PRINCIPLES OF QUANTUM
ELECTRODYNAMICS

PURE AND APPLIED PHYSICS

A SERIES OF MONOGRAPHS AND TEXTBOOKS

CONSULTING EDITOR

H. S. W. MASSEY

University College, London, England

Volume 1. F. H. FIELD and J. L. FRANKLIN, Electron Impact Phenomena and the Properties of Gaseous Ions. 1957

Volume 2. H. KOPFERMANN, Nuclear Moments. English Version Prepared from the Second German Edition by E. E. SCHNEIDER. 1958

Volume 3. WALTER E. THIRRING, Principles of Quantum Electrodynamics. Translated from the German by J. BERNSTEIN. With Additions and Corrections by WALTER E. THIRRING. 1958

IN PREPARATION

U. FANO and G. RACAH, Irreducible Tensorial Sets

J. IRVING and N. MULLINEUX, Mathematics in Science and Technology

E. P. WIGNER, Group Theory and its Application to the Quantum Mechanics of Atomic Spectra. With Additions and Corrections by E. P. WIGNER. Translated from the German by J. J. GRIFFIN

FAY AJZENBERG-SELOVE (ed.). Nuclear Spectroscopy

ACADEMIC PRESS INC., NEW YORK AND LONDON

PRINCIPLES OF QUANTUM ELECTRODYNAMICS

WALTER E. THIRRING

Universität Bern, Switzerland

TRANSLATED FROM THE GERMAN BY

J. BERNSTEIN

The Institute for Advanced Study
Princeton, New Jersey

WITH CORRECTIONS AND ADDITIONS BY

WALTER E. THIRRING

1958

ACADEMIC PRESS INC., PUBLISHERS
NEW YORK · LONDON

Originally Published in 1955 under the title
EINFÜHRUNG in die QUANTENELEKTRODYNAMIK
by Franz Deuticke, Vienna.

PRINTED IN THE UNITED STATES OF AMERICA

FOREWORD TO THE GERMAN EDITION

Elementary particles, their properties and interrelationships, have in recent years come to the forefront of fundamental research in physics. The only theory which one has at one's disposal, as yet, to describe the behavior of such systems is the quantum theory of fields. Although this theory represents one of the most fundamental that we possess—it not only unifies elementary quantum mechanics, but it is also the first theory that brings together quantum theory and relativity—it is still not an area in which most physicists feel at home. The reason may be that in field theory one needs to draw on a considerable amount of higher mathematics, hiding much of the development behind a dense smoke screen of formalism. Hence, one may get the impression that field theory is a dry mathematical scheme in which work may be done when one has mastered the necessary rules, but which does not require any special physical insights. In this book we shall concentrate on one of the best understood parts of quantum field theory, quantum electrodynamics. We shall endeavor to emphasize the physical basis of the theory and to avoid purely mathematical details. For this reason, the book should not be taken as a handbook of field theory, but rather as a compendium of the most characteristic and interesting results which have been obtained up to now.

The advances which have been made most recently in quantum electrodynamics depend essentially on the new formal structure which the theory has been given. One may now condense its starting points into a few fundamental postulates from which everything else may be deduced. As we shall learn, correspondingly significant simplifications have been made in the computation of specific processes. On these aesthetic developments we shall put special emphasis in the body of the book. Not only will the mathematics be made as simple as possible, but it is hoped that the connections with the current literature will be made easier.

As for mathematical background, some analysis and linear algebra are necessary for the text. Less familiar tools, such as Dirac γ matrices and invariant Green's functions, are discussed in the two appendices. The notation is explained in a separate section. As far as physics is concerned, the reader will need a knowledge of special relativity and quantum mechanics. The notation and concepts of Dirac's book, "Principles of Quantum Mechanics," (Oxford, 1947) will be used. Further applications of the theory can be found in W. Heitler, "Quantum Theory of Radiation" (Oxford, 1954). The mathematical aspects of the theory are treated in a more elementary fashion by G. Wentzel, "Quantum Theory of Fields" (Interscience, 1949). Other references are given only for details which are not treated in the text. Therefore neither are the references complete nor is attention paid to priority.

To illuminate the physical background the book starts with a chapter in which the orders of magnitude of the various effects, to be calculated later in detail, are discussed. They will be estimated by heuristic arguments which may seem somewhat arbitrary at the beginning. Such arguments become more convincing when they are backed by calculations, and the reader should return to this section after having worked through the rest of the book. For practicing the calculational techniques, problems with solutions are given for each part of the book.

FOREWORD TO THE ENGLISH EDITION

In the six years that have passed since the German edition of this book was written, no essential new discoveries have been made on the subject of the book. However, considerable progress has been made in the understanding of the physics underlying the post-war developments. Since the main purpose of the original book was the discussion of the physical principles involved, it was necessary to do considerable rewriting and expansion of the text to justify the publication of an English edition. In particular, the section on renormalization theory had to be brought up to date and discussed more elaborately.

In the meantime, two other books in this field have appeared, namely, J. M. Jauch and F. Rohrlich, "The Theory of Photons and Electrons," (Addison-Wesley, 1955), and H. Umezawa, "Quantum Field Theory," (Interscience Publishers, 1956). In these books many mathematical and formal details are elaborated. We did not, therefore, endeavor to achieve more completeness in these respects since the references above can be consulted for this purpose. However, we have tried to give a reasonably detailed discussion of physical concepts which are not treated adequately in the literature.

The English edition has been prepared in collaboration with Dr. J. Bernstein. We are indebted to Professors H. Feshbach and F. Low, to W. H. Nichols, S.J., and to Professor F. Scarf for reading part of the manuscript and for valuable criticism.

CONTENTS

Foreword to the German Edition... v
Foreword to the English Edition... vii
Notation... xi
PART I. GENERAL INTRODUCTION
   1. Units and Orders of Magnitude.................................. 3
      A. Structure of Atoms... 3
      B. Emission of Photons.. 7
      C. Scattering of Particles..................................... 10
      D. Quantum Effects of the Electric Field...................... 12
   2. Classical Electrodynamics...................................... 17
   3. The General Formalism of the Quantum Theory of Fields....... 27
PART II. FREE FIELDS
   4. General Discussion.. 45
   5. Special Fields.. 51
   6. Matrix Elements.. 65
   7. Fluctuation Phenomena.. 77
PART III. FIELDS WITH EXTERNAL SOURCES
   8. General Formulae... 89
   9. Emission of Light... 97
  10. The Dirac Field in an External Electric Field................. 109
  11. The Limitations of Measurability............................. 127
PART IV. INTERACTING FIELDS
  12. General Orientation.. 137
  13. Scattering Processes... 147
  14. Renormalization Theory...................................... 161
  15. Higher Order Corrections.................................... 177
  16. Outlook... 191

APPENDIXES

   Appendix I.. 203
   Appendix II... 207
Problems.. 217
Solutions... 219
Subject Index... 231

NOTATION

Hilbert Space

Operators in Hilbert space will be denoted by capital Roman letters, e.g., O, A, T_{ik}, Q, etc.; ordinary numbers, such as eigenvalues, coordinates, and indices, will be denoted by small letters like o', x, k, and α. Vectors in Hilbert space will be written in Dirac fashion as $|\ )$; conjugate vectors, as $(\ |$. Generally, the eigenvector associated with an eigenvalue o' will be denoted by $|\ o')$. The symbol for the product of two vectors will be $(\ |\ )$; and for an operator and a vector, $O\ |\ )$. Both operations may be combined into $(\ |\ O\ |\ )$. We shall also use the following notations and definitions.

Ordinary numbers

Complex conjugate: α^*

Real part: $\mathrm{Re}\ \alpha$

Imaginary part: $\mathrm{Im}\ \alpha$

Signum function: $\epsilon(\alpha) = \quad 1$ for $\alpha > 0$

$$= -1 \text{ for } \alpha < 0$$

Step function: $\theta(\alpha) = 1$ for $\alpha > 0$

$$= 0 \text{ for } \alpha < 0$$

$$\theta(\alpha) = \tfrac{1}{2}\ (1 + \epsilon(\alpha))$$

δ function: $\delta(\alpha) = 0$ for $\alpha \neq 0$, $\displaystyle\int_{-\epsilon}^{\epsilon} d\alpha \delta(\alpha) = 1$

$$\theta(\alpha) = \int_{-\infty}^{\alpha} d\beta \delta(\beta), \qquad \delta(-\alpha) = \delta(\alpha)$$

$$\frac{d}{d\alpha}\, \delta(\alpha) = -\delta(\alpha)/\alpha$$

$$\delta(f(\alpha)) = \sum_{\alpha_0} |\, f'(\alpha_0)^{-1}\, |\, \delta(\alpha - \alpha_0)$$

with

$$f(\alpha_0) = 0. \tag{N.1}$$

Operators

Transposed operator: O^T $(c' \mid O^T \mid c'') = (c'' \mid O \mid c')$

Hermitian conjugate operators: $O^\dagger$; $(c' \mid O^\dagger \mid c'') = (c'' \mid O \mid c')^*$

Inverse operators: O^{-1}, $O^{-1}O = 1$

Commutators: $[A, B]_-$ or $[A, B] = AB - BA$

Anticommutators: $[A, B]_+$ or $\{A, B\} = AB + BA$

Defining equations

Hermitian operators: $O^\dagger = O$

Unitary operators: $O^\dagger = O^{-1}$

Symmetric operators: $O^T = O$

Operators representing interacting fields will be distinguished by bold face type: $\mathbf{A}$, $\boldsymbol{\psi}$.

Spin space

The operators acting in spin space are the Dirac γ's and expressions containing them. For γ invariants, that is, scalar products constructed from a four vector and a γ vector, we introduce the notation

$$\mathbf{p} = p_k\gamma^k \qquad \mathbf{e} = e_k\gamma^k \tag{N.2}$$

and so forth. Vectors comprising the spin space (spinors) are denoted by ψ or u. Matrix indices are always lower case Greek letters, for example, $\gamma_{\alpha\beta}\psi_\alpha$. However, spin indices will usually be suppressed, so that we will write $\gamma^k\gamma^i\psi$ for $\gamma^k_{\alpha\beta}\,\gamma^i_{\beta\delta}\psi_\delta$, or

$$\bar{\psi}\psi \;\; = \bar{\psi}_\alpha\psi_\alpha$$
$$\mathrm{Tr}\, M = M_{\alpha\alpha}. \tag{N.3}$$

The rest of the notation is the same as in Hilbert space.

Ordinary space

We use real world-coordinates with the metric

$$g = \begin{pmatrix} 1 & 0 & 0 & 0 \\ 0 & -1 & 0 & 0 \\ 0 & 0 & -1 & 0 \\ 0 & 0 & 0 & -1 \end{pmatrix} \qquad \begin{matrix} x^0 = t \\ x^1 = x \\ x^2 = y \\ x^3 = z. \end{matrix}$$

The space part of a four vector is designated by setting a bar under the letter, as $\underline{x}$. Tensor indices are usually lower case Roman letters, contravariant indices are raised, and covariant indices are lowered

$$g^{ik}p_k = p^i \qquad g^{ik}g_{kl} = \delta^i_l .$$

The scalar product $a_i b^i = a_0 b^0 - ab$ is sometimes denoted by round brackets (ab) and sometimes by writing ab.

If a vector is a sum of vectors $b = c + d$ then we write $(a, c + d)$ for (ab).

Momentum space

For the Fourier transform we write

$$f(x) = \frac{1}{(2\pi)^4} \int dk e^{-ikx} f(k), \qquad f(k) = \int dx e^{ikx} f(x)$$

where dk is the four-dimensional volume element and k any four vector; sometimes we will use p instead of k.

The Fourier representation of the four-dimensional δ-function $\delta(x)$

$$\int dx' f(x') \delta(x' - x) = f(x)$$

is given by

$$\delta(x) = \frac{1}{(2\pi)^4} \int dk e^{-ikx}. \tag{N.4}$$

Differential and integral symbols

Partial differentiation $\partial/\partial x^i f(x)$ is sometimes denoted by $\partial_i f$ and sometimes by an index following a comma $f_{,i}$.

$$\Box^2 = g^{ik}\partial_i \, \partial_k = \frac{\partial^2}{\partial t^2} - \Delta.$$

An $\dot{x}$ will stand for differentiation with respect to proper time. The symbol $f \overleftrightarrow{\partial}_\mu g$ will be useful and stands for $fg_{,\mu} - f_{,\mu}g$. If not otherwise indicated all integrations will run from $-\infty$ to ∞ .

We write the four-dimensional volume element as $dx = dx^0 dx^1 dx^2 dx^3$. The surface element of a three-dimensional surface, a covariant vector directed normal to the surface, we denote by

$$d\sigma_i = (dx^1 dx^2 dx^3, \, dx^0 dx^2 dx^3, \, dx^0 dx^1 dx^3, \, dx^0 dx^1 dx^2).$$

Any surface for which $d\sigma_i$ is timelike for all points will be called spacelike. The four-dimensional generalization of Gauss' theorem can be given by $\int dx \partial_i f = \int d\sigma_i f$, where σ is the surface of the four-dimensional volume under consideration. For a divergence-free vector $f^i (f^i_{,i} = 0)$ which vanishes sufficiently strongly at infinity (spatially) the value of the integral $\int d\sigma_i f^i$ taken over a spacelike surface does not depend upon the particular choice of surface. This follows directly from the relation

$$\int_{\sigma_1} d\sigma_i f^i - \int_{\sigma_2} d\sigma_i f^i = \int_V dV \, \partial_i f^i \tag{N.5}$$

where V is the volume between σ_1 and σ_2. Conversely, if $\int d\sigma_i f^i$ is independent of σ, then $\partial_i f^i = 0$. In this case we are entitled to call $\int d\sigma_i f^i$ a scalar, since observers in different Lorentz frames would obtain the same values by integrating over a surface defined by $t = \text{constant}$ in their frames. In the same way, tensors of higher rank can only be obtained by integrating divergence-free expressions.

If a function f vanishes sufficiently strongly on infinitely remote parts of spacelike surfaces then one has the lemma

$$\int_\sigma d\sigma_i \, \partial_k f - \int_\sigma d\sigma_k \, \partial_i f = 0. \tag{N.6}$$

The proof proceeds by showing that $\partial_i \partial_k f - \partial_k \partial_i f = 0$ implies that the left side of Eq. (N.6) is independent of the surface σ. Hence one may evaluate the integrals on a spacelike surface defined by a constant time t. In this case only $d\sigma_0$ differs from zero and the terms with $\partial_{1,2,3}$ reduce by the generalized Gauss theorem to vanishing surface integrals. To complete the proof we note the obvious fact that Eq. (N.6) holds for $i = k = 0$.

As a final matter of notation we remark that if a surface σ or, more generally, any region ΔV, contains a point x, then this will be denoted by $x \subset \sigma$ or $x \subset V$.

Frequently recurring symbols

$A(x)$	electric vector potential
$D(x)$	invariant function
e	elementary charge
e^i	small displacement

e^{ik}	small rotation
$f(x)$	arbitrary function
f_{ik}	electric field strength
F	generator of a transformation
g_{ik}	metric tensor
$j_i(x)$	current density
J_{ik}	total angular momentum
$L(x)$	Lagrange function
m	electron or meson mass
n	integer or surface normal
P_i	energy-momentum vector
P	time ordering operation
Q	total charge
r	$\lvert \underline{x} \rvert$
s	proper time
S	scattering matrix
$S(x)$	invariant function
Tr	trace
$T_{ik}(x)$	energy-momentum tensor
$u(x)$	wave function
U	unitary transformation
v	velocity four vector
V	four-dimensional volume
$\underline{V}$	three-dimensional volume
W	action integral
Z	nuclear charge
α	fine structure constant
δ_i^k	$= 1$ for $i = k$, $= 0$ for $i \neq k$
$\Delta(x)$	invariant function
ϵ_{iklm}	totally antisymmetric tensor with elements 0, ± 1 and $\epsilon_{0123} = 1$
ϕ	scalar or pseudo-scalar field
$\lambda(x)$	gauge potential
$\psi(x)$	Dirac field
ω	circular frequency
Ω	solid angle

Part I

GENERAL INTRODUCTION

1. Units and Orders of Magnitude

The explored part of the microcosmos is governed by a few dimensionless constants. To understand an atomic process means to understand the role which these constants play in it.

If one attempts to obtain an intuitive picture of the atomic world one encounters the difficulty that in the formulae of atomic physics constants occur whose magnitudes are difficult to conceive when viewed on a macroscopic scale. On the other hand, these sizes are easily visualized when considered in relation to each other. Hence, in understanding the microcosmos it is necessary to separate out the macroscopic constants and to make use of atomic units as building blocks in the description of atomic events. In a theory which contains both relativistic and quantum mechanical effects it is therefore useful to set $\hbar = c = 1$. Thus all physical quantities become expressible as powers of a length unit which we keep explicit, since at this time we do now know which length in nature is to be taken as fundamental. With this choice of dimensions, energy = frequency = mass, and all become inverse lengths.

A second difficulty in microscopic physics is that atomic processes in which wave phenomena play a role can only be treated by the application of considerable mathematical technique. One is therefore in danger of losing oneself in a forest of formulae and altogether missing the trees. Many phenomena can be qualitatively understood from the point of view of a naive classical particle picture if in addition the uncertainty relations of wave mechanics are superimposed. Although the finer details cannot be treated so simply we would like to indicate how one may estimate in this way the orders of magnitude of the elementary processes of electrodynamics.

A. Structure of Atoms—The essential quantity which determines the magnitudes of ordinary atomic phenomena is the fine structure constant[1]

$$\alpha = \frac{e^2}{4\pi} = \frac{1}{137}.$$

[1] Heaviside units are used for the charge. Properly, α should be called the coarse structure constant, since it determines the scale of the gross structure phenomena of atoms.

3

It measures the strength of the interaction of elementary charged particles with the electric field. The spatial extension of phenomena in which electrons play a role, such as those of the atomic shell, is defined by the Compton wave length of the electron $m^{-1} = 3.81 \times 10^{-11}$ cm. This is equal to the 2πth part of the wave length of a photon whose energy is equal to the rest energy of an electron; $m = 0.51$ Mev. It is also the smallest size within which the electron can be compressed without increasing its kinetic energy over its rest energy. Because of the uncertainty relation (U.R.)

$$\Delta p \cdot \Delta x \sim 1$$

every accurate localization of the electron results in an increase in the spread of its momentum distribution and an associated expenditure of kinetic energy $p^2/2m$. These energies must be of the order of the rest energy m if the electron is to be located in a region of dimension m^{-1}. Let us first see how the size of the atom is determined by this length, which is fundamental for the electron, and by the strength of the elementary electric charge. In an atom the wave packet of an electron is held together by the Coulomb energy in the field of the nucleus $-Z\alpha/r$. Here Z is the *effective* nuclear charge, taking the screening of the other electrons into account in a rough way. In the quantum theory, unlike classical physics, the smallest value for the total energy

$$\frac{p^2}{2m} - \frac{Z\alpha}{r} = E$$

is not attained by making r arbitrarily small, for a strong concentration of the wave packet corresponds to an increased kinetic energy. If we suppose, in the sense of the uncertainty relations, that coordinates and momenta are related by[2] $r \cdot p = 1$, then the total energy assumes a minimum for

$$r = \frac{1}{Z\alpha m} \ (= Z^{-1} \cdot 0.5 \times 10^{-8} \text{ cm}).$$

The corresponding velocity of the electron is $Z\alpha$ and the binding energy $E_0 = -m(Z\alpha)^2/2 (= Z^2 \cdot 13$ volts, which corresponds to $Z^2 \times 10^5$ degrees Kelvin). Corrections to this electrostatic energy through magnetic interactions and relativistic mass effects are of order

[2] Quantum theoretically r and p stand for expectation values, and these are about as large as Δr and Δp.

$v^2 = \alpha^2 Z^2$ and are unimportant for elements which are not too heavy. The angular momentum in quantum theory is always integral or half-integral and is small for the ground state since $p \cdot r \sim 1$.

While the size and ionization energy of atoms reveal themselves more or less directly, the speed of the electrons shows up in more subtle effects like the scattering of light by atoms or the magnetic properties of matter. Although the scattered radiation from *free* electrons is monochromatic, the motion of the electrons in an atom produces a frequency distribution of the emitted light. This spectral broadening arises because the incident light has a different color for electrons moving with different velocities (Doppler effect); hence, the broadening will be of the order

$$\frac{\Delta \nu}{\nu} = v = Z\alpha.$$

Furthermore, the strength of magnetic interactions is measured by ev rather than e, and thus the smallness of the velocity of the electron compared to c manifests itself by the weakness of the magnetic properties of matter. To see this we note that the departure of the dielectric constant from unity is itself of the order of unity since it is of the order of the volume of an atom relative to the volume available to an atom in condensed matter. The corresponding magnetic quantity is less by a factor v^2; about 10^{-4}.

Let us finally recognize the magnitudes characterizing photons emitted by atoms. The frequency of the radiated photon corresponds to the energy difference between excited states. For the first excited state above the ground state these energy differences are the same order of magnitude as the ground state energy itself, $-m(Z\alpha)^2/2$. Thus the frequency of the photons is of the order of the frequency of the electrons, which is velocity/diameter $= m(Z\alpha)^2 = Z\alpha \cdot$ atomic radius ($\sim Z^2\,10^{15}\,\mathrm{sec}^{-1}$ corresponds to a wave length of $Z^{-2}\,10^{-5}$ cm). Hence the geometry of the atomic shell is determined in its main features by $Z\alpha$, which gives the ratio of the Compton wave length to the diameter, and the ratio of the diameter to the wave length of emitted light and the corresponding energies and times.

Having sketched the coarse structure of atoms let us draw our attention to some more subtle details which are important for the main subject of this book. The fine structure of the energy levels is of considerable interest because it reveals delicate features of the electron which are not ordinarily observed. Apart from the abovementioned magnetic and relativistic mass effects there is a contribution from spontaneous pair creation (Darwin term) which is of the same order in $Z\alpha$. The spontaneous pair creation occurs as a virtual process in which the energy of the particles is not conserved. The length of time during which the virtual pair can exist is determined by the U.R. $\Delta t \cdot \Delta E \sim 1$ to be $\Delta t \sim 1/\Delta E \sim 1/m$. Within this time the pair cannot propagate farther than $\Delta x \sim 1/m$ even if it moves with relativistic velocities. It can happen that the original electron annihilates the positron of the virtual pair, leaving the other electron at a distance Δx; see Fig. 1. Consequently, the localization of an electron within a region smaller than Δx is impossible, and an electron in an electromagnetic field feels the average of this field over a region $(\Delta x)^3$. This fact can also be described by an effective square fluctuation,

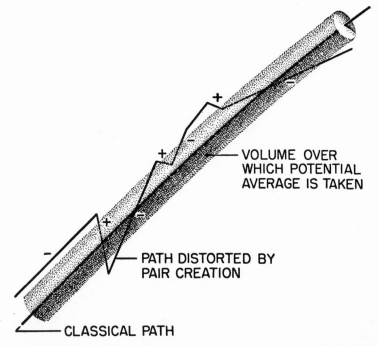

FIG. 1. The broken line segment indicates the zigzag path of the electron in its "zitterbewegung". Strictly speaking, the notion of a "classical path" does not apply to the electron's motion, but the diagram is meant to *indicate* position fluctuations which the electron undergoes due to virtual pair creation processes. In this diagram and in all future ones the sense of time is to be taken toward the top of the page.

$(\Delta x)^2 \sim m^{-2}$, of the position of the electron. This changes the energy of those electrons which are in close contact with the nucleus (S-electrons) where the value of the potential is different from the average over the neighborhood. The equation $\Delta V = -Ze\delta(x)$ says that inside the nucleus there is a deviation of the potential from the local average. The potential energy inside the nucleus is of the order of Ze^2/r if r is the nuclear radius. It is easily estimated that due to the fluctuation Δx this potential is changed by a factor $(\Delta x)^2\Delta V \sim e^2Z/m^2r^3$. Thus, the energy shift is of the order $\delta E =$ (change of potential energy inside the nucleus)·(probability of finding the electron in the nucleus). The last factor is approximately the ratio of the volume of the nucleus to that of the atom. Thus

$$\delta E = \frac{Z\alpha}{m^2r^3}\cdot(mZ\alpha)^3\cdot r^3 = m(Z\alpha)^4$$

i.e., $(Z\alpha)^2$ times the level spacing.

B. Emission of Photons—After these static phenomena we wish to discuss processes which arise due to the presence of photons. These are described in essence by the Larmor formula, which says that the energy radiated by a unit electric charge e in a unit time is proportional to $\alpha\dot{v}^2$.[3] If an electron changes its velocity by Δv in a time Δt, then it gives up an energy $\Delta E \sim \alpha(\Delta v)^2(\Delta t)^{-1}$ to the electric field. The spectrum of emitted light reproduces the Fourier analysis of the motion of the charge, which will involve frequencies of order $(\Delta t)^{-1}$. Quantum theoretically this process is to be understood as arising because the electron emits photons[4] with a certain probability. The energy of these quanta is given by their frequency and is thus of the order $(\Delta t)^{-1}$. Since quantum mechanically we expect the electron to lose to the field an amount of energy, on the average, equal to the above energy, the photon emission probability w must be of order $w = \alpha(\Delta v)^2$. The probability for emitting several photons is even less likely, because successive emissions are to a certain extent independent, and thus the probability for emission of two photons is $[\alpha(\Delta v)^2]^2$. In this way, the probability that an oscillator of frequency ω and velocity v (Δv per ω equals v) emits a photon in a unit time becomes $\alpha\omega v^2$. Hence, the emission of a photon by an oscillator is a slow process, for an oscillator must, on the average, carry out $137/v^2$ oscil-

---

[3] We have omitted numerical factors such as, in this case, $\frac{2}{3}$; see Chapter 2.
[4] The single emission of a photon is much more likely than multiple emissions, as will be shown later.

lations before it generates a quantum. Neglecting finer details of the electron's motion, the radiation of an atom equals that of a linear oscillator with the frequency of the electron. Hence, the lifetime τ of an excited atomic state is of the order

$$\tau = \frac{1}{\alpha\omega\underaccent{\tilde}{v}^2} = \frac{1}{\alpha m(\alpha Z)^4} \sim (Z^{-4} \cdot 10^{-9} \text{ sec}).$$

This is $1/\alpha(\alpha Z)^2$ times longer than the revolution time of the electrons. This factor also gives the ratio of the interval between energy levels to their intrinsic width since the U.R. $\Delta E \Delta t \sim 1$ implies that the latter quantity is of the order of the inverse lifetime of the level. Another interpretation of this same factor is as the number of waves in the emitted wave train. Thus the coherence length of the light is of order $Z^{-4}(\alpha^5 m)^{-1} \sim 10 Z^{-4}$ cm. The emission of photons is inhibited, because they must always carry at least one unit of angular momentum, and in this way they become coupled to $\underaccent{\tilde}{v}$. In fact, even if a photon carries only one unit of angular momentum, it had to be created by the electron at a distance $1/\omega = 137/Z \cdot$ (atomic radii) away from the atom—thinking of it as a classical particle with momentum ω. This would make the process practically impossible, because electrons never get that far away from the atom. In the quantum theory, however, the photon is not so accurately localized that the process is forbidden, but the greater the angular momentum of the photon the less probable is its emission.

It is remarkable that even the annihilation of matter into radiation follows essentially the same laws. Here the energy-momentum conservation relations forbid the creation of only one photon in the process of annihilation of an electron and a positron. However, positronium,[5] for example, can decompose into one photon for short times within the energy fluctuation allowed for by $\Delta E \cdot \Delta t \sim 1$. Strictly speaking, the electron and positron can annihilate each other only if they are in the same place. Because of the fluctuations of position which come about by virtue of the pair effects discussed earlier, it is sufficient if they come as close together as m^{-1}. They then start annihilating by creating one photon with energy $\neq 2m$. This process is again governed by the Larmor formula where the frequency is $\sim m$ and $\Delta \underaccent{\tilde}{v} \sim 1$, since the position of the particles is defined to within m^{-1}. Thus, the probability for annihilation per unit time is

[5] Positronium is a hydrogen atom in which the proton has been replaced by a positron.

$\sim \alpha m^{-1}$. Since the state with one photon violates energy conservation by m, it lasts only for a time $\Delta t \sim m^{-1}$. That is to say, on the average the particles spend a fraction of time α converted into a photon. To get the probability for finding positronium decomposed we must multiply this time fraction by the probability of finding the particles within a distance m^{-1}. The ground state of positronium has about the same spatial extension as the hydrogen atom, so that the electron and positron are confined to a region of order $(\alpha m)^{-1}$. The probability that the electron and positron are close enough to annihilate is thus of order α^3. In this way positronium becomes a photon for a small fraction of time α^4 (a millionth per cent) which affects the energy of the triplet S ground state by an amount $\delta E \sim$ (probability of the virtual state)·(energy defect of the virtual state) $\sim m\alpha^4$. As one would expect, this is again of the order of the fine structure. Since angular momentum, like linear momentum, is conserved in virtual processes, and since a photon has at least one unit of angular momentum, an energy shift does indeed occur only in the triplet S-state where the spin is one (spins parallel). Hence, one can observe the one photon virtual annihilation as an energy separation of the S-states.

There can also be an annihilation process in which two photons are created. In this case, energy and momentum can be conserved by emitting the two photons in opposite directions, each with an energy m. Two photon annihilations can be observed as *real* processes in which the final state can last for an unlimited time. Virtual processes, such as the one photon positronium annihilation, can take place only for a finite time which is fixed by the uncertainty relations. The disintegration probability into two photons per $1/m$ is compounded from the following probabilities; see Fig. 2: a) the probability that the electron and positron are sufficiently close together, and b) the probability for emission of two photons per $1/m$. Putting these together gives a disintegration probability per unit time of order $m\alpha^5$, or a lifetime of the ground state of order $\tau = 1/m\alpha^5 (\sim 10^{-9}$ sec), which is the order of the lifetimes for transition of excited states to the ground state. Consequently, the width of the ground state is also smaller than the fine structure splitting by a factor α. Because of the conservation of angular momentum the triplet S-state of positronium (with total angular momentum one) can disintegrate only into three or more photons, and will therefore have a life time which is 137 times longer than that of the singlet S-state.

C. Scattering of Particles—Another process which involves the interaction of charged bodies with the radiation field is the scattering of light by an electron. Classically, an electric wave with an amplitude E gives the electron an acceleration of order eE/m. This implies that the electron radiates an energy $\alpha(eE/m)^2$ in a unit time. If one divides this by the incident energy flux per unit time and surface area, $E^2/4\pi$, then one obtains a scattering cross section (Compton cross section) $\sigma \sim (\alpha/m)^2 (\sim 10^{-25}$ cm$^2)$. This number has an intuitive meaning as the area which the electron presents to the incident photon beam for scattering.

From the particle point of view the scattering event consists of an absorption and re-emission of the photon. In this process a relativistic effect plays a role even at low energies. This is because one might expect that the absorption and emission probabilities go as $\alpha(\Delta\underline{v})^2$, where the change in velocity $\Delta\underline{v}$ occurs when the electron absorbs a photon of momentum ω, and hence would be ω/m, implying that the cross section would go to zero with ω. However, the initial photon can create a virtual pair after which the positron annihilates the original electron, leaving an electron and a new photon; see Fig. 3. Clearly, this process will also look like an electron-photon scattering event. As explained before, the process can take place only if the pair is created as close as m^{-1} to the original electron. The probability for the over-all process is again compounded from the following individual probabilities: a) that the proton is close enough to the electron, b) that a pair is created, c) that the pair is annihilated with the emission of a photon.

If the photon is contained in a normalization volume V, then the

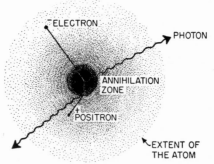

FIG. 2. This diagram illustrates the two-photon annihilation of the positronium atom as described in the text.

probability that it is sufficiently close, per unit time, to the electron will be given by the ratio of the volume of a cube with cross section m^{-2} and length 1 to the normalization volume V; i.e., $(1/V)(1/m^2)$. Since the pair can have relativistic velocities, both other probabilities are equal to α for, in this case, $\Delta v \sim 1$. To find the interaction cross section we must divide out the incident flux of photons per unit time and surface area which equals $1/V$. Putting these things together we obtain the same cross section as computed before, $(\alpha/m)^2$.

The length $r_0 = \alpha/m (= 2.8 \cdot 10^{-13}$ cm) is considered in classical electrodynamics to be the radius of the electron, since the electrostatic energy of a charge concentrated within a radius α/m would be just m. Quantum theoretically, the applicability of these considerations is limited, because the uncertainty relations say that the energy of the electron can only be regarded as m if it is not localized in a region smaller than $1/m$. In the process of more accurate localization pair creation will occur. In fact, we shall see that for a radius of the electron $r < m^{-1}$ the self energy behaves like $\alpha m \ln (rm)$, so that the classical result goes completely wrong.

This same length, however, plays a role in the scattering of charged particles. We may ask how near an electron must come to a proton

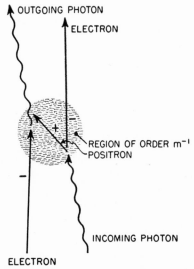

FIG. 3. This diagram illustrates Compton scattering of photons from electrons, a process which takes place via a virtual creation and reannihilation of an electron-positron pair.

in a collision for its momentum to be appreciably changed. If its trajectory passes at a distance d from a proton then it is subjected to a force at most of order α/d^2 during a time d/v. If we demand that its change of momentum, $(\alpha/d^2)(d/v)$, be of the order of the initial momentum, then $d \sim \alpha/mv^2$. Hence, we see that the classical electron radius is the characteristic length for the large angle scattering of fast charged particles. We must keep in mind, however, that for large scattering angles and $v \sim 1$, relativistic features appear as they did in the fine structure problem. The spreading of the electron's charge because of virtual pairs decreases the scattering for impact parameters $<m^{-1}$.

Furthermore, the electron experiences a time-varying electric field strength which acts on its magnetic moment during the scattering. If the electron has spin up, for example, then this force will have opposite signs for trajectories which pass to the right or left of the proton. Hence, an azimuthal asymmetry will be introduced in the angular distribution of the scattering of polarized electrons and unpolarized electrons will become partially polarized. For electron positron scattering there is the additional possibility of one photon virtual annihilation if the impact parameters are less than m^{-1}. This too will manifest itself in the high-energy large-angle scattering. All of these interesting possibilities have, in fact, been verified experimentally.

The probability for emission of a photon during the scattering (*bremsstrahlung*) is also easy to estimate. If, for a fast particle, we place $v \sim \Delta v \sim 1$, then the cross section for *bremsstrahlung* is approximately the scattering cross section times the emission probability: $\sigma = \alpha(\alpha Z/m)^2 \sim (Z^2 \cdot 10^{-28} \text{ cm}^2)$. This corresponds to a mean free path of 300 meters in air or $\frac{1}{2}$ cm in lead.

D. Quantum Effects of the Electric Field—The free electromagnetic field which obeys a field equation, $\square^2 A(x) = 0$, is equivalent to a set of oscillators located throughout space, each coupled to its neighbors. Such a system is treated quantum mechanically by introducing normal coordinates, which serves to uncouple the oscillators. We may represent these coordinates by plane waves of frequency ω and amplitude q_ω, which are normalized in a unit volume. The nth excited state of such an oscillator with an energy $n\omega$ corresponds to n photons in this particular mode with frequency ω. In this case the uncertainty in the amplitude, Δq_ω, is of the order $1/\sqrt{\omega}$. If the field A and, therefore, the q_ω, are to have sharply defined values, the state of the system must be a superposition of states with many photons in each mode. Generally speaking, electromagnetic phenomena show particle or field properties, depending upon whether the quantum numbers of the oscillators are small or large. A source of the electromagnetic field corresponds to an external force imposed on the oscillators. A static point source, for instance, which weights all Fourier components equally corresponds to adding eq_ω to the Hamiltonian $\frac{1}{2}(p_\omega^2 + \omega^2 q_\omega^2)$ of each oscillator.[6] This shifts the center of each individual oscillator by $\delta q_w = e/\omega^2$. The ground state of the perturbed system has a probability of being in an excited state of the free system (states with photons) which is of the order of

$$\text{(shift of } q_\omega/\text{zero point fluctuation of } q_\omega)^2 = \left[\frac{\delta q_\omega}{\Delta q_\omega}\right]^2 \cong \frac{\alpha}{\omega^3}.$$

This is usually expressed by saying that there is a cloud of virtual photons around the charge. In a time-dependent description the charge emits and reabsorbs photons.

It should be emphasized that the concept of a classical path is not really adequate for describing such virtual absorptions and emissions, for one might be tempted to ask for the detailed trajectories of these quanta, a concept which does not make quantum mechanical sense. It is better to think of these virtual processes as being similar to the leakage of light into a dense medium in the process of total reflection or to the diffusion of particles into energetically forbidden areas in α-decay.

The probability of finding a photon in the frequency range $\omega_{max} \gtrless \omega \gtrless \omega_{min}$ near the source is obtained by integrating the above expression times the number of waves per frequency interval. The latter is given by the Rayleigh-Jeans formula as $\sim\omega^2\, d\omega$, which gives an expression $\alpha \ln (\omega_{max}/\omega_{min})$ for the probability. Clearly this is only valid for frequency ranges in which the whole expression is <1. For multiply-charged particles α is replaced by $Z^2\alpha$ and many oscillators are in higher excited states. Therefore, the above estimate fails. In other words, while one may apply the photon picture to elementary particles, macroscopic bodies which are multiply-charged require the field description.

An alternative estimate of the bremsstrahlung cross section provides a good application of the concept of virtual photons around a

---

[6] The reader who gets confused with the dimensions in the following expressions should remember that we chose the volume of the radiation field as unit volume.

charged particle. From this point of view, the incoming particle scatters a virtual photon, which becomes real in the process. We found a probability $\alpha(d\omega/\omega)$ for the presence of a virtual photon within a frequency range $d\omega$. Because of the uncertainty relations such photons will be confined to a volume of extension ω^{-3} around the charge. If the incoming particle moves across this volume it has a chance of scattering the photon equal to

(probability for presence of photon)(scattering cross section)

$$\cdot (\text{surface area})^{-1} = \alpha(d\omega/\omega) \cdot (\alpha/m)^2 \cdot \omega^2.$$

This gives a cross section

$$\sigma = (\text{surface area})(\text{probability of scattering}) = (\alpha/m)^2 \alpha(d\omega/\omega)$$

for bremsstrahlung of a photon within the range $d\omega$, which shows that our previous estimate of α^3/m^2 for the total cross section is correct save for the log $(\omega_{max}/\omega_{min})$. This quantity is actually divergent for $\omega_{min} \to 0$, which reflects the infinite range of the Coulomb field. Hence, particles passing the charge at a great distance are enabled to emit photons. If we confine our attention to photons with appreciable energy this divergence is irrelevant.

In like manner, the probability αv^2 for emission of a photon when a charged particle is set into motion can be estimated. The moving Coulomb field is Lorentz contracted and only the photons of the rest field which overlap those of the moving field follow the charge. The photons that are left, which are a fraction $1 - \sqrt{1 - v^2} \sim v^2$, are radiated. This gives us for the radiation probability αv^2 times a logrithm which depends upon the details of the motion.

The striking features introduced by quantizing an oscillator are the zero point energy and vibration. One has not yet found a way of relating the zero point energy to any observable quantity. However, the zero point fluctuations of the oscillator amplitudes cause detectable effects. For a particular frequency the mean square fluctuation is given by $(\Delta A_\omega)^2 \sim 1/\omega$. This gives the electric field strength belonging to a frequency ω a fluctuation $(\Delta E_\omega)^2 \sim \omega$. Since the E_ω are independent we have to add the square fluctuations to get the total fluctuation. Multiplying by the Rayleigh-Jeans density $\omega^2 d\omega$ and integrating up to a certain maximum frequency ω_{max} we get $(\Delta E)^2 \sim \omega_{max}^4$. This yields $\Delta \bar{E} \sim L^{-2}$ as the value for the total fluctuation $\Delta \bar{E}$, of the average of E over a space region which is of order L^3 (where frequencies greater than $L^{-1} = \omega_{max}$ are averaged out and do not contribute). Such a result is surprising because it implies that the fluctuations of the electric field in an atom with radius r are of order $1/r^2$ and hence are greater than the Coulomb field which is $\sim e^2/r^2$. However, the fluctuating field contains mostly high frequencies and hence is not as effective as the Coulomb field, which acts for long times in the same direction. A field E_ω with frequency ω gives a displacement $(\Delta x_\omega)^2 \sim (eE_\omega/m\omega^2)^2$. Putting $E_\omega{}^2 = \omega$ and integrating over frequency with the weighting factor $\omega^2 \, d\omega$ we get $(\Delta x)^2 = \alpha/m^2 \ln (\omega_{max}/\omega_{min})$. In atomic systems frequencies less than those of the electrons, $\alpha^2 m$, are averaged out and frequencies greater than m are quenched by relativistic effects, so that $\ln (\omega_{max}/\omega_{min})$ is $\ln \alpha^2$ and is actually a number of order 5. This effect gives fluctuations in the electron position which are, in fact, less than the relativistic fluctuations discussed above which gave $(\Delta x)^2 \sim m^{-2}$.

However, these fluctuations like the relativistic ones tend to shift the S-levels up, but only by $\Delta E \sim m\alpha^5 \ln \alpha$. This effect has even been measured experimentally by Lamb and Retherford. In the particle description this fluctuation would be attributed to the recoil of the electron when it emits and absorbs virtual quanta. Specifically, when an electron emits a virtual photon of momentum ω, it obtains a recoil velocity ω/m. The U.R. tells us that such a photon will be reabsorbed after a time ω^{-1} during which the electron will be displaced by a distance m^{-1}. Since the photons are emitted in random directions, we have to add square displacements as before. Integrating the probability of photon emission $\alpha\omega^3$ times the photon density $\omega^2 \, d\omega$ we have, as before, $(\Delta x)^2 \sim e^2/m \ln (\omega_{max}/\omega_{min})$.

The presence of virtual photons and pairs also influences the magnetic moment of the electron. This and similar effects are quite involved, since there are many factors which contribute with complicated phase relations and cannot be estimated easily. When both relativistic and quantum phenomena are taken into account at the same time the total interaction between elementary particles becomes very intricate. Indeed, the deep and complex mathematical structure which we are now going to build is necessary primarily for the calculation of these subtle phenomena.

2. Classical Electrodynamics

Many of the notions of quantum electrodynamics are inferred from classical electrodynamics. Hence, we shall give a short review here of the classical theory.

If one unites the electric and magnetic field strengths as the time and space components of a single antisymmetric four tensor $f_{ik}(x) = -f_{ki}(x)$, then the Maxwell equations can be written in the compact form

$$f_{,k}^{ik} = j^i(x) \tag{1.1}$$

$$\epsilon^{qrst} f_{rs,t} = 0. \tag{1.2}$$

Here $j^i(x)$ is the current density vector. Equation 1.2 is identically satisfied if we represent f_{ik} by the four-dimensional curl of the four potential $A_i(x)$

$$f_{ik} = A_{i,k} - A_{k,i}. \tag{1.3}$$

If we subject A_i to the restriction

$$A_{,i}^{i} = 0 \tag{1.4}$$

then Eq. 1.1 takes the form

$$\Box^2 A^i(x) = j^i(x). \tag{1.5}$$

The continuity equation

$$j_{,i}^{i} = 0 \tag{1.6}$$

insures the consistency of Eq. 1.4 with Eq. 1.5.

The energy-momentum tensor of the electromagnetic field is given by

$$T_k^{i} = f^{ij} f_{jk} + \tfrac{1}{4} f^{jl} f_{jl} \delta_k^{i}. \tag{1.7}$$

T_k^{i} has a vanishing trace; $T_i^{i} = 0$, and obeys, as one may easily verify, using Eqs. 1.1 and 1.2 (see problem 1), the equation

$$T_{,i}^{ik} = -j_l f^{lk}. \tag{1.8}$$

This set of equations describes the energy-momentum transfer between the electromagnetic field and charged bodies by means of the force density $j_l(x)f^{lk}(x)$. In the following we shall suppose that the charged bodies are point particles and therefore we will be able to calculate only quantities for which the detailed structure of the particles is irrelevant. Needless to say we cannot obtain a complete description of the elementary charged particles in this way but, in any case, the classical description is not sufficient. However, many of the classical relations referring to structure-independent features also hold in quantum theory. The motion of a point particle with no internal degrees of freedom can be described by its four space-time coordinates z_i as a function of the proper time s. The relevant mechanical and electrical quantities appropriate to such a particle; i.e., the energy-momentum tensor and current vector are given by

$$\mathfrak{I}^{ik}(x) = m \int_{-\infty}^{\infty} ds \dot{z}^i(s)\dot{z}^k(s)\delta(x - z(s)). \qquad (1.9)$$

Here $\delta(x)$ is the four-dimensional δ function given in Eq. (N.4) of the section on Notation.[1]

$$j_i(x) = e \int_{-\infty}^{\infty} ds \dot{z}_i(s)\delta(x - z(s)). \qquad (1.10)$$

If only electromagnetic forces act on the charges, the equations of motion will assume the familiar form

$$m\ddot{z}_i(s) = e\dot{z}^k(s)f_{ki}(z(s)). \qquad (1.11)$$

In this case the change of energy momentum of the field and that of the particles balance each other (see problem 2)

$$\frac{d}{dx_i}(T^{ik} + \mathfrak{I}^{ik}) = 0. \qquad (1.12)$$

From the definition of s it follows that

$$\dot{z}^2 = 1 \qquad \dot{z}\ddot{z} = \dot{z}\dddot{z} + \ddot{z}^2 = 0. \qquad (1.13)$$

Eq. (1.13) is essential for the consistency of Eq. (1.11) (since $\dot{z}_i\dot{z}_k f^{ik} = 0$).

---

[1] One easily sees that Eqs. (1.9) and (1.10) have the right form in the rest system. Since they are invariant equations, $\mathfrak{I}$ and j will have these forms in all systems.

The general solution of Eq. (1.5) is composed of an arbitrary solution of the homogeneous equation and a special solution of the inhomogeneous equation. Applying the Greens' functions, Eq. (A2.15) in Appendix, we may define two solutions of the source-free equation, A^{in} and A^{out}, with the expression

$$A(x) = A^{in}(x) + \int dx' D^{ret}(x - x') j(x')$$
$$= A^{out}(x) + \int dx' D^{adv}(x - x') j(x'). \tag{1.14}$$

In a physical sense, A^{in} means the incoming field, which is not generated by j. This can be seen by switching on the charge at some given time. Since D^{ret} is only different from zero inside the forward light cone, by taking $j = 0$ for $x_0 < -t$ we have $A = A^{in}$ for $x_0 < -t$. In like manner, we can think of A^{out} as the outgoing field which is left after the charge has been switched off.

The radiation field

$$A^{rad}(x) = A^{out}(x) - A^{in}(x) = \int dx' D(x - x') j(x') \tag{1.15}$$

plays an essential role. It will be used to describe irreversible energy transferred by the charge to the field.

If there is no incoming field, then we may derive, with the aid of Eqs. (A2.15) and (N.1)

$$A_i(x) = e \int_{-\infty}^{\infty} ds \dot{z}_i(s) D^{ret}(x - z(s))$$
$$= \frac{e}{4\pi} \frac{\dot{z}_i(s_0)}{(\dot{z}(s_0), x - z(s_0))}. \tag{1.16}$$

D^{ret} is essentially a δ function with whose help the integral over ds can easily be evaluated. By s_0 we shall mean the proper time of the point of intersection of the backward light cone of x and the world line of the charge.

$$(z(s_0) - x)^2 = 0 \qquad x_0 > z_0(s_0). \tag{1.17}$$

Since s_0 depends on x, it is useful for computing the field strength to differentiate with respect to x under the integral sign in Eq. (1.6) and then to partially integrate

$$A_{i,k}(x) = e \int ds \dot{z}_i(s) \frac{d}{ds} D^{\mathrm{ret}}(x - z(s)) \left\{ \frac{d}{ds} (x - z(s))^2 \right\}^{-1} (x - z(s))^2_{,k}$$

$$= e \int ds D^{\mathrm{ret}}(x - z(s)) \frac{d}{ds} \frac{\dot{z}_i(s)(x - z(s))_k}{(\dot{z}(s), x - z(s))}$$

$$f_{ik}(x) = \frac{e}{4\pi} (\dot{z}, x - z)^{-1}$$

$$\cdot \frac{d}{ds} \left\{ [\dot{z}_i(x - z)_k - \dot{z}_k(x - z)_i](\dot{z}, x - z)^{-1} \right\} \big|_{s=s_0} \quad (1.18)$$

$$= \frac{e}{4\pi} (\dot{z}, x - z)^{-3} [(\dot{z}, x - z)\ddot{z}_i(x - z)_k - (\ddot{z}, x - z)\dot{z}_i$$

$$\cdot (x - z)_k + \dot{z}_i(x - z)_k - (i \leftrightarrow k)] \big|_{s=s_0}.$$

The last symbols mean antisymmetrization with respect to i and k. The f is composed of a part which depends on $\ddot{z}$ and a part which depends only on $\dot{z}$. The former terms arise from the acceleration of the charge and have two powers of $x - z$ in the numerator, whereas the latter are multiplied by only one power. As is known from the Hertz solutions, an accelerating charge generates a field which falls off as $1/r$, while the static field falls off as $1/r^2$. The asymptotic field $f^{(\ddot{z})}_{ik}(z)$ has the property that the electric and magnetic field strengths are orthogonal to each other and to the space part of $x - z$

$$f^{(\ddot{z})}_{ik}(x - z)^k = f^{(\ddot{z})}_{mn}(x - z)_k \epsilon^{ikmn} = f^{(\ddot{z})}_{ik} f^{(\ddot{z})}_{mn} \epsilon^{ikmn} = 0. \quad (1.19)$$

If we wish to learn what the radiated energy-momentum vector is

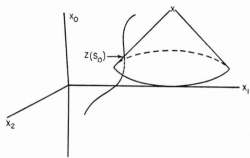

FIG. 4. This diagram will be useful for understanding Eq. (1.17) and what follows.

at infinity, then we need just the energy-momentum tensor generated by $f_{ik}^{(\ddot{z})}$. Only those terms which do not fall off more rapidly than $1/r^2$ contribute to the energy flux through the surface of an infinitely remote sphere. This part of the energy-momentum tensor can be calculated to be (problem 4)

$$T_{ik}^{(\ddot{z})}(z) = -\left(\frac{e}{4\pi}\right)^2 \frac{(x-z)_i(x-z)_k}{(\dot{z}, x-z)^4} \left\{\ddot{z}^2 + \left[\frac{(\ddot{z}, x-z)}{(\dot{z}, x-z)}\right]^2\right\}_{s=s_0}. \quad (1.20)$$

If we calculate T_{00} in the rest system of $\dot{z}(s_0)$, then Eq. (1.20) shows, since $\ddot{z}^2 < 0$, that the energy density is always positive. Furthermore, the strongest radiation is generated at right angles to $\ddot{z}$, which is spacelike in this system. The energy-momentum change of the particle ΔP, which is absorbed by the electromagnetic field in a definite space-time region V bounded by a surface σ, becomes

$$\Delta P^i = -\int_V dx T_{,k}^{ik} = -\int d\sigma_k T^{ik}. \quad (1.21)$$

In order to compute the radiation from a segment ds of the world line of the charge, we choose for σ a surface defined by the upper light cones through the beginning and end points of ds. The four-volume between these is closed at infinity by a surface σ' whose normal γ is orthogonal to $\dot{z}(s_0)$.

In the system where $\dot{z}(s_0)$ is timelike, γ is purely spacelike and σ' is an infinite spherical shell around $z(s_0)$.

If x is the integration point on σ, it follows that

$$(x-z)^2 = 0 \qquad (\gamma, \dot{z}) = 0. \quad (1.22)$$

If we define r by $x - z = r\dot{z} + \gamma$, then we may prove the relations

$$(\gamma, x-z) = \gamma^2 = -r^2$$
$$(\dot{z}, x-z) = r \qquad (1.23)$$
$$(\ddot{z}, x-z) = (\ddot{z}, \gamma).$$

Since the normal to the light cone is orthogonal to $x - z$, only σ' contributes to Eq. (1.21). The surface element of this part of σ can be written in the reference frame where $\dot{z}(s_0)$ is timelike.

$$d\sigma_i = ds d\Omega r \gamma_i \quad (1.24)$$

where $d\Omega$ has the meaning of the spatial solid angle. In this reference frame $\ddot{z}$ is purely spatial [$\dot{z} = (1, 0, 0, 0)$], which enables us to make

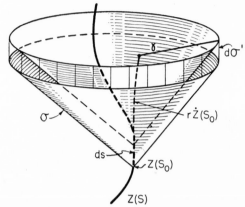

Fig. 5. This diagram illustrates the geometrical quantities defined by Eqs. (1.22) and (1.23).

a simple evaluation of the energy loss by combining Eqs. (1.20), (1.23), and (1.24).

$$\Delta P_k = \left(\frac{e}{4\pi}\right)^2 ds \int d\Omega r^{-1}(\gamma + r\dot{z})_k \left[\ddot{z}^2 + \left(\frac{\ddot{z}, \gamma}{r}\right)^2\right]$$
$$= \frac{2}{3}\frac{e^2}{4\pi} ds \dot{z}_k \ddot{z}^2. \tag{1.25}$$

Integration over the directions of γ will average out odd powers of γ and $\left(\frac{\ddot{z}, \gamma}{r}\right)^2$ becomes simply $-\ddot{z}^2/3$. The energy-momentum loss per ds

$$\frac{\Delta P}{ds} = \frac{2}{3}\frac{e^2}{4\pi}\dot{z}\ddot{z}^2 \tag{1.26}$$

is in the rest system of $\dot{z}$ a purely timelike vector with negative 0 component. Hence, in this frame, there is no momentum loss and one can write

$$\frac{\Delta P_0}{dx_0} = \frac{2}{3}\frac{e^2}{4\pi}\ddot{z}^2. \tag{1.27}$$

In the previous calculation we have treated the electromagnetic field at an infinite distance from the charge. One may try to calculate the radiation which does not get to infinity. In order to investigate this, we rewrite, with the help of Eqs. (1.8) and (1.15), the expression for the energy-momentum vector transferred from the particle to the field

$$\Delta P_k = \int dx j^u \left[f_{\mu k}^{\text{in}} + \frac{1}{2} (f_{\mu k}^{\text{rad}} + f_{\mu k}^{\text{ret+adv}}) \right]. \tag{1.28}$$

The first term represents the interaction between the charge and the external field f^{in}. We wish to show now that the energy-momentum loss arising from interaction with the radiation field stems from the second term while the third term has, for a point charge, only an inertial effect.

The integral over dx in Eq. (1.28) in conjunction with Eq. (1.10) tells us that we have to take the field on the world line of the body. We shall now see that f^{rad} is finite on the world line. Referring to Eqs. (1.15) and (1.18) we note that

$$f_{ik}^{\text{rad}}(x)$$

$$= e \int ds D(x - z(s)) \left(\frac{d}{ds} \left\{ \frac{\dot{z}_i(s)(x - z(s))_k}{(\dot{z}(s),\, x - z(s))} \right\} - (i \leftrightarrow k) \right). \tag{1.29}$$

This has to be evaluated for a point x on the world line. We associate the value $s = 0$ with this point $z(0)$ and evaluate $f_{(z(0))}^{\text{rad}}$ by expanding in powers of s (z's without argument refer to $s = 0$)

$$z(s) - z(0) = s\dot{z} + \frac{s^2}{2!}\ddot{z} + \frac{s^3}{3!}\dddot{z} + \cdots$$

$$\dot{z}(s) = \dot{z} + s\ddot{z} + \frac{s^2}{2}\dddot{z} + \cdots \tag{1.30}$$

Inserting in Eq. (1.29) and keeping as many powers of s as necessary we get, interpreting $\delta(s^2)$ as $\lim_{\alpha \to 0} \delta(s^2 - \alpha^2)$,

$$\frac{1}{2} f_{ik}^{\text{rad}}(z(0)) = -\frac{e}{4\pi} \int_{-\infty}^{\infty} ds \epsilon(s)\delta(s^2) \frac{d}{ds}$$

$$\cdot \left[\frac{\left(\dot{z}_i + s\ddot{z}_i + \frac{s^2}{2}\dddot{z}_i \right)\left(\dot{z}_k + \frac{s}{2}\ddot{z}_k + \frac{s^2}{6}\dddot{z}_k \right)}{\left(\dot{z} + s\ddot{z} + \frac{s^2}{2}\dddot{z} \right)\left(\dot{z} + \frac{s}{2}\ddot{z} + \frac{s^2}{6}\dddot{z} \right)} \right] - (i \leftrightarrow k)$$

$$\frac{1}{2} f_{ik}^{\text{rad}}(z(s)) = \frac{e}{4\pi} [\dot{z}_i(s)\dddot{z}_k(s) - \dot{z}_k(s)\dddot{z}(s)] \cdot \frac{2}{3} \tag{1.31}$$

In the last equation we used s rather than 0 as the argument since it obviously holds for all points on the world line. Integrating with respect to x in Eq. (1.28) over two spacelike surfaces intersecting the world line at s and $s + ds$ we only get contributions from the world line when $j \neq 0$. This gives, for the field reaction

$$\frac{dP_k^{\text{rad}}}{ds} = \frac{e^2}{4\pi} \frac{2}{3} (\dot{z}_k \ddot{z}^2 + \dddot{z}_k). \tag{1.32}$$

The first term is the radiated energy-momentum which we found at infinity. Its zero component is always negative and represents an irreversible energy transfer from the particle to the field. Its space part is a force which, like a viscous force, is proportional to the negative momentum of the charged particle. The second part of Eq. (1.32) is a total differential of a quantity referred to as the acceleration energy. In contrast to the first term, the zero component of the second can have either sign and is an energy which is reversibly stored in the field. The charge regains this energy when it takes on the original value of $\ddot{z}$. This part of the field energy remains in the neighborhood of the charge and does not appear at infinity. The space component of this term is a force which acts in the direction of the change of $\ddot{z}$. Therefore, this term may tend to increase the energy[2] and momentum of the particle. This remarkable effect has its origin in a tendency of the accelerated charge to radiate more in the backward than into the forward direction. In fact, the two terms can cancel each other, as happens for hyperbolic motion which is characterized by $\ddot{z}^2 = -a^2$, $\dddot{z} = z/a^2$, $\dddot{z} = \dot{z}/a^2$. In this case, the charge radiates energy which it "borrows" from the field in the near zone.

One may wonder why the self force $e^2/4\pi(2/3)\dddot{z}$ changes sign under $t \leftrightarrow -t$ whereas the original Eqs. (1.1) to (1.6) are invariant under this transformation. The point is that the positive time direction becomes distinguished from the negative one when we put $A^{\text{in}} = 0$ rather than $A^{\text{out}} = 0$. Thus, the sign of the reaction force is determined by our belief that certain initial conditions at $t = -\infty$ have more probability of realization than others at $t = +\infty$.

---

[2] The reader will note that $(e^2/4\pi)(2/3)\dddot{z}_0$ can be arbitrarily large, which means that the charge can borrow arbitrarily large amounts of energy from the field. This seems to be in strong contradiction to the positive definite character of the field energy. Such a peculiarity of the point model is explained by the positively infinite self energy of a point charge, which can always compensate the acceleration energy.

The last term on the right hand side of Eq. (1.28) is infinite since $f^{\text{ret}} + f^{\text{adv}}$ is singular on the world line. Here the δ model for the charge fails and assumptions about the structure of the charged body have to be made. For a charged sphere of radius R, one obtains $dP/ds \sim -\ddot{z}(e^2/8\pi R)$ plus terms which vanish for $R \to 0$. Since $D^{\text{ret}+\text{adv}}$ is an even function of x_0, all contributions from this term are proportional to even derivatives of z_μ and, for dimensional reasons, the term $\ddot{z}$ must be proportional to R^{-1}. The term which becomes infinite as R goes to zero has only the effect of increasing the mass of the charged body. Having calculated the action of the self field we may write the equations of motion

$$\left(m + \frac{e^2}{8\pi R}\right)\ddot{z}_\mu - \frac{e^2}{4\pi}\frac{2}{3}\left(\dddot{z}_\mu + \dot{z}_\mu \ddot{z}^2 + 0(R)\right) = e\dot{z}^r f^{\text{in}}_{r\mu} \qquad (1.33)$$

where $0(R)$ contains terms which vanish for $R \to 0$. The mass which is relevant for the motion of the body in a slowly varying f^{in} is $m' = m + e^2/8\pi R$. This quantity may therefore be called the observable mass. It has to be remembered that for a charged body of finite extension nonelectromagnetic forces have to be introduced to overcome Coulomb repulsion. Otherwise the equations of motion, Eq. (1.1) are not satisfied inside the body. This has the consequence that $T_{ik} + \mathfrak{z}_{ik}$ is not divergence-free and the corresponding energy-momentum vector does not transform like a four-vector. Many attempts have been made to contsruct a model of a closed relativistic theory where this would not happen. For instance, one might try to find a limiting process which corresponds to $R \to 0$ in which the equations of motion are satisfied. The papers discussing the difficulties one runs into by doing so (and with proposals for saving the situation) are legion. We shall not enter into these problems, since they are purely academic and do not correspond to anything in physics. In the classical theory, difficulties arise if particles are as small as e^2/m. However, in quantum theory, relativistic effects begin to appear at distances as large as the Compton wave length $1/m$. These phenomena dominate for smaller distances and, therefore, results of the classical theory where distances $\sim e^2/m$ are involved cannot be taken seriously. It seems that in nature methods other than clever mathematics are used to solve the difficulties of classical electrodynamics.

It is possible to derive the classical equations of motion from a Hamiltonian function

$$H = (p(s) - eA(q(s))^2)/2m. \qquad (1.34)$$

The canonical equations

$$m\dot{q}_i = (p - eA)_i \qquad \dot{p}_i = \frac{e}{m}(p - eA)_k A^k,_i \qquad (1.35)$$

are equivalent to Eq. (1.11).

The laws of electrodynamics can be presented in a still more condensed form, by means of an action principle in which the electromagnetic field is eliminated and only the motion of the charged particles is treated explicitly. If one has a number of charged particles differentiated by Greek indices, then Eqs. (1.1), (1.2), and (1.11) are combined in the action integral of Fokker, Schwarzschild, and Tetrode

$$W = \sum_\alpha \int ds \dot{z}_\alpha^2 \frac{m_\alpha}{2} + \sum_{\alpha > \beta} e_\alpha e_\beta \int ds\, ds'$$
$$\cdot \{\dot{z}_\alpha(s)\dot{z}_\beta(\dot{s})\bar{D}(z_\alpha(s) - z_\beta(s'))\}. \qquad (1.36)$$

If one varies the world lines of the bodies and regards W as the integral of a Lagrange function along these world lines, then the Euler equations

$$\frac{d}{ds}\frac{\partial L}{\partial \dot{z}_\alpha(s)} = \frac{\partial L}{\partial z_\alpha(s)} \qquad (1.37)$$

are indeed equivalent to the equations of motion in Eq. (1.11). The field generated by the other particles effects the motion of a given particle according to Eq. (1.37) as follows:

$$m_\alpha \ddot{z}_{\alpha k} = e_\alpha \dot{z}_\alpha{}^i(s) \sum_{\beta < \alpha} \int ds' \left[\dot{z}_{\beta i}(s') \frac{\partial}{\partial z_\alpha{}^k(s)} \right.$$
$$\left. - z_{\beta k}(s') \frac{\partial}{\partial \dot{z}_\alpha{}^i(s)} \right] \bar{D}(z_\alpha(s) - z_\beta(s')). \qquad (1.38)$$

Because Eq. (1.36) is symmetric with respect to the subscripts α and β, one is forced to use the average of the retarded and advanced interaction in Eq. (1.36). By choosing α is greater than β in the double sum in Eq. (1.36), one avoids the infinite self energy and thereby loses terms representing the radiation field of the particle acting back upon itself. On the basis of the above action at a distance concept, one cannot build a consistent theory which gives subtle effects like the Lamb shift. This shows that the field concept which associates separate degrees of freedom with the electric field gives the proper description of these phenomena.

3. The General Formalism of the Quantum Theory of Fields

In the quantum theory the observables of a system, such as energy or charge are represented by operators O.[1] These act on vectors $|\,)$ in an infinite dimensional vector space (commonly called Hilbert space) in such a way that a vector $|\,\alpha)$ is taken into a vector $|\,\beta)$ by the operation: $O\,|\,\alpha) = |\,\beta)$. In particular, a vector $|\,o')$ is said to be an eigenvector of O corresponding to the eigenvalue o' of O if

$$O\,|\,o') = o'\,|\,o') \tag{1.39}$$

where o' is an ordinary number. (In a matrix representation a number is a simple multiple of the unit matrix.)

The two essential axioms for the interpretation of the mathematical formalism are:

I. The result of any measurement of an observable can only be one of the eigenvalues of the operator associated with it.

II. The state of a system is characterized by a vector $|\,)$ in Hilbert space.[2] Further, the probability $w_{o'}$ that in the measurement of an observable O a particular eigenvalue o' is measured is equal to the absolute value squared of the component of the state vector along the eigenvector $|\,o')$ belonging to the eigenvalue o'

$$w_{o'} = |\,(|\,o')\,|^2. \tag{1.40}$$

Since the result of a measurement must be a real number, the first axiom implies that an observable can only be represented by Hermitian operators: $O^\dagger = O$. Hermitian operators furthermore have

[1] For instance, in elementary wave mechanics the momentum of a particle is represented by the differential operator $-i(\partial/\partial x)$, which acts on the Schrödinger function (state vector). See P. A. M. Dirac, "Principles of Quantum Mechanics," 3rd ed., Chapter II. Oxford Univ. Press, London and New York, 1947.

[2] In the text we take the standpoint of the so-called Heisenberg representation, in which the state vector is fixed in time while the entire time-dependence of the system is manifested in the eigenstates of the observables.

the property that eigenvectors belonging to two different eigenvalues are orthogonal.[3]

Equation (1.39) defines eigenvectors only up to a numerical factor which we restrict by the normalization[4]

$$(o' \mid o'') = \delta(o' - o''). \qquad (1.41)$$

The mean value[5] of many measurements, $\int do'o'w_{o'}$, is simply equal to $(\mid o \mid)$; as one sees by expanding the state vector $\mid)$ in a basis of eigenvectors of O, $\mid) = \int do'(o' \mid) \mid o')$, and by using Eqs. (1.40) and (1.41).

If one subjects an operator O to a similarity transformation U, that is, writes

$$\bar{O} = UOU^{-1} \qquad (1.42)$$

then the eigenvalue spectrum does not change; the eigenvector of $\bar{o}$ belonging to the eigenvalue o' of O is given by

$$\mid \bar{o}') = U \mid o') \qquad (1.43)$$

that is

$$\bar{O} \mid \bar{o}') = o' \mid \bar{o}').$$

In order to preserve the Hermiticity of operators and the normalization, Eq. (1.41), of eigenvectors, one must insist that U be unitary: $U^\dagger = U^{-1}$. Unitary transformations are the generalization of rotations for complex vectors. The matrix representations of U on the basis of eigenvectors of $\bar{O}$ or O are given by

$$(o' \mid U \mid o'') = (o' \mid \bar{o}'') \qquad (1.44)$$

which follows directly from Eq. (1.43). If the eigenvectors $\mid o')$ and

---

[3] One multiplies Eq. (1.39) with $(o'' \mid$ and $(o'' \mid O = o'' \mid o'')$ with $\mid o')$ and subtracts the resulting equations.

[4] Here we suppose that the δ symbol is equal to the Dirac δ function if the spectrum is continuous and to the Kronecker δ if the spectrum is discrete. The integrals over eigenvalues which follow are to be taken as summations if the eigenvalues are discrete.

[5] Often this is referred to as an "expectation value," but since it needn't be equal to an eigenvalue, one cannot, in general, expect to measure the "expectation value."

$| \bar{o}')$ are normalized, then Eq. (1.44) is unitary. The inverse theorem, that two Hermitian operators are unitarily equivalent if they have the same eigenvalue spectrum, is usually true as well. Since energy operators of a closed system, for instance, have the same eigenvalue spectrum at different times, they must be connected by a unitary transformation

$$O(t_1) = U_{12} O(t_2) U_{12}^{-1} \qquad | o'_{t_1}) = U_{12} | o'_{t_2}) \qquad (1.45)$$

Thus it is as if the eigenvectors of O had been rotated in the time interval between t_1 and t_2. If a system is in an eigenstate $| o')$ of an operator O (the state vector $|) = | o'))$ then the second axiom implies that the probability that the measurement of another observable P will yield an eigenvalue p' is given by $| (o' | p') |^2$. Hence, the time development of a system is governed by U_{21}, which is the product of eigenvectors of O at times t_1 and t_2

$$(o'_{t_1} | o''_{t_2}) = (o'_{t_2} | U_{12}^{-1} | o''_{t_2}), \qquad U_{12}^{-1} = U_{21}. \qquad (1.46)$$

This fundamental property of unitary matrices—that they can be represented by scalar products between basic vectors in the old and the new system—can be directly inferred from Eq. (1.43).

Because of the group property of rotations it is sufficient to characterize transformations differentially, that is, to give the infinitesimal variation of the transformation matrices U due to an infinitesimal rotation of the operators. Since the product of two unitary operators is unitary one can produce unitary operators which differ infinitesimally from U simply by multiplying U by the infinitesimal unitary operator $1 - iF$

$$U + \delta U = (1 - iF)U \qquad (1.47)$$

where F is an infinitesimal Hermitian operator. The change produced in an operator O by an infinitesimal similarity transformation is given by the relation[6]

$$O + \delta O = (1 - iF)O(1 + iF) = O + i[O, F]. \qquad (1.48)$$

In the matrix representation defined by Eq. (1.46), Eq. (1.47) can be written

$$\delta(o_{t_1} | o''_{t_2}) = (o'_{t_2} | \delta U_{12}^{-1} | o''_{t_2}) = i(o'_{t_1} | F_{12} | o''_{t_2}). \qquad (1.49)$$

[6] We always retain only the linear terms in F.

The nature of F is restricted by the group property of the transformations U

$$U_{13} = U_{12}U_{23}$$

or

$$(o'_{t_1} \mid o'''_{t_3}) = \int do''(o'_{t_1} \mid o''_{t_2})(o''_{t_2} \mid o'''_{t_3}). \tag{1.50}$$

The variation of Eq. (1.50) gives

$$(o'_{t_1} \mid F_{13} \mid o'''_{t_3}) = \int (o'_{t_1} \mid F_{12} \mid o''_{t_2}) do''(o''_{t_2} \mid o'''_{t_3})$$

$$+ \int (o'_{t_1} \mid o''_{t_2}) do''(o''_{t_2} \mid F_{23} \mid o'''_{t_3}) \tag{1.51}$$

$$= (o'_{t_1} \mid F_{12} + F_{23} \mid o'''_{t_3}).$$

Hence, the multiplicative nature of U implies the additivity of F.

The third and final axiom of the quantum theory yields a prescription for the construction of the generators F.[7]

III. To every canonical transformation of a classical system there is associated a unitary transformation of the corresponding quantized system, so that the generator of the infinitesimal unitary transformation is constructed in the same way as the generator of the corresponding classical canonical transformation.[8]

In the classical canonical formalism the generators of infinitesimal transformations are constructed out of variations of the action integral W. Thus, for the motion of a free particle with one coordinate q and a Lagrangian L we have

$$W = \int_{t_0}^{t} dtL(q, \dot{q}) \qquad \delta W = p\delta q - H\delta t.$$

The change in time or with q of any observable O is $\delta O/\delta t = [O, H]$ or $\delta O/\delta q = [O, p]$ where [ ] refers to the Poisson brackets, which will correspond to the commutators of Eq. (1.48) in the quantum mechanical formalism. Thus, in either classical or quantum mechanics, the change in any quantity by an infinitesimal transformation is determined by the Poisson bracket (in the classical case) or the commutator (in quantum mechanics) of the quantity with the generator of the transformation, while the latter is given by the

[7] See Dirac, Section 26, and J. Schwinger, *Phys. Rev.* **82**, 914 (1951).

[8] Systems without classical analogs can also be quantized along these lines.

corresponding change in the action integral. In this way, an observable may be changed through its time dependence or by the variation of some other parameter in the Lagrangian. This formula for quantization leads in particle mechanics to the Schrödinger equation. Thus, it is plausible to utilize these formal rules for the quantization of fields. In fact, these quantization rules are thought to be of much more general validity and to be applicable to any system. They have been used to describe the field of elastic displacements in a crystal or the motion of a liquid. In such cases the description of the system in terms of an infinite number of degrees of freedom is redundant and only a finite number of the modes correspond to the underlying mechanical situation.

In what follows we shall be dealing with fields like $\psi^\alpha(x)$ the electromagnetic or electron fields, for which one does not have a mechanical model in the background. All that one knows to start with about such fields are several invariance properties and equations of motion which are inferred from macroscopic and atomic phenomena. One may very well inquire about the limits of the field description for electrons and photons since we know that, for example, the field picture of a crystal breaks down in the atomic domain. In fact, when distances of less than 10^{-13} cm and correspondingly high energies are involved, the electric field begins to create particles other than electrons, and a great variety of new structures spring up. The principles governing these phenomena are hardly understood as yet. Therefore, the theory we are going to develop can only be applied with any certainty to phenomena between macroscopic and nuclear dimensions. In any event, we shall develop the quantum theory of fields under the assumption that it is invariant under the Lorentz group, with no thought of how precisely this is realized in nature.

From the analogy of particle mechanics we may anticipate that the field equations for[9] ψ^α will be the Euler equations of a variational principle based on the action W, which is given by the four-dimensional integral of the Lagrangian[10]

$$W = \int dx L(\psi^\alpha(x), \psi_{,i}{}^\alpha(x)). \tag{1.52}$$

[9] The index α is meant to differentiate among components of ψ when ψ is, for example, a vector or a spinor.

[10] In the sequel we treat only second-order field equations, so that L depends only on $\psi_{,i}$, the first derivative of ψ. The general considerations which now follow will be illustrated by examples in Chapter 5.

In order to deal with the Lorentz invariance of the theory, it is convenient to replace the essentially nonrelativistic idea of all space at one time by the notion of a spacelike, but otherwise arbitrary, surface. This allows one to drop the specialization to a definite coordinate system and always to work with general regions composed of physically independent points.

Thus, when we integrate quantities such as the total energy, we replace $\int dV$ by an integration over σ, $\int d\sigma$. Correspondingly, we have in mind the eigenvectors of an observable $\mid o'$) on a spacelike surface and not on a plane corresponding to t equals constant. The expression of particle mechanics for the action integral $W_{12} = \int_{t_2}^{t_1} dtL(q, \dot{q})$ is generalized to

$$W_{12} = \int_{\sigma_2}^{\sigma_1} dxL. \tag{1.53}$$

Axiom III can be written symbolically as

$$\delta(o'\sigma_1 \mid o''\sigma_2) = i\,(o'\sigma_1 \mid \delta \int_{\sigma_2}^{\sigma_1} dxL \mid o''\sigma_2)\,. \tag{1.54}$$

The additivity of F, Eq. (1.51), is guaranteed, since obviously $\delta W_{13} = \delta W_{12} + \delta W_{23}$. In order for $1 + i\delta W$ to be unitary to first order in δ, one must choose, in a quantized theory, a Hermitian L. The Lorentz and reflection invariance of Eq. (1.54) requires L to be a scalar.

We will now construct the generators of variations which are composed of a variation $\delta_0\psi^\alpha$ of the field variables and a variation of σ by δx.

The variation of W can be written

$$\delta W_{12} = \int_{\sigma_2}^{\sigma_1} dx\delta_0 L + \left(\int_{\sigma_1} - \int_{\sigma_2}\right) d\sigma_j \delta x^j L$$

$$\delta_0 L = \delta_0\psi^\alpha \frac{\partial L}{\partial \psi^\alpha} + \delta_0\psi^\alpha{}_{,k} \frac{\partial L}{\partial \psi^\alpha{}_{,k}} \tag{1.55}$$

$$= \left(\frac{\partial L}{\partial \psi^\alpha} - \frac{\partial}{\partial x^k} \frac{\partial L}{\partial \psi^\alpha{}_{,k}}\right) \delta_0\psi^\alpha + \frac{\partial}{\partial x^k}\left(\delta_0\psi^\alpha \frac{\partial L}{\partial \psi^\alpha{}_{,k}}\right).$$

Since ψ^α and $\delta_0\psi^\alpha$ are in general noncommuting quantities, in this expression and the following it is to be understood that the position of $\delta_0\psi$ is defined by the position of the corresponding ψ in the non-varied Lagrange function. If δx and $\delta_0\psi$ vanish on σ_1 and σ_2, the δW_{12} must also vanish. In this case the observables and the associated eigenvector system are not varied on σ_1 and σ_2 and hence the transformation function is fixed. The δW_{12} consists of a surface integral which vanishes under these conditions, and a volume integral over $(\delta L/\delta\psi^\alpha - (\partial/\partial x^k)\delta L/\delta\psi^\alpha{}_{,k})\delta_0\psi^\alpha$, where $\delta_0\psi^\alpha$ is arbitrary.

The Euler equations

$$\frac{\partial L}{\partial \psi^\alpha} - \frac{\partial}{\partial x^k}\frac{\partial L}{\partial \psi^\alpha{}_{,k}} = 0 \tag{1.56}$$

are therefore necessary for the consistency of our quantization procedure. The remaining divergence in Eq. (1.55) can be turned into a surface integral, and δW_{12} is now constructed from quantities referring only to σ_1 and σ_2. We shall, in addition, always suppose that all of the field variables ψ vanish strongly enough at infinity spatially so that contributions to surface integrals arise only from the regions of σ_1 and σ_2, which are not infinitely remote.

$$\delta W_{12} = F(\sigma_1) - F(\sigma_2)$$

$$F(\sigma) = \int d\sigma_j(L\delta x^j + \pi^{\alpha j}\delta_0\psi^\alpha), \qquad \pi^{\alpha j} = \frac{\partial L}{\partial \psi^\alpha{}_{,j}}. \tag{1.57}$$

The δW corresponds, therefore, to unitary transformations on σ_1 and σ_2 with the generators F. In the sequel we limit ourselves to rigid variations of σ, which are composed from infinitesimal rotations and displacements.[11] Thus, we set

$$\delta x^i = x'^i - x^i = e^i + e^{ik}x_k, \qquad e^{ik} = -e^{ki}. \tag{1.58}$$

As in particle mechanics, the total variation of ψ,[12] $\delta\psi$, is produced from both $\delta_0\psi$ and the variation of ψ induced by δx. Now we can see that it is through the infinitesimal rotation e^{ik} that the transformation

[11] Time reflection is an exception, since it generates no unitary transformation. It expresses the possibility of changing the sign of i everywhere, which leaves the observable consequences of the theory invariant. For details, see J. M. Jauch and F. Rohrlich, "Theory of Photons and Electrons." Addison-Wesley, Reading, Massachusetts, 1955. On the other hand, spatial reflections can be represented by unitary transformations, as we shall see later.

[12] One notes in the following that $\delta\psi_{,k} = \partial_k\delta\psi$ must be fulfilled.

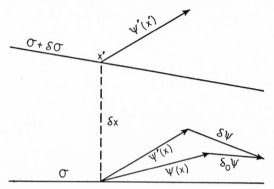

Fɪɢ. 6. This diagram indicates the variations which are considered in the arguments following Eq. (1.59) of the text.

character of ψ^α relative to the Lorentz group plays a role. If we designate ψ in the new system by ψ' then we have

$$\psi'^\alpha(x') - \psi^\alpha(x) = \tfrac{1}{2}e^{ik}S_{ik}^{\alpha\beta}\psi^\beta(x) \qquad S_{ik}^{\alpha\beta} = -S_{ki}^{\alpha\beta}. \quad (1.59)$$

Hence

$$S = 0 \text{ if } \psi \text{ is a scalar}$$

$$S_{ik}^{\alpha\beta} = (\gamma_i\gamma_k - \gamma_k\gamma_i)^{\alpha\beta}/4 \text{ if } \psi \text{ is a spinor}^{13}$$

$$S_{ik}^{\alpha\beta} = (g_i{}^\alpha g_{k\beta} - g_k{}^\alpha g_{i\beta}) \text{ if } \psi \text{ is a vector.}$$

Thus (see Fig. 6)

$$\delta\psi^\alpha = \delta_0\psi^\alpha + \psi^\alpha{}_{,k}\delta x^k - \tfrac{1}{2}e^{ik}S_{ik}^{\alpha\beta}\psi^\alpha = \delta_0\psi^\alpha + \psi^\alpha(x) - \psi'^\alpha(x)$$

which we may insert in Eq. (1.57) and write

$$F(\sigma) = \int d\sigma_j\left(\pi^{\alpha j}\delta\psi^\alpha + L\delta x^j - \pi^{\alpha j}\psi^\alpha{}_{,k}\delta x^k + \pi^{\alpha j}\frac{e^{ik}}{2}S_{ik}^{\alpha\beta}\psi^\beta\right).$$

We may transform the last term on the right-hand side with the introduction of

$$f_{jik} = -f_{ijk} = \tfrac{1}{2}(\pi_j{}^\alpha S_{ik}^{\alpha\beta}\psi^\beta + \pi_k{}^\alpha S_{ij}^{\alpha\beta}\psi^\beta + \pi_i{}^\alpha S_{kj}^{\alpha\beta}\psi^\beta) \quad (1.60)$$

and the use of Eqs. (1.58) and (1.59)

$$\tfrac{1}{2}e^{ik}\pi_j{}^\alpha S_{ik}^{\alpha\beta}\psi^\beta = e^{ik}f_{jik} = -\partial^i(f_{jik}\delta x^k) + \delta x^k\partial^i f_{jik}.$$

[13] See Eq. (A1.9).

The first term gives no contribution to F since $f_{jik} = -f_{ijk}$ and

$$\int d\sigma_j \partial_i f = \int d\sigma_i \partial_j f. \tag{N.6}$$

Thus, F takes the final form

$$F(\sigma) = \int d\sigma_j (\pi^{\alpha j} \delta \psi^\alpha - T^{jk} \delta x_k) \tag{1.61}$$

$$T^{jk} = \pi^{\beta j} \psi^{\beta,k} - \partial_i f^{jik} - Lg^{jk}.$$

The field equations only fix the Lagrangian up to the addition of an arbitrary divergence, since the Euler equations are invariant under the substitution

$$L \rightarrow L + \partial_i h^i \tag{1.62}$$

W_{12} is not invariant under Eq. (1.62). We will now show that the change in W_{12} expresses the possibility of altering the basis of eigenvectors on σ_1 and σ_2. We can again restrict our considerations to infinitesimal transformations, and we shall call the generator which produces infinitesimal changes of bases $H(\sigma): |\bar{o}') = (1 - iH) |o')$. Then we have, for the new W_{12}

$$(\bar{o}'(\sigma_1) | \bar{o}''(\sigma_2)) = (o'(\sigma_1) |1 - iH(\sigma_2) + iH(\sigma_1) | o''(\sigma_2))$$

and with

$$H(\sigma) = \int d\sigma_j h^j$$

this is equivalent to changing W_{12}, as indicated in Eq. (1.62), by

$$\delta W_{12} = \int_{\sigma_2}^{\sigma_1} dx \partial_j h^j.$$

As a corollary, if we choose $h^j = -\delta(\pi^{\alpha j} \psi^\alpha)$, δW_{12} becomes

$$-\int d\sigma_j \delta(\pi^{\alpha j} \psi^\alpha)$$

and we have for F a second equivalent representation

$$F(\sigma) = -\int d\sigma_j (\psi^\alpha \delta \pi^{\alpha j} + T^{jk} \delta x_k). \tag{1.63}$$

Equations (1.61) and (1.63) correspond to the well-known expressions $\delta W = p\delta q - H\delta t$ and $\delta W = -q\delta p - H\delta t$ of particle mechanics. The quantities which correspond to q and p are ψ^α and the component π^α of $\pi^{\alpha j}$ along the normal n_j to the surface σ at the point x, $\pi^\alpha(x) = n_j \pi^{\alpha j}(x)$. As in particle mechanics, we presume that $\int d\sigma_j \pi^{\alpha j}\delta\psi^\alpha$ is the generator of the transformation $\psi \to \psi - \delta\psi$, $\pi \to \pi$, and that $-\int d\sigma_j \psi^\alpha \delta\pi^{\alpha j}$ is the generator for $\pi \to \pi - \delta\pi$, $\psi \to \psi$. (The $\delta\psi$ is defined by Fig. 6.) Referring back to Eq. (1.48), we are led to the commutation relations

$$\left[\psi^\beta(x), \int d\sigma_j \pi^{\alpha j}(x')\delta\psi_\alpha(x') \right] = i\delta\psi^\beta(x)$$

$$\left[\pi^\beta(x), \int d\sigma_j \pi^{\alpha j}(x')\delta\psi^\alpha(x') \right] = 0$$

$$\left[\psi^\beta(x), \int d\sigma_j \psi^\alpha(x')\delta\pi^{\alpha j}(x') \right] = 0 \tag{1.64}$$

$$-\left[\pi^\beta(x), \int d\sigma_j \psi^\alpha(x')\delta\pi^{\alpha j}(x') \right] = i\delta\pi^\beta(x)$$

for x and x' on the spacelike surface σ, i.e., $(x - x')^2 < 0$.

In classical mechanics, $\delta\psi$ and $\delta\pi$ can be chosen freely on a spacelike surface,[14] and there is no question about commutativity. In the present case, in order to eliminate $\delta\psi$ and $\delta\pi$ from Eq. (1.64) we must know something about their commutation properties with ψ and π. Here it is sufficient to consider the simplest kinds of variations, when $\delta\psi$ and $\delta\pi$ are ordinary numbers with the following qualification. It can be shown that a consistent charge symmetric theory can be constructed only if one supposes that $\delta\psi$ and $\delta\pi$ commute with all quantities if ψ^α is a scalar, a vector, or some more general tensor, and anticommute if ψ^α is a spinor. This classification corresponds to integer or half-integer spins of the particles described by the ψ fields.

If one uses the algebraic identity

$$[A, BC] = [A, B]_\pm C - B[C, A]_\pm$$

and the fact that $\delta\psi$ and $\delta\pi$ as functions of x on σ are arbitrary, then from Eq. (1.64) there follows a natural generalization of the commu-

---

[14] Sometimes this is not so, in which case care must be exercised in using these rules.

tation relations $[q_j , p_k] = i\delta_{jk}$ for systems with a discrete number of degrees of freedom

$$[\psi^\alpha(x), \pi^\beta(x')]_\pm = i\delta_\beta{}^\alpha \delta(x - x')$$
$$[\psi^\alpha(x), \psi^\beta(x')]_\pm = [\pi^\alpha(x), \pi^\beta(x')]_\pm = 0$$

(1.65)

for $(x - x')^2 < 0$ where, in accordance with the comments above, $\pm$ on the brackets indicates whether we deal with particles of half-integer or integer spin.[15]

Invariance of the action integral against particular variations produces conservation theorems, for $\delta W_{12} = F(\sigma_1) - F(\sigma_2) = 0$ means that the F under consideration is independent of σ, and hence is *a fortiori* independent of time.

We now consider variations of x alone. Equations (1.58) and (1.61) yield $- F(\sigma) = e^i P_i + \frac{1}{2} e^{ik} J_{ik}$ with $P^i = \int d\sigma_k T^{ki}$ and $J^{ik} = \int d\sigma_m M^{mik}$ where

$$M^{mik} = -M^{mki} = T^{mi}x^k - T^{mk}x^i.$$

(1.66)

If L does not depend explicitly on x, then rigid translations and rotations on σ only correspond to a redefinition of the integration variables, and thus leave W_{12} invariant. Hence, we have

$$P(\sigma_1) = P(\sigma_2) \qquad J(\sigma_1) = J(\sigma_2).$$

(1.67)

$P^i e_i$ is the counterpart of $H\delta t$ in particle mechanics, so that P^i is the four-dimensional analog of energy, the energy-momentum vector.[16] T^{ik} is, correspondingly, the energy-momentum tensor, and J^{ik} and M^{mik} are to be interpreted as the total angular momentum and the angular momentum tensor. The three space components of J^{ik} are the angular momenta; the three time components describe the center of gravity motion. Since σ_1 and σ_2 are arbitrary, one can use Eq. (N.5) and write Eq. (1.67) in differential form

$$\partial_k T^{ki} = 0 \qquad \partial_m M^{mik} = 0.$$

(1.68)

[15] The expressions in Eq. (1.65) are only correct if the sequence of factors is really written as in Eq. (1.64). In the examples to come later we always choose the sequence of factors in L in order to fulfill this requirement.

[16] The fact that L is independent of σ enables us to denote P as a vector and to extend the integration over an arbitrary spacelike surface.

From Eqs. (1.66) and (1.68) it immediately follows that T^{ik} is symmetric: $T^{ik} = T^{ki}$. Equation (1.68) can also be verified by direct calculation with Eq. (1.56).

The conservation of energy, momentum, and angular momentum and the center of mass theorem rest only on the fact that L is independent of x. In other words, they are grounded on the homogeneity and isotropy of the space-time continuum. These are the general precepts of our theory.

Particles with internal degrees of freedom are represented by fields with several components. In the case of spin, for example, the different components correspond to different spin states. In this instance a Lorentz transformation generates a linear transformation among the field components. There are, however, internal degrees of freedom which are not connected with any space-time property and where a Lorentz transformation does not mix field components corresponding to different states representing such a degree of freedom. It appears that electric charge is such a quantity and that charge conservation originates from an invariance property of the Lagrangian other than Lorentz invariance. For the description of charged particles one must double the number of components of the field. This makes it possible for L to be invariant under linear transformations among these components.

In general, the invariance of the Lagrangian under a continuous group of transformations among the field components $\psi_\alpha \rightarrow t_{\alpha\beta}\psi_\beta$ implies the existence of a constant of the motion. Such a quantity will be a scalar, as distinguished from the ten constants of the motion which originate from Lorentz invariance. The F corresponding to an infinitesimal transformation $(e^2 \rightarrow 0)$

$$T = 1 - iet, \qquad \delta\psi_\alpha = iet_{\alpha\beta}\psi_\beta$$

is given by

$$F(\sigma) = \int d\sigma_k j^k(x) \qquad j^k(x) = ie\pi^{\alpha k}(x)t^{\alpha\beta}\psi^\beta(x). \tag{1.69}$$

The invariance of L implies that $F(\sigma_1) = F(\sigma_2)$ or $\partial_k j^k(x) = 0$. Correspondingly, the F generated by the transformation associated with the charge will be interpreted as the total charge Q,[17] and $j_k(x)$ as the

[17] It is interesting to note that P, J, and j, but not T and M, are invariant against Eq. (1.62), which renders the local energy and angular momentum ambiguous in our theory.

current density. We shall see in the next section that the eigenvalues of Q are integer multiples of the eigenvalues of et. Particles with charges 0, $\pm e$ can, therefore, be characterized by the simplest representation of the one and two-dimensional rotation group, $t = 0$ and $t = \begin{pmatrix} 0 & i \\ -i & 0 \end{pmatrix}$, respectively. In the latter case it is convenient to unite the two components ψ_1 and ψ_2 in one complex field

$$\psi = (\psi_1 + i\psi_2)\frac{1}{\sqrt{2}} \qquad \psi^\dagger = (\psi_1 - i\psi_2)\frac{1}{\sqrt{2}}$$

in which case the invariance described above is guaranteed if L depends only on the Hermitian combination $\psi\psi^\dagger = \psi_1^2 + \psi_2^2$. In this notation the effect of T is an infinitesimal phase transformation $T\psi = e^{ie}\psi$ and $T\psi^\dagger = e^{-ie}\psi^\dagger$.

Quantities invariant under this transformation will commute with the generating operator Q. Furthermore, the L above is invariant[18] under a change of sign of ψ_2, which corresponds to a reflection in this two-dimensional space and anticommutes with the rotation t. Therefore, this operation reverses the sign of Q and is called charge conjugation. It can be accomplished by a unitary transformation which transforms all states into identical states except that the particles have opposite signs of their charges. States in which no particular sign of the charge is preferred must be invariant under this transformation and must be eigenstates of Q with zero eigenvalue.

According to the general rule in Eq. (1.54), P, J, and Q are the generating operators of infinitesimal displacements, rotations, and phase transformations. The commutation relations which express this are[19]

$$[\psi^\alpha(x), P_k] = i\partial_k\psi^\alpha(x)$$

$$[\psi^\alpha(x), J_{jk}] = i(x_k\partial_j - x_j\partial_k)\psi^\alpha(x) + iS_{kj}^{\alpha\beta}\psi^\beta(x)$$

$$[\psi^\beta(x), Q] = ec\psi^\beta. \qquad (1.70)$$

Here c is 0 or ± 1, and we have employed a representation which

---

[18] For spinor fields charge conjugation is somewhat more complicated, as we shall see in Section 5. In theories with several kinds of charged particles one can construct quantities like $\phi_1\psi_2 - \phi_2\psi_1$ which are rotation- but not reflection-invariant. If L contains terms with this structure, U_c may not exist, although the charge is conserved.

[19] Q is the generator for $\psi \rightarrow \psi - \delta\psi = \psi - iec\psi^\beta$.

diagonalizes t. As can be shown by direct calculation, these commutation relations are also a result of the commutation relations already expressed in Eq. (1.64), since all of the quantities occurring in Eq. (1.70) are functions of the ψ^β and $\pi^{\alpha k}$.

As the generator of infinitesimal phase transformations, Q commutes with all Hermitian quantities. Therefore, we have

$$[Q, P^i] = [Q, J^{ik}] = 0$$

which, conversely, shows that Q is a rotation and displacement invariant. Since P is itself a displacement invariant

$$[P_i, P_k] = 0 \tag{1.71}$$

while under rotations P transforms like a vector

$$\tfrac{1}{2}e_{mn}[P^k, J^{nm}] = ie^{kl}P_l. \tag{1.72}$$

This, together with the antisymmetry of J, leads to the expression

$$[P^k, J^{nm}] = i(g^{km}P^n - g^{kn}P^m). \tag{1.73}$$

Conversely, this measures the change in J, caused by a displacement which comes about because of the explicit dependence of J on the coordinates, as seen in Eq. (1.66). In an analogous way the tensor character of J implies the following commutation relations of the J's among themselves

$$[J^{ji}, J^{kl}] = i(g^{ki}J^{lj} + g^{il}J^{jk} + g^{jk}J^{il} + g^{lj}J^{ki}). \tag{1.74}$$

If the superscripts in Eqs. (1.72) and (1.73) are set equal to 1, 2, and 3, then the familiar commutation laws for momentum and angular momentum result. However, the superscripts involved with J_{0i} need further discussion. J_{0i} can be written in nonrelativistic notation as

$$x_i(t) - P_i t, \text{ where } x_i(t) = \int d^3\underline{V}T_{00}(x)x_i \text{ is the center of gravity.}$$

The latter depends, as does the center of charge $\int d\sigma_\mu j^\mu x_i$, on σ, and does not have simple transformation properties like J_{0i}. From the previous work it follows that

$$[x_k, P_j] = i\delta_{kj}E, \qquad [x_k, E] = iP_k.$$

These are the field theoretic forms of the position-momentum commutation laws. However, the transformation characteristics are concealed by the noncovariant notation. We may note, in addition, that the different components of x fail to commute; the commutator being the angular momentum.

The F's of Eq. (1.66) form a representation of the inhomogeneous Lorentz group. The commutation relations in Eqs. (1.71), (1.73), and (1.74) are determined by the commutation relations of the corresponding elements of the Lorentz group. If we treat two infinitesimal coordinate transformations of the group

$$\delta x_j^{(\alpha)} = e_j^{(\alpha)} + e_{jk}^{(\alpha)} x^k \tag{1.75}$$

in succession, then $\delta^{(1)}\delta^{(2)}x$ is again a transformation of the same kind.

$$(\delta^{(1)}\delta^{(2)} - \delta^{(2)}\delta^{(1)})x_i = e_{ij}^{(2)}e^{(1)j} - e_{ij}^{(1)}e^{(2)j} + (e_{ij}^{(2)}e^{(1)jk} - e_{ij}^{(1)}e^{(2)jk})x_k$$
$$= e_i^{(12)} + e_{ik}^{(12)}x^k \tag{1.76}$$

is in the group as well.

The generators of Eq. (1.75) are

$$-F^{(\alpha)} = e_i^{(\alpha)}P^i + \tfrac{1}{2}e_{ik}^{(\alpha)}J^{ik}$$

so that Eq. (1.76) expresses the unitary transformation

$$[1 + iF^{(1)}, 1 + iF^{(2)}] = -[F^{(1)}, F^{(2)}] = iF^{(12)}.$$

It is easy to convince oneself that the commutation relations in Eqs. (1.71) to (1.74) follow from the expression

$$-F^{(12)} = e_i^{(12)}P^i + \tfrac{1}{2}e_{ik}^{(12)}J^{ik}.$$

From the perspective of this chapter one can say that the mathematical formalism of the quantum theory of fields is dictated by the precepts of quantum theory and the kinematical structure which these are given through our notion of a pseudo-Euclidean space-time continuum.

Part II

FREE FIELDS

4. General Discussion

Having developed the general mathematical framework in the last part we will now study some problems concerning the physical interpretation of the theory. We ask whether the quantization procedure we have adopted actually introduces quantum characteristics and, if so, how these are expressed by the formalism. As a first step we shall determine what the eigenvectors of P are. In this part of the book we will restrict our attention to those cases in which the fields appear quadratically in the Lagrangian; thereby dealing with linear differential equations, which will be shown to govern the fields of noninteracting particles. These equations will imply that the Fourier transform $b(k)$ of ψ is different from zero only when $k^2 = m^2$, where m is the mass of the particles under consideration. That is to say, the k-vector has to be in or on the forward or backward light cone since it obeys the equation of the energy-momentum vector of a free particle.

In subsequent sections the modifications introduced by interacting particles and coupled differential equations will be examined. In general, however, we will only consider systems having a positive definite energy operator. This means, in particular, that the energy eigenvalues will be bounded below. The state corresponding to the lower bound is called the vacuum, since it may reasonably be supposed that the state of least energy and that of no particles will coincide. In order to define the vacuum as invariant we must assume that all observers find vanishing energy-momentum vectors in this state. Mathematically this is expressed by the formula

$$P_k \,|\, 0) = 0. \tag{2.1}$$

The Lagrangian of the system is to be adjusted so that this condition is fulfilled. In order to determine the consequence of this assumption we expand ψ in terms of plane waves which are the eigenfunctions of the differential operator ∂_k .

The fundamental commutation relation, Eq. (1.70), $[P_j, \, \psi^\alpha] = -i\partial_j\psi^\alpha$ becomes, using the fact that

$$\psi^\alpha(x) = \frac{1}{(2\pi)^4} \int dk e^{-ik \cdot x} b^\alpha(k)$$

$$P_j b^\alpha(k) - b^\alpha(k)P_j = -k_j b^\alpha(k). \tag{2.2}$$

45

If we multiply Eq. (2.2) with $| 0)$, then we learn that $P_j b^\alpha(k) | 0) = -k_j b^\alpha(k) | 0)$. Hence, $b^\alpha(k) | 0)$ is an eigenvector (although not normalized) of P, belonging to the eigenvalue $-k$. Since P^0 is positive definite it can have no negative eigenvalues, and $b^\alpha(k) | 0) = 0$ for $k_0 > 0$. We may decompose b into its positive and negative frequency parts; i.e., $b = b^- + b^+$, $b^+(k) = 0$ for $k_0 < 0$, and $b^-(k) = 0$ for $k_0 > 0$. Then we have, for the vacuum, $\psi^+|0) = 0$. This decomposition into positive and negative frequency parts is a Lorentz invariant concept only when the k-vectors are in or on the light cones. Hence, these arguments can only be applied to operators ψ which obey the linear equations mentioned above, and not to products of ψ or operators obeying nonlinear equations.

One can see by induction[1] from Eq. (2.2) that $| nk) = [b^-(k)]^n | 0)$ is an eigenvector of P belonging to the eigenvalue $-nk$ (n being a positive integer). If one multiplies Eq. (2.2) for $k_0 < 0$ with $| nk)$, then one learns that

$$P_j b^-(-k) | nk) = (n + 1)k_j b^-(-k) | nk).$$

More generally, a state[2]

$$| n_1 k_1, n_2 k_2, \cdots n_i k_i)$$
$$= [b^-(-k_1)]^{n_1}[b^-(-k_2)]^{n_2} \cdots [b^-(-k_i)]^{n_i} | 0). \tag{2.3}$$

obeys an equation

$$P_j | n_1 k_1, n_2 k_2 \cdots n_i k_i)$$
$$= (n_1 k_1{}^j + n_2 k_2{}^j + \cdots n_i k_i{}^j) | n_1 k_1 \cdots n_i k_i). \tag{2.4}$$

Keeping in mind that the k's are not arbitrary vectors, but that $b(k)$ is different from zero only when $k^2 = m^2$, we get the following fundamental theorem:

Any sum of integer multiples of vectors obeying $k^2 = m^2$ is an eigenvalue of the energy-momentum vector.

The eigenvalue $p^j = n_1 k_1{}^j + n_2 k_2{}^j + \cdots n_i k_i{}^j$ is just the energy-momentum vector of a system of n_1 free particles with energy-momentum vectors k_1, n_2 particles with k_2, etc. Since our first fundamental axiom assures us that eigenvalues are the only possible results

---

[1] The method is analogous to that of Dirac, Section 34.

[2] We mention without proof that in this way one obtains a complete set of eigenstates of P; i.e., any eigenvector can be written this way.

of measurement we find the quantum nature of the field expressed in the following way:

Any measurement of the energy-momentum vector can only give a value which equals the sum of energy-momentum vectors of an integer number of free particles, all having the same mass. The state corresponding to this eigenvalue will naturally be interpreted as a state where n_1 particles with energy-momentum vector k_2, n_2 particles with k_2, and so forth, are present. We shall see here and in future sections how such a state exhibits other characteristics one expects for particles, such as quantized values for charge and angular momentum. Since P_j and, therefore, its eigenstates, is a constant of the motion, the energy-momentum vectors are not altered in the course of time. This means that the theory as we have developed it up to now does not describe any process in which the motion of the particles is changed. In particular, we shall soon see that the probability of finding a particle at a later time in any position is not influenced by the presence of other particles except by the Pauli principle. The more interesting case of nonlinear systems, when this is no longer true and particle interactions can occur, will be discussed in Part IV.

The relationship between energy and frequency, and momentum and wave number, depends formally only on the property of the energy-momentum vector as a displacement operator, and is an essential consequence of quantum theory; one which is wholly absent in classical physics. It stands beside the Planck relationship $E = h\nu$ as the basis of quantum theory and expresses the content of the Einstein light quantum hypothesis and the de Broglie relation.

Just as the energy and momentum do, the angular momentum also has a quantum structure. In fact, an analogous commutation relation obtains, Eq. (1.70)

$$-[\psi^\alpha(x), J_{mn}] = i(x_m\partial_n - x_n\partial_m)\psi^\alpha(x) + iS_{mn}^{\alpha\beta}\psi^\beta(x). \quad (2.5)$$

The total angular momentum can be split into a spin and an orbital part, $J = J^{\text{orb}} + J^{\text{spin}}$, with $T_{ik}^{\text{orb}} = \pi_i^\beta\psi_k^\beta - g_{ik}L$ and $T_{ik}^{\text{spin}} = \partial^j f_{jik}$. J^{orb} as one can show by calculation and as is evident from the last section, generates space-time rotations, while the change induced in the field components by J^{spin} depends upon their transformation character with respect to the Lorentz group.

$$-[\psi^\alpha(x), J_{mn}^{\text{orb}}] = i(x_m\partial_n - x_n\partial_m)\psi^\alpha(x)$$
$$-[\psi^\alpha(x), J_{mn}^{\text{spin}}] = iS_{mn}^{\alpha\beta}\psi^\beta(x). \quad (2.6)$$

In order to determine the eigenvalues of J^{orb} we develop ψ in a series of eigenfunctions $Y_l^{\ m}$ of the rotation operators $i(x_m \partial_n - x_n \partial_m)$; ie, $\psi(x) = \sum_{l,m} b_l^{\ m} Y_l^{\ m}(x)$. ($Y_l^{\ m}$ is the usual spherical harmonic associated with the eigenvalues l, m.) It is well known that the three space components of the rotation operators have integers as eigenvalues. Let us take one of these space components, for example, J_{12}, and use its commutation relation with ψ^α, where we have decomposed ψ^α into the $Y_l^{\ m}$ as above. We will learn, after a spatial integration in which the orthogonality of the $Y_l^{\ m}$ is used, that $b_l^{\ m} J_{12}^{\text{orb}} - J_{12}^{\text{orb}} b_l^{\ m} = m b_l^{\ m}$. From this it follows that J_{12}^{orb} is an integer multiple of m and therefore has itself integer eigenvalues. $b_l^{\ m} \mid 0)$ is an eigenstate of J_{12}^{orb} with the eigenvalue m.

For a scalar field there is no J^{spin}. However, for a vector field $A_i(x)$, the expression for $S_{mn}^{\alpha\beta}$, which is given following Eq. (1.59), implies the following commutation relations for the spin part of J

$$[J_{12}^{\text{spin}}, A_1] = -iA_2 \qquad [J_{12}^{\text{spin}}, A_2] = iA_1 \tag{2.7}$$

or, if we transform from linear to circular components

$$A_1 + iA_2 = A_l \qquad A_1 - iA_2 = A_r$$
$$[J_{12}^{\text{spin}}, A_l] = -A_l \qquad [J_{12}^{\text{spin}}, A_r] = A_r . \tag{2.8}$$

From these one can conclude, as above, that the eigenvalues of J_{12}^{spin} are integers for states of the vector field containing quanta which have been produced by A_l and A_r. Multiplying the eigenvector of the z-component of the spin, J_{12}^{spin}, by A_r or A_l leads to a new eigenvector with an eigenvalue which is increased or decreased by one, respectively. Since A^- raises and A^+ lowers the energy and the number of quanta we can say:

A_r^- emits right circularly polarized quanta
A_r^+ absorbs left circularly polarized quanta
A_l^- emits left circularly polarized quanta
A_l^+ absorbs right circularly polarized quanta.

For a spinor field we have, from Eq. (1.59), $-[J_{mn}^{\text{spin}}, \psi^\alpha] = \frac{1}{2}\sigma_{mn}^{\alpha\beta}\psi^\beta$, from which it follows that the associated particle has spin $\frac{1}{2}$, since σ_{mn} has eigenvalues $\pm 1 (\sigma^2 = 1)$. Our result, therefore, is as follows.

The angular momentum has integer or half-integer eigenvalues. These results follow from the commutation relations in Eq. (1.74) alone and are therefore a consequence of the structure of the rotation group.[3]

---

[3] See Dirac, p. 144.

The last commutation relation of Eq. (1.70),

$$[\psi^{\alpha}(x), Q] = e\psi^{\alpha}(x)$$

$$[\psi^{\dagger\alpha}(x), Q] = -e\psi^{\dagger\alpha}(x)$$

for any complex field, gives us the information that the total charge is a multiple of e. In order for the vacuum to be invariant under charge conjugation we must also have $Q \mid 0) = 0$. Since the same derivation applies for arbitrarily small volumes it is not possible to "smooth out" the quantum nature of the charge. In fact, Eq. (1.70) holds for

$$\Delta Q = \int_{\Delta\sigma} d\sigma_k' j^{\cdot k}(x') \tag{2.9}$$

so long as the region $\Delta\sigma$ contains the point x. $\psi(x)$ commutes (or anticommutes) with $\psi(x')$ if x and x' are separated by a spacelike interval so that the commutator, Eq. (1.70), has contributions from Q only at the point x and all other points can be ignored. Furthermore, this indicates that the field quanta have the properties of point particles with no finite extension of their charge distribution. Since ψ, $(\psi^{\dagger})$, decreases, (increases), ΔQ for any $\Delta\sigma$ containing x, we may say that $\bar{\psi}(x)$ creates a point particle at the point x in space-time. We shall see, however, that virtual pair production will prevent the particles from displaying their point nature and in many processes they will act as if they had a charge distribution of extension $1/m$.

The eigenvalues of the energy in a finite volume are only integer multiples of the wave number, if the corresponding cube of the wave length is substantially smaller than the volume. Although Eq. (1.70) holds for the energy ΔP in an arbitrary volume around the point x, one may come to the conclusions in Eq. (2.2) only if $1/k^3$ is much smaller than the volume. The spin always has integer or half-integer eigenvalues, no matter how small the volume is. One might wonder whether it is possible to obtain a relativistic description of extended particles. At first sight, it would seem plausible to associate a current

$$\mathcal{J}_{\mu}(x) = \int dx' F(x - x') j_{\mu}(x')$$ with the fields, where F is an invariant

form factor. Although $Q = \int d\sigma_{\mu} \mathcal{J}_{\mu}(x)$ is an invariant for certain

forms of F, it does not depend on derivatives of only finite order of the fields on the surface σ. This leads to grave difficulties when one wants to use g as a source for the electromagnetic field. Hence, we shall confine ourselves to the point model.

Since b in Eq. (2.2) or, more generally, any expansion coefficient of ψ in an arbitrary eigenfunction system, has the same commutation relations with Q as ψ itself, $\psi(x)$ and $b(k)$ lower the charge by e. The conjugate functions $\bar{\psi}(x)$ or $\bar{b}(x)$ raise the charge by e. If we call particles with charge e electrons and particles with charge $-e$ positrons, then the operators below, for example, take on essentially the following meanings:

$\psi^-(x)[b^-(k)]$ emits positrons at coordinate x (with momentum k)

$\psi^+(x)[b^+(k)]$ absorbs electrons at coordinate x (with momentum k)

$\bar{\psi}^-(x)[\bar{b}^-(k)]$ emits electrons at coordinate x (with momentum k)

$\bar{\psi}^+(x)[\bar{b}^+(k)]$ absorbs positrons at coordinate x (with momentum k).

The notion of a particle at a point requires some qualification, as will be shown in Section 6.

Hence, the formal prescription for quantization reproduces the quantum characteristics of momentum, angular momentum, and charge which are in nature.

5. Special Fields

We wish to illustrate the formalism developed above with some specific examples. We will restrict ourselves to fields which obey linear differential equations of second order. Fields which obey equations of higher than second order do not have a positive definite energy and hence do not have any state of smallest energy. Such fields will not be considered in this book.

The formally simplest case is a scalar or pseudo-scalar[1] field which is represented by a Hermitian operator $\Phi(x)$. The Lagrange function must be of the form

$$L(x) = \tfrac{1}{2} : \partial_k \Phi(x) \partial^k \Phi(x) - m^2 \Phi(x) \Phi(x) : \qquad (2.10)$$

where m is a number with the dimensions of a reciprocal length.[2] In order for the vacuum expectation value of L to be zero

$$(0 \mid L \mid 0) = 0 \qquad (2.11)$$

along with that of T and J (this must be the case on general invariance grounds) we choose the sequence[3] of factors in L so that the positive frequency parts of the fields, Φ^+, always stand to the right of the negative frequency parts Φ^-. With this in mind we introduce the notation: ... : to mean

$$\begin{aligned} :\Phi(x)\Phi(x'): = \Phi^+(x)\Phi^+(x') &+ \Phi^-(x)\Phi^+(x') \\ &+ \Phi^-(x')\Phi^+(x) + \Phi^-(x)\Phi^-(x'). \end{aligned} \qquad (2.12)$$

From the Hermiticity of Φ it follows that $(\Phi^-)^\dagger = \Phi^+$, and hence the Hermitian conjugate of the vacuum definition $\Phi^+ \mid 0) = 0$ reads $(0 \mid \Phi^- = 0$. Thus $(0 \mid : \ldots : \mid 0) = 0$ is guaranteed in general. Furthermore : ... : does not destroy the Hermiticity of L and similar quantities. The Euler equation, Eq. (1.56), becomes here

$$(\Box^2 + m^2)\Phi(x) = 0 \qquad (2.13)$$

---

[1] A pseudo-tensor has the same transformation properties as an ordinary tensor except that it undergoes an additional change of sign under reflection.

[2] Because of the variational principle in Eq. (1.54), $L(x)$ has the dimensions of L^{-4}, so that Φ must have the dimensions of L^{-1}.

[3] $[\Phi^+(x), \Phi^-(x)]$ is an ordinary number, so that this reordering of L and, hence, of the observables, redefines the latter by only an additive constant.

and the quantity conjugate to Φ is

$$\pi^k = \partial^k \Phi \tag{2.14}$$

and

$$T^{mn} = {:}\partial^m \Phi \partial^n \Phi - \frac{g^{mn}}{2}(\partial^k \Phi \partial_k \Phi - m^2 \Phi\Phi){:}. \tag{2.15}$$

The energy density which we wish to be positive definite is, in fact

$$T_{00} = \tfrac{1}{2}{:}(\partial_0 \Phi \partial_0 \Phi + \partial_1 \Phi \partial_1 \Phi + \partial_2 \Phi \partial_2 \Phi + \partial_3 \Phi \partial_3 \Phi + m^2 \Phi\Phi){:}. \tag{2.16}$$

Furthermore, the canonical commutation relations become, Eq. (1.65)

$$[\Phi(x), \Phi(x')] = 0$$

$$\int_{x'\copyright\sigma'} [\Phi(x), \partial'^k \Phi(x')]f(x') = if(x) \tag{2.17}$$

with $(x - x')^2 < 0$, and for arbitrary f. For linear equations one can explicitly exhibit the commutators among the Φ not only for points on a spacelike surface, but for arbitrary points. The Φ is given throughout all of space-time by the field equations, if it is known on a spacelike surface along with its derivatives in the direction of the surface normal. This construction of Φ is done with the aid of the Δ function, Eq. (A2.12)

$$\Phi(x) = \int d\sigma_j''(\Delta(x - x'')\partial''^j\Phi(x'') - \Phi(x'')\partial''^j\Delta(x - x'')). \tag{2.18}$$

We can replace $\Phi(x)$ in the commutator $[\Phi(x), \Phi(x')]$ by an expression involving Φ and its normal derivatives on a spacelike surface through x', and then make use of the commutation relations, Eq. (1.65).[4]

$$[\Phi(x), \Phi(x')] = \int_{x'\copyright\sigma''} d\sigma_j''[\Delta(x - x'')\partial''^j\Phi(x'')$$

$$- \Phi(x'')\partial''^j\Delta(x - x''), \Phi(x')] = -i\Delta(x - x'). \tag{2.19}$$

[4] One can verify that $\Delta(x)$ is necessarily—for the consistency of Eqs. (2.17) and (2.19)—an invariant, odd, real solution of Eq. (2.13) with the property shown in Eq. (A2.9).

For the positive and negative frequency parts this gives

$$[\Phi^+(x), \Phi^-(x')] = -i\Delta^+(x - x')$$
$$[\Phi^+(x), \Phi^+(x')] = [\Phi^-(x), \Phi^-(x')] = 0. \tag{2.20}$$

Such relations were anticipated in the discussion in the preceeding section. Because of them, the field quanta behave like free particles.

If the Lagrangian is the sum of L's for two Hermitian scalar fields, Φ_1 and Φ_2, with the same mass, a new invariance property appears. Since L is in this case quadratic in Φ it depends only on $\Phi_1^2 + \Phi_2^2$ and $\sum_{i=1}^{2} \Phi_{i,\mu} \Phi_i^{,\mu}$. If we consider Φ_1 and Φ_2 as components of a vector in a two-dimensional space then L is invariant under rotations in this space. Introducing the non-Hermitian linear combinations $\Phi = (\Phi_1 + i\Phi_2)/\sqrt{2}$ and $\Phi^\dagger = (\Phi_1 - i\Phi_2)/\sqrt{2}$, which correspond to eigenvectors of infinitesimal rotations, we may write $L = :\Phi_{,\mu}\Phi^{\mu\dagger} - m^2\Phi\Phi^\dagger:$. In this representation L is invariant under the phase transformation $\Phi \to \Phi e^{ie}$. The commutation relations are now

$$[\Phi(x), \Phi^\dagger(x')] = -i\Delta(x - x')$$
$$[\Phi(x), \Phi(x')] = [\Phi^\dagger(x), \Phi^\dagger(x')] = 0 \tag{2.21}$$

and, for the current we find

$$j_\mu = e:(\Phi_{1,\mu}\Phi_2 - \Phi_{2,\mu}\Phi_1): = ie:(\Phi_{,\mu}\Phi^\dagger - \Phi\Phi_{,\mu}^\dagger):. \tag{2.22}$$

As mentioned in Section 3, L and the commutation rules are invariant under charge conjugation U_c.

$$U_c\Phi U_c^{-1} = \Phi^\dagger.$$

Furthermore, T_{ik} is invariant under U_c, whereas j changes sign, as one would expect. From the discussion in the last section it follows that U_c changes the emission operator of a positive particle into the emission operator of a negative particle. The same holds for absorption operators. If we fix the arbitrary phase factor in U_c by the convention $U_c \mid 0) = \mid 0)$ we see that U_c just changes positive into negative particles, and vice versa, in any state. This is the property of U_c mentioned in Section 3 which is used for its explicit construction. In general, the invariance of L and the commutation rules imply the existence of a corresponding unitary matrix. In this case one can even see explicitly which states are carried into each other under the transformation.

The possibility of splitting Φ into Φ^+ and Φ^-, both obeying Eq. (2.13), enables us to define, even in the case of one Hermitian field, a divergence free vector density

$$d_\mu = i\,(\Phi^-\Phi^+_{,\mu} - \Phi^-_{,\mu}\Phi^+) \qquad d^\mu_{,\mu} = 0. \quad (2.23)$$

Thus, we can define the invariant

$$N = \int d\sigma_\mu\, d^\mu \qquad (2.24)$$

which has the properties (problem 16)

$$N(0) = 0 \quad [N, \Phi^\pm(x)] = \pm\Phi^\pm(x).$$

This shows that $\Phi^-(x_1)\Phi^-(x_2)\cdots\Phi^-(x_n)\,|0\rangle$ or any linear combinations of such states is an eigenstate of N, belonging to the eignvalue n. Since in this way, as will be shown shortly, we can build the most general state with n particles present, we conclude that N is the operator corresponding to the number of particles and d is the particle density. From the invariance properties of N one has

$$[P_i, N] = [J_{ik}, N] = [Q, N] = 0. \qquad (2.25)$$

That is to say, a state with a definite number of particles can be an eigenstate of total charge, energy-momentum, angular momentum, or center of gravity (see end of Section 3). It is important to recognize that N, like P_k but unlike Q, fails to commute with local observables such as $T_{ik}(x)$ or $j_i(x)$. This seems surprising if we consider the following:

We have seen that the quanta of the field have, in some respects, the properties of point particles with no intrinsic extension, but only the spread in position dictated by the uncertainty relation. This would lead one to suppose that a state with exactly localized particles present would be an eigenstate of, say, $j_0(x)$ for all space points at a given time. This state should have eigenvalue zero everywhere except for some δ-like singularities. In fact, we can easily construct a state of this kind in a quantized nonrelativistic Schrödinger field. Such a localized state will not, of course, be an eigenstate of energy and momentum. This is expressed by the failure of P_k to commute with $j_0(x)$.

It is a typical feature of relativistic theories that such states do not contain a definite number of particles; i.e., $[N, j_0(x)] \neq 0$. This arises from the possibility of particle creation which is absent in nonrelativistic theories. For instance, the vacuum is not an eigenstate of $j_0(x)$ because of the pair creation term $\Phi^-\Phi^-$. In nonrelativistic theories it is also possible to define the number of particles in a finite volume. However, the operator ΔN obtained by integrating Eq. (2.24) over a finite space volume $\Delta\sigma$ does not possess the commutation properties of Eq. (2.25) for x in $\Delta\sigma$ in the way that ΔQ does. This stems formally from the fact that $[\Phi^+(x), \Phi^-(x')] = -i\Delta^+(x - x')$, which does not vanish for spacelike intervals $x - x'$, but decays like e^{-mr}. The $\Phi^-(x) \,|\, 0)$ is not, therefore, an eigenstate of ΔN but something quite different when $\Delta\sigma \sim m^{-3}$ and $x \subset \Delta\sigma$. The physical interpretation is that in the attempt to measure the number of particles in such a small volume new particles will be created and, therefore, the original number of particles will be changed.

Today it is well established that the π meson is a pseudo-scalar particle. There are three kinds of π's, π^+, π^-, and π^0; where π^0 has almost the same mass as $\pi^\pm$. L is, therefore, the sum of the L's of the three fields and is approximately invariant against the three-dimensional rotation group. Charge conjugation requires the exact invariance against $\Phi \leftrightarrow \Phi^\dagger$, and this manifests itself in the exact equality of masses and lifetimes of the free π^+ and π^-.[5]

In the case of heavier particles there seem to be more internal invariance properties than properties connected with electric charge. These invariance properties, some only approximate, are a striking feature of this new branch of physics and are beyond the scope of this book, which deals mainly with electrons and photons.

In order of formal complication the next case to consider is a Hermitian multicomponent field where the different components are connected with space-time properties. An example is furnished by the electromagnetic field. It can be described by the vector potential $A_k(x)$. In the absence of interaction with charges each component

[5] Actually, in any Lorentz invariant theory π^+ and π^- must have equal masses, even if U_c does not exist. It is a characteristic prediction of relativistic field theories that for any charged particle there must be a corresponding particle of opposite charge. No exception to this rule is known experimentally. In nonrelativistic theories it is perfectly consistent to have particles with one sign of charge without oppositely charged counterparts.

obeys an equation of the type in Eq. (2.13). Because photons have rest mass zero the equations reduce to[6]

$$\Box^2 A_k(x) = 0. \tag{2.26}$$

Correspondingly, L is the sum of L's of the type in Eq. (2.10) for the individual components. However, Lorentz invariance prevents us from giving all the contributions the same sign.

Equation (2.26) is the Euler equation of a Lagrange function of the form

$$L(x) = -\tfrac{1}{2} : \partial_k A^i(x) \partial^k A_i(x) :. \tag{2.27}$$

The energy-momentum tensor, Eq. (1.61), is composed additively of the individual components of A, although the spacelike components are given a positive sign, while the timelike components are given a negative sign.

$$T^{ik} = - : \partial^i A_m \partial^k A^m - \tfrac{1}{2} g^{ik} \partial^m A_n \partial_m A^n :. \tag{2.28}$$

For simplicity we have omitted the spin part, Eq. (2.6). Because $f^{jik} = -f^{ijk}$ and the generalized partial integration formula Eq. (N.5), it does not contribute to P. We may derive the commutation relations in a way entirely analogous to our previous work

$$[A^k(x), A^j(x')] = ig^{kj} D(x - x'). \tag{2.29}$$

The electromagnetic field has the formal complication that the field equations Eq. (2.26), are only equivalent to the Maxwell equations if we impose the condition $\partial_k A^k = 0$. This condition is also necessary if the energy is to be positive definite, as one best sees by going over into momentum space. The negative sign of A_0 is compensated by the sign of the longitudinal[7] component of A (problem 10).

One cannot impose this condition directly on the operators A_k for, applied to the commutation relations in Eq. (2.29), it would lead to the false equation $\partial_j D(x - x') = 0$. One way out of this difficulty is to understand this auxilliary condition as holding for a certain set of states

$$\partial_k A^k(x) \mid) = 0. \tag{2.30}$$

---

[6] Here we treat the vacuum equations, which correspond to the case in which no charges are present in the field. Equation (2.26), as one can see by comparing with Eq. (2.13), reflects the fact that the photon has no rest mass.

[7] This is the component of A which is in the direction of the momentum of the photon. The other components are called transverse.

For these states alone the Maxwell equations hold in expectation value form.

By excluding all other states as physically inadmissable we obtain a restricted Hilbert space within which the energy is positive and the Maxwell equations hold. Also, the transversality of photons is guaranteed by Eq. (2.30), as the following argumentation shows.

In Section 3 we learned that $A_1^- \pm iA_2^-$ creates a photon with spin parallel or antiparallel to, for example, the z-direction. If we take a Fourier component $A^-(k)$ with k in the z-direction, this creates a photon with its momentum in the z-direction. $A_1^-(k) \pm iA_2^-(k)$ applied to any state obeying Eq. (2.30) leads to another state obeying Eq. (2.30). Thus, a state of a photon with its spin parallel or antiparallel to its momentum is allowed. On the other hand, the application of the quantity $A_2^-(k) \pm iA_3^-(k)$ gives a state violating Eq. (2.30), so that it is not permissable for a photon to have its spin perpendicular to its momentum.

In classical electrodynamics, all observable effects of the electromagnetic field are described by the field strengths $f_{ik} = A_{i,k} - A_{k,i}$. These are invariant against the gauge transformation

$$A_k \rightarrow A_k + \partial_k \lambda \qquad (2.31)$$

where $\lambda(x)$ is an arbitrary function of space and time. This suggests the hypothesis that all the physical consequences of the theory are independent of any particular choice of gauge. In order to maintain the commutation relations in Eq. (2.39) under gauge transformations, we restrict the meaning of λ to that of an ordinary numerical function which commutes with all field quantities.

Furthermore, if the auxilliary condition, Eq. (2.30), is adopted, then one must have

$$\Box^2 \lambda(x) = 0. \qquad (2.32)$$

Our Lagrangian L is not gauge invariant as it stands. However, it differs from the gauge invariant form $L = -\frac{1}{4}f_{ik}f^{ik}$ only by a divergence and a term whose expectation value vanishes because of Eq. (2.30).

$$\frac{1}{4}f_{ik}f^{ik} = \frac{1}{2}A_{i,k}A^{i,k} - \frac{1}{2}\partial_k(A_iA^{k,i}) + \frac{1}{2}A_i\partial^iA_{,k}^k. \qquad (2.33)$$

Similarly, the expectation value of the energy-momentum vector which arises from Eq. (2.28) is equal to the expectation value of the energy-momentum vector arising from

$$T_k{}^i = f_{il}f_k{}^l + \tfrac{1}{4}g_{ik}f^{mn}f_{mn} .\tag{2.34}$$

We would have derived this expression, which is the usual Maxwell tensor, by inserting the gauge invariant L into Eq. (1.61). As we have mentioned, the simple expressions, Eqs. (2.27) and (2.28), generally suffice.

The connection between gauge invariance and the auxiliary condition becomes apparent by considering the generator of the infinitesimal gauge transformation[8]

$$\sum = - \int d\sigma_k (\lambda A^{i,k}_{,i} - \lambda^{,k}A^i_{,i}).\tag{2.35}$$

One shows that $\sum$, because of the D'Alembertian equation for λ and A and Eq. (N.5), is independent of σ. With the aid of the commutation relations, Eq. (2.29), and the properties, Eqs. (A2.10) and (A2.11), of the D function, one verifies that the generator $\sum$ satisfies the desired commutation relation: $[A_k, \sum] = i\lambda_{,k}$. Since $\sum$ involves only $\partial^k A^i_{,i}$ and $A^i_{,i}$, all quantities which commute with $A^i_{,i}$ also commute with $\sum$ and hence are gauge invariant. Conversely, all gauge invariant quantities commute with A^k_k. This means that if we multiply any vector fulfilling the auxiliary condition in Eq. (2.30) with a gauge invariant quantity we again get a vector satisfying Eq. (2.30). If we restrict ourselves to gauge invariant quantities or their equivalents then we never go beyond the Hilbert space defined by Eq. (2.30).

For the electromagnetic field the vacuum state is the state of lowest energy compatible with Eq. (2.30). Hence, we cannot just use the definition. $A_k{}^+(x) \mid 0) = 0$ will not do as the definition of the vacuum since it is not consistent with gauge invariance or the auxiliary condition. Furthermore

$$[A_k{}^+(x), A^j_{,j}(x')] = i\partial_k'D^+(x - x')$$

and hence cannot give zero when multiplied from both sides with the vacuum state, since D^+ is an ordinary number. As explained below, $A_0{}^+$ is an emission operator and there is no state in which the emission of particles can be forbidden. That $A_0{}^+$ is[9] an emission operator for

---

[8] After B. Zumino (unpublished).

[9] One can notice a sign difference in the commutation relations of A_0 and $A_{1,2,3}$. L in Eq. (2.27) is in the form of the sum of L's of four independent fields, but because of the Lorentz invariance a sign difference is introduced which causes this complication.

quanta of negative energy follows from the fact that the contribution of A_0 to the energy is negative. Since we have seen generally that the application of A^+ decreases the energy of a state, A_0^+ must emit photons. A state obeying Eq. (2.30) can be constructed explicitly by expanding $A_k(x)$ in a series of plane waves (problem 11). It turns out that Eq. (2.30) involves only the longitudinal and timelike components of A and demands that $|\,)$ must be a mixture of all states containing as many longitudinal as timelike quanta in every momentum. Since a timelike photon has negative energy, the energy of these photons cancel exactly. Thus, we get an eigenstate of P_j by imposing the further condition that there be no transverse quanta present. These conditions are summarized in the gauge and Lorentz invariant form[10]

$$f_{ik}^+(x) \mid 0) = 0. \tag{2.36}$$

Any state permitted by Eq. (2.30) is not an eigenstate of the number of particles, if the later are constructed, as in the scalar case, by repeated application of the creation operators. This is usually expressed by saying that the longitudinal and timelike parts of the field remain unquantized. Ordinarily, when one refers to a state of n photones one means transverse photons.

As the final case, we consider a Dirac field where both kinds of internal degrees of freedom occur, those connected with angular momentum and those connected with charge. This field supplies the approximate description of the electron and positron. The Dirac equation is generated by the Lagrange function[11]—for notation, see Eq. (A1)

$$L(x) = :\bar{\psi}(x)(\partial - m)\psi(x):, \partial = i\gamma^k\partial_k$$
$$(\partial - m)\psi = \bar{\psi}(\partial + m) = 0. \tag{2.37}$$

The ψ is a four-component field which we take to be non-Hermitian, so that it describes charged particles. Altogether this gives us eight independent fields. These represent four kinds of particles which are distinguished by spin and charge. For this we need a description in terms of twice as many fields, since the Dirac equation is of first order, as opposed to the second order Klein-Gordon equation.

The L in Eq. (2.37) is not Hermitian, but can be used, since it dif-

[10] After B. Zumino (unpublished).

[11] By applying $(\partial + m)$ we learn that $(\square^2 + m^2)\psi = 0$, from which it follows that our equations describe particle of mass m.

fers from the Hermitian-Lagrange function $\frac{1}{2}(L +$ Hermitian conjugate) by a divergence $-\frac{1}{2}i\partial_k:\bar{\psi}\gamma^k\psi:$.

The canonically conjugate field,[12] the energy-momentum tensor (without the spin part),[13] and the current density vector can all be computed from Eq. (2.37) by the field equations ($L = 0$)

$$\pi^k = i\bar{\psi}\gamma^k$$
$$T^{mn} = i:\bar{\psi}\gamma^m\partial^n\psi: \tag{2.38}$$
$$j^k = e:\bar{\psi}\gamma^k\psi:.$$

Since we are dealing with a field of half-integer spin, it turns out in this case that in the canonical commutation relations, Eq. (1.65), we must take anticommutators

$$\int_{x'\copyright\sigma} d\sigma_k\{\psi(x'), \bar{\psi}(x)\gamma^k\} f(x) = f(x') \tag{2.39}$$

for arbitrary f.

We shall see shortly what difficulties one would run into by using commutators. Similarly we have

$$\int_{x'\copyright\sigma} d\sigma_k\{\psi(x), \gamma^k\psi(x')\} = 0.$$

If we use Eq. (A2.20), as above, we learn[14]

$$\{\psi(x), \bar{\psi}(x')\} = i\{\psi(x), \int_{x\copyright\sigma''} d\sigma_k''\bar{\psi}(x'')\gamma^k S(x'' - x)\}$$
$$= iS(x - x') \tag{2.40}$$
$$\{\psi(x), \psi(x')\} = \{\bar{\psi}(x), \bar{\psi}(x')\} = 0.$$

In order to make the commutation relations in Eqs. (1.64) and (1.65) consistent with each other we must define the : ... : product, keeping in mind the anticommutivity of the ψ, in the following way

$$:\bar{\psi}\psi: = \bar{\psi}^+\psi^+ + \bar{\psi}^-\psi^+ - \psi^-\bar{\psi}^+ + \bar{\psi}^-\psi^-. \tag{2.41}$$

[12] Here, the canonically conjugate field to ψ is identically equal to zero, a difficulty which would not have arisen if we had used the Hermitian Lagrange function. However, it is easy to see that our L leads to the same commutation relations that one would have found with the latter.

[13] With this $T_{mn} \to \frac{1}{2}(T^{mn} + T^{nm})$.

[14] In spin space $\int d\sigma\{\psi_\alpha, (\bar{\psi}\gamma)_\beta\} = \delta_{\alpha\beta}$, $\{\psi_\alpha, \bar{\psi}_\beta\} = iS_{\alpha\beta}$.

With these definitions it is possible to find a unitary transformation U_c which has the properties of a charge conjugation. In the spin $\frac{1}{2}$ case one cannot simply assume that charge conjugation takes ψ into $\psi^\dagger$, since $\psi^\dagger$ does not even obey the same equation except for a special representation of the γ's. However, as shown in Eq. (A1), a particular combination of the $\psi_\alpha{}^\dagger$'s, namely, $\psi' = C\psi^\dagger$, obeys the same equation and can be used. In fact, one readily sees that if U_c acts on ψ—the notation is as in Eq. (A1.12)—in the following fashion

$$U_c\psi U_c^{-1} = \psi'$$
$$U_c\bar{\psi}U_c^{-1} = \bar{\psi}'. \tag{2.42}$$

then the commutation rules are not changed (problem 18). Furthermore, we shall now see that T is unaffected by this transformation, whereas j changes sign. We can, therefore, use the previous prescription to construct an explicit representation of U_c in terms of states with definite numbers of particles.

If we split the commutation relations, Eq. (2.40), into positive and negative frequency parts then we find

$$\{\psi^+(x), \bar{\psi}^-(x')\} = iS^+(x - x')$$
$$\{\psi^-(x), \bar{\psi}^+(x')\} = iS^-(x - x')$$

and

$$\{\psi^+, \psi^-\} = \{\bar{\psi}^+, \bar{\psi}^-\} = \{\psi^+, \bar{\psi}^+\}$$
$$= \{\psi^-, \bar{\psi}^-\} = \{\psi^+, \psi^+\} = \{\psi^-, \psi^-\} = \{\bar{\psi}^+, \bar{\psi}^+\}$$
$$= \{\bar{\psi}^-, \bar{\psi}^-\} = 0. \tag{2.43}$$

Now, using, Eqs. (A1.11) and (A1.12),

$$\psi'^\pm = C\bar{\psi}^\pm, \quad \bar{\psi}'^\pm = -\psi^\pm C^{-1} \qquad C = -C^T$$
$$C^{-1} = C^\dagger \qquad C^{-1}\gamma C = -\gamma^T \tag{2.44}$$

$$:\bar{\psi}'\psi': = -\psi^+\bar{\psi}^+ - \psi^-\bar{\psi}^+ + \bar{\psi}^-\psi^+ - \psi^-\bar{\psi}^- = :\bar{\psi}\psi:$$
$$:\bar{\psi}'\gamma\psi': = \psi^+\gamma^T\bar{\psi}^+ + \psi^-\gamma^T\bar{\psi}^+ - \bar{\psi}^-\gamma^T\psi^+ + \psi^-\gamma^T\bar{\psi}^-$$
$$= -:\bar{\psi}\gamma\psi:. \tag{2.45}$$

The sign of j is therefore reversed by charge conjugation. The T which we get from the simplified Lagrangian, Eq. (2.37), goes into its Hermitian conjugate under charge conjugation. However, the P

that we get by integrating T is Hermitian and agrees, therefore, with the one obtained by using $\frac{1}{2}(L + L^\dagger)$. Thus, as long as we do not consider the localization of energy, we may use the non-Hermitian L.

If we had quantized with commutators instead of anticommutators then, as one easily shows, T changes sign under charge conjugation and j does not. This implies, in particular, that P cannot be positive definite and one does not get an acceptable theory in this way.[15]

Conversely, it is impossible to quantize a scalar field with anti-commutators which, because of the field equations, leads to commutation relations of the form $\{\psi(x), \psi(x')\} = i\Delta(x - x')$. This entails an outright mathematical contradiction, because replacing x by x' leaves the left hand side of the equation invariant and changes the sign of the right hand side.[16]

As we have seen in Part I, the transformation going from one solution of the field equations, ψ, to an infinitesimally neighboring one, $\psi + \delta\psi$, is canonical and hence the commutation relations are left unchanged.[17] The latter is clearly true if $\delta\psi$ is chosen to commute or anticommute with all field quantities.

As we have done for free scalar particles, we can define an operator N corresponding to the number of particles

$$N = \int d\sigma_k [\bar{\psi}^- \gamma^k \psi^+ + \psi^- \gamma^{kT} \bar{\psi}^+]. \qquad (2.46)$$

We can readily show that N has the desired commutation properties and is invariant under Lorentz transformations and charge conjugation.

If we expand ψ in the complete set of functions u_k

$$\psi(x) = \sum_k b_k u_k(x)$$

then the commutations relations in Eq. (2.40) imply

$$\{b_k^-, b_{k'}^-\} = 0$$

or, for $k = k'$

$$(b_k^-)^2 = 0. \qquad (2.47)$$

[15] The original reason anticommutators were used here was that only in this way would a positive definite energy result. Charge symmetry was only recognized later, for the positron was originally regarded as a "hole" in an infinite sea of vacuum electrons. These difficulties arise only because of a clumsy formalism.

[16] See Pauli, W., *Phys. Rev.* **58,** 716 (1940).

[17] One notes that the right hand side of the commutation relations are ordinary numbers which cannot be changed by a unitary transformation.

Now, b_k^- produces a positron in the state $u_k(x)$. Hence, these commutation relations imply that it is impossible for two electrons or positrons to be produced in the same state; i.e., the double application of b_k^- on any state gives zero. This corresponds to the Fermi statistics in which a given state may be occupied by only one particle at a time. Thus we see that Fermi statistics go along with quantization by anti-commutation, while Bose statistics[18] correspond to quantization by commutation, in which an arbitrary number of identical particles can be produced in a given state. This gives the fundamental result that:

   a. *particles with integer spin obey Bose statistics, and*
   b. *particles with half-integer spin obey Fermi statistics.*

This theoretical connection between spin and statistics has been confirmed experimentally without exception and is one of the greatest successes of quantized field theory.

[18] In states which are characterized by the number of particles alone, the individuality of the particles cannot be determined as would be necessary for Boltzman statistics.

6. Matrix Elements

Before we return to the discussion of the physical consequences of the theory we must orient ourselves as to the general form of matrix elements of operators involving field quantities. If Φ is a real scalar field, then Φ^+, according to Section 4, absorbs single particles; that is, it has nonvanishing matrix elements between states in which the number of particles differ by one. The matrix of Φ^+ between a state $|u)$ in which a particle is present and the vacuum state is a complex numerical function $u(x)/\sqrt{2}$ which certainly obeys the Klein-Gordon equation and only involves positive frequencies. In formulae this is written

$$\Phi^+(x) \mid u) = \frac{u(x)}{\sqrt{2}} \mid 0), \qquad \Phi^+(x) \mid 0) = 0$$

and the conjugate relations become

$$(u \mid \Phi^-(x) = (0 \mid \frac{u^*(x)}{\sqrt{2}}, \qquad (0 \mid \Phi^-(x) = 0. \qquad (2.48)$$

If we compute the expectation value in this state of the fundamental bilinear scalar

$$:\Phi(x)\Phi(x): \ = \ \Phi^+(x)\Phi^+(x) \ + \ \Phi^-(x)\Phi^-(x) \ + \ 2\Phi^-(x)\Phi^+(x) \quad (2.49)$$

then only the last term contributes and

$$(u \mid :\Phi(x)\Phi(x): \mid u) = 2(u \mid \Phi^-(x)\Phi^+(x) \mid u)$$

$$= 2(u \mid \Phi^-(x) \mid 0)(0 \mid \Phi^+(x) \mid u) = u^*(x)u(x). \quad (2.50)$$

With this technique matrix elements can easily be evaluated. The expectation value of an observable quadratic in the Φ for a state $|u)$ is obtained by replacing the quantized Φ by the unquantized u; for example

$$(u \mid j^\mu(x) \mid u) = \frac{1}{i} \, (u \mid \Phi^-\Phi^+_{,\mu} - \Phi^-_{,\mu}\Phi^+ \mid u) = \frac{1}{2i} \, (u^* \overset{\leftrightarrow}{\partial} u) \quad (2.51)$$

where we employ the notation

$$A \overleftrightarrow{\partial} B = A \left[\frac{\partial}{\partial x} B \right] - \left[\frac{\partial}{\partial x} A \right] B. \qquad (2.52)$$

This shows that u plays the role of the Schrödinger function of the unquantized theory. One can proceed conversely by considering a positive frequency solution of the Klein-Gordon equation u^+ and constructing the corresponding state $| u \rangle$. Since Φ^- creates a particle and one finds the appropriate state, as we shall show below, by multiplying Φ^- with $u(x)$ and operating on the vacuum in the following way

$$| u \rangle = \frac{i}{\sqrt{2}} \int d\sigma_j \Phi^-(x) \partial^{\,j} u(x) \, | 0 \rangle. \qquad (2.53)$$

In fact, this state has the properties asserted above

$$\Phi^+(x) \, | u \rangle = \frac{1}{\sqrt{2}} \int_{x \circledcirc \sigma'} d\sigma_j{}' \Delta^+(x - x') \overleftrightarrow{\partial'^{\,j}} u(x') \, | 0 \rangle$$

$$= \frac{1}{\sqrt{2}} \int_{x \circledcirc \sigma'} d\sigma_j{}' \Delta(x - x') \overleftrightarrow{\partial'^{\,j}} u^+(x') \, | 0 \rangle \qquad (2.54)$$

$$= \frac{u^+(x)}{\sqrt{2}} \, | 0 \rangle.$$

In this calculation we have first used the commutation relations for Φ^- and Φ^+ and the vacuum definition. Equation (2.53) is independent of σ' because $\partial_j[\Phi^-(x) \overleftrightarrow{\partial^j} u(x)] = 0$, so that we can choose for σ' a surface containing x and then use Eq. (A2.12). Since u has only positive frequencies the negative frequency part of Δ does not contribute.

By multiplying Eq. (2.53) by the adjoint equation we find, using Eq. (2.54), that states corresponding to different u's are normalized and orthogonal if

$$i \frac{1}{2} \int d\sigma_j u_A{}^*(x) \overleftrightarrow{\partial^{\,j}} u_B(x) = \delta_{AB}. \qquad (2.55)$$

For charged fields, states containing a positive or negative particle with a wave function u can be constructed in the same way provided one uses the appropriate creation operators in Eq. (2.53), $(\Phi_1{}^- + i\Phi_2{}^-)/\sqrt{2}$ or $(\Phi_1{}^- - i\Phi_2{}^-)/\sqrt{2}$.

A state with a photon with wave function

$$| f_i) = \frac{i}{\sqrt{2}} \int d\sigma_j A_k^-(x) \overleftrightarrow{\partial^j} f_k(x) \mid 0) \tag{2.56}$$

satisfies Eq. (2.30) only if $\square^2 f_k = 0$ and $f_{k}{}^{,k} = 0$.

For a complex spinor field the somewhat different commutation rules require the following form for the one electron state and the wave function normalization

$$| v) = \frac{i}{\sqrt{2}} \int d\sigma_j \bar{\psi}^-(x) \gamma^j v(x) \mid 0)$$

$$\frac{1}{2} \int d\sigma_j \bar{v}_A \partial^j v_B = \delta_{AB}. \tag{2.57}$$

N commutes with P, J, and Q. Therefore, we can construct one-particle states which are eigenstates of P or J. On the other hand, $[Q, \bar{\psi}^-] = e\bar{\psi}^-$ assures us that Eq. (2.57) is already an eigenstate of Q. We obtain an eigenstate of the angular momentum for a spinless particle by using for u in Eq. (2.53) an eigenfunction of the rotation operator. This is apparent because J_{12}, say, induces an infinitesimal rotation of Φ around the z-axis. By partial integration we can make the derivatives in the rotation operator work on u, which gives u times the corresponding eigenvalue.

To obtain this formally we use

$$J_{12}\Phi(x) \mid 0) = [J_{12}, \Phi(x)] \mid 0) = -i \frac{\partial}{\partial \phi} \Phi(x) \mid 0). \tag{2.58}$$

Now

$$J_{12} \mid u) = \frac{i}{\sqrt{2}} J_{12} \int d\sigma_j \Phi^-(x) \overleftrightarrow{\partial^j} u(x) \mid 0)$$

$$= -\frac{1}{\sqrt{2}} \int d\sigma_j \Phi^-(x) \overleftrightarrow{\partial^j} \frac{\partial}{\partial \phi} u(x) \mid 0) = m \mid u) \tag{2.59}$$

if

$$u(x) \sim Y_l^{*m}(\theta, \phi) u(r).$$

As in elementary wave mechanics we get a state of angular momentum zero or one if u is invariant under rotation or transforms like a vector. We shall use this general result at the end of the present section.

Similarly, we can build eigenfunctions of the momentum by using plane waves for u. Such a state, however, will not satisfy the normalization condition in Eq. (2.53), which reads in momentum space

$$\frac{1}{(2\pi)^3} \int_{k_0>0} d^4k\delta(k^2 - m^2)u_A{}^*(k)u_B(k) = \delta_{AB}$$

if we put

$$u(x) = \frac{\sqrt{2}}{(2\pi)^3} \int_{k_0>0} d^4k e^{-ik\cdot x}\delta(k^2 - m^2)u(k). \qquad (2.60)$$

Equation (2.55) diverges for $A = B$ and $u_A = \delta^3(k - k_A)$, but can be made finite by approximating the δ function by a narrow Gaussian distribution. For practical calculations it is not necessary to use such a wave packet explicitly. However, one might as well start with a finite space volume $\underline{V}$, in which case the normalized u is given by

$$u_A(x) = \frac{e^{-ip\cdot x}}{\sqrt{\underline{V}p_0}}, \qquad p_0 = + \sqrt{p^2 + m^2}. \qquad (2.61)$$

Going to the limit $\underline{V} \to \infty$ will be possible for physically reasonable quantities and will restore relativistic invariance. Equation (2.61) or a superposition of such states with the same p_0 provides an eigenstate of P_0. For photons the corresponding state has the form

$$f_i = \frac{e_i e^{-ik\cdot x}}{\sqrt{k_0\underline{V}}} \qquad (2.62)$$

with $k_0 = |\underline{k}|$, $e^2 = 1$, and $e\cdot k = 0$.

One may wonder whether wave functions can be found which have a δ character in coordinate space analogous to the behavior of Eqs. (2.61) and (2.62) in momentum space. To study this it is instructive to evaluate for a state with wave function $u(x)$ the probability amplitude $w(\Delta x)$ for finding the particle in the state $u(x + \Delta x)$. If u is a localized state the square of this amplitude gives the probability of finding the particle at time $t + \Delta t$ at the point $\underline{x} + \Delta\underline{x}$ when we know it was at the point $\underline{x}$ at time t. The scalar product between these states is found to be, introducing Fourier transforms

$$w(\Delta x) = \frac{1}{(2\pi)^3} \int_{k_0>0} dk e^{-ik\Delta x}\delta(k^2 - m^2) \, |\, u(k) \,|^2. \qquad (2.63)$$

If u is a δ function in x space, $u(k) \sim k_0$, then we find $w(\Delta x) \neq 0$, for $\Delta\underline{x} \neq 0$, $\Delta t = 0$. Such a state cannot, therefore, be interpreted as being perfectly localized, since this would imply that the particle occupies several positions simultaneously. For $u(k) \sim \sqrt{k_0}$, $w(\Delta x) = \delta(\Delta x)$ for $\Delta t = 0$. However, $w(\Delta x) \neq 0$ for $|\Delta x| > \Delta t \neq 0$. That is to say, if this state is supposed to describe a particle at a definite position then the particle can change its position with a velocity greater than one. Furthermore, such states are not relativistically invariant, so that different observers would not agree as to whether the particle was localized. Finally, the expectation values in these states do not show δ-character for all densities like $T_{ik}(x)$, $M_{ijk}(x)$, and $j_i(x)$. This indicates that the notion of the position of a particle does not have as simple a meaning in relativistic theories as it has in nonrelativistic mechanics. There is no contradiction here with the point character of the field quanta, rather, the effect comes about because of virtual pair creation. One can see this because the departures from δ distributions decay exponentially with a half width of the Compton wave length. This is the extension of the virtual pair cloud which is required by the uncertainty relations.

If u represents a wave packet much larger than the Compton wave length, $u(\underline{k}) \cong e^{-\underline{k}^2 b^2/2}$, $b \ll m^{-1}$, then $w(\Delta x)$ gives the usual result for the diffusion of wave packets.

$$| w(\Delta x) |^2 = \frac{b^2}{\left[b^4 + \left(\dfrac{\Delta t}{2m} \right)^2 \right]^{1/2}} e^{-(b^2(\Delta x)^2/4[b^4 + (\Delta t/2m)^2])}. \qquad (2.64)$$

Hence, $\Delta^+(x)$, from which $w(\Delta x)$ was directly inferred, has the simple meaning of describing the propagation of a relativistic particle. The discussion of these questions for spin one half particles proceeds completely analogously and is left to the reader.

A state with two particles can be constructed in a similar fashion. For a neutral Bose field we see that

$$\int d\sigma_i \, d\sigma_j{}' \Phi^-(x) \Phi^-(x') \overleftrightarrow{\partial}^i \overrightarrow{\partial}_j' f(x, x') \mid 0 \rangle \qquad (2.65)$$

has the desired properties if f satisfies the Klein-Gordon equation with respect to both arguments and contains only positive frequencies. In this case Eq. (2.65) is independent of σ and σ'. One can, therefore, use the same surface $t = $ constant for both. Furthermore, we can restrict ourselves to f's which are symmetric with respect to exchange of both x and x'. Because of the symmetry of the other factors in Eq. (2.65) any antisymmetric part would drop out.

For fields with internal degrees of freedom the symmetry require-ment has to be correspondingly extended. For an electromagnetic field for instance, the wave function $f_{il}(x, x')$ for the two photon state

$$\int d\sigma_j \, d\sigma_k' A_i^-(x) A_l^-(x') \overleftrightarrow{\partial^j} \overleftrightarrow{\partial'^k} f_{il}(x, x') \mid 0\rangle \qquad (2.66)$$

will satisfy

$$f_{il}(x, x') = f_{li}(x', x). \qquad (2.67)$$

For a charged scalar field we require, similarly, the symmetry of the wave function under exchange of coordinate and charge variables. For a spinor field the two electron state will be, with all indices made explicit

$$\int d\sigma_i \, d\sigma_j' \bar{\psi}_\alpha(x) \bar{\psi}_{\alpha'}(x') \gamma^i_{\alpha\beta} \gamma^i_{\alpha'\beta'} U_{\beta\beta'}(x, x') \mid 0). \qquad (2.68)$$

Because of the anticommutivity of the ψ, U will be antisymmetric

$$U_{\beta\beta'}(x, x') = -U_{\beta'\beta}(x', x). \qquad (2.69)$$

These symmetry properties of the wave functions are well-known from elementary wave mechanics.

In working out the normalization and orthogonality relations for two particle wave functions we find[1] a factor $\frac{1}{2}$ stemming from the identity of the particles.

$$\frac{1}{(2\pi)^6} \int_{\substack{k_0>0 \\ k_0'>0}} dk^4 \, dk'^4 [\delta(k^2 - m^2)\delta(k'^2 - m^2)$$

$$(2.70)$$

$$F_A^*(k, k') F_B(k, k')] = \frac{\delta_{AB}}{2!}.$$

F is defined in analogy to Eq. (2.60). If the particles also have dis-crete degrees of freedom the integral in Eq. (2.70) includes summa-tions over the corresponding variables.

To study the influence of statistics on the propagation of particles we calculate as before the scalar product $w(\Delta x_1, \Delta x_2)$ of a two particle state with wave function $f(x_1, x_2)$ and one with $f(x_1 + \Delta x_1, x_2 + \Delta x_2)$.

[1] For the reader who is bored by this algebra, we may remark that this factor of two is actually observed experimentally. Because of it the annihilation cross section for positrons is only half as big as it would be if the photons were non-identical.

This is computed as before by commuting Φ^+ to the right in the expression

$$(0 \mid \Phi^+(x_1')\Phi^+(x_2')\Phi^-(x_1)\Phi^-(x_2) \mid 0) \tag{2.71}$$

and using the properties of the vacuum state. We get two terms

$$\Delta^+(x_1' - x_1)\Delta^+(x_2' - x_2) + \Delta^+(x_1' - x_2)\Delta^+(x_2' - x_1)$$

which gives in momentum space

$$w(\Delta x_1 , \Delta x_2) = \frac{1}{(2\pi)^6} \int_{\substack{k^0_1 > 0 \\ k^0_2 < 0}} dk_1{}^4 \, dk_2{}^4 \mid F(k_1 , k_2) \mid^2 \tag{2.72}$$

$$\delta(k_1{}^2 - m^2)\delta(k_2{}^2 - m^2)[e^{i(k_1 \cdot \Delta x_1 + k_2 \cdot \Delta x_2)} + e^{i(k_2 \cdot \Delta x_1 + k_1 \cdot \Delta x_2)}]$$

We notice that even when the particles are uncorrelated— $F(k_1 , k_2) = G(k_1)G(k_2)$—$w$ does *not* factor into $u(\Delta x_1)u(\Delta x_2)$, so that the particles are not quite independent. This effect is, however, not an interaction in the usual sense, as can be recognized from the following consideration. The states we deal with here are not necessarily in the momentum continuum as would result from a true scattering. Here we can very well have states where the particles have just the momenta k_1 and k_2. If the particles are identical in the quantum mechanical sense then one just cannot say which one has the momentum k_1 and which k_2. It is, however, a typical feature of the quantum theory that these two possibilities can interfere, so that Bose particles naturally stick together and Fermi particles stay apart. This can be seen if the state specifies only the relative position of the particles, $f = f(x_1 - x_2)$, $F = \delta^3(k_1 + k_2)G(k_1)$. Thus, the factor in the square bracket of Eq. (2.72) becomes $\cos [k_1 \cdot (\Delta x_1 - \Delta x_2)]$. For Fermi particles one obtains a similar expression. However, the anticommutivity of the ψ results in a change of sign and we get $\sin [k_1 \cdot (\Delta x_1 - \Delta x_2)]$ instead of cos. If the particles have other degrees of freedom the exchange term appears only if the particles are identical with respect to these quantum numbers as, for instance, spin parallel and the same charge.

This shows that equivalent Fermi particles avoid each other within a wave length, whereas equivalent Bose particles have a maximum probability for occupying the same position. There are many striking consequences of this fact as, for instance, in the angular distributions for the scattering of identical particles. These, however, fall in the domain of elementary wave mechanics and are not particularly characteristic of relativistic quantum theory. We shall not explicitly discuss them any further, but they will appear throughout our further investigations.

As an important application of our general development we shall now investigate the restriction imposed by Eq. (2.30) on the possible states of photons. For this purpose it is convenient to introduce $a_i(k)$ by

$$A_i(x) = \frac{1}{(2\pi)^3} \int_{k_0 > 0} d^4k e^{-ik \cdot x} \delta(k^2) a_i(k) \qquad (2.73)$$

which enables us to define the one photon state in the invariant form

$$| f) = \frac{1}{(2\pi)^3} \int d^4k \delta(k^2) F_i(k) a_i^-(k) \mid 0) \qquad (2.74)$$

with f defined by Eq. (2.56). First, we shall show that because $k^i F_i(k) = 0$ it is impossible to obtain a one photon state with angular momentum zero. That is to say, the Lorentz condition excludes states in which the spin angular momentum and the orbital angular momentum are antiparallel. This is to be expected, because the Lorentz condition demands the transversality of photons, which means that the spin is parallel to the momentum and therefore perpendicular to the orbital angular momentum. Formally, the construction of a state with angular momentum zero amounts to finding a state in which no particular direction is distinguished. The only space vector available in Eq. (2.74) is $\underline{k}$. Hence, we must have $F = \underline{k}G(\mid \underline{k} \mid)$. $F_i k^i = 0$ yields $F_i(k) = k_i G(\mid k \mid)$, which gives zero in Eq. (2.74), since $k^i a_i^- \mid 0) = 0$.

In the more familiar three-dimensional language the preceding derivation goes as follows. We note that in the sum over i in Eq. (2.74) the contributions come from terms in which the polarization vector $\underline{e}$, which is represented by the subscript i, is normal to $\underline{k}$. When we put the 1-direction parallel to k our condition implies that $F_0 = F_1$, and the Lorentz condition leaves only $a_2 F_2 + a_3 F_3$. The wave function must be a scalar proportional to $\underline{e}$. Since the only scalar $\underline{e} \cdot \underline{k}$ vanishes, we cannot construct a state of angular momentum zero.

Although we have not yet spoken about interactions we shall discuss here some consequences of the possible eigenvalues for the angular momentum for photon states when transitions arising from electromagnetic interactions are considered. The only thing we assume about the interactions is that they conserve angular momentum.

That is to say, when we know that an initial state has angular momentum zero we are certain that this state can never develop into a one photon state. Our result has important consequences in atomic physics, since it predicts that in transitions with no change of angular momentum, e.g., $0 \leftrightarrow 0$ transitions, more than one photon must be emitted.

Less obvious is the fact that a two-photon state cannot have an angular momentum one. To show this we can, without loss of generality, go to the system in which the total momentum is zero (the barycentric or center of mass frame), so that $\underline{k}_1 = -\underline{k}_2$. It is now more appropriate to use the three-dimensional description. In this we have three vectors, the two polarization vectors $\underline{e}_1$ and $\underline{e}_2$ and the momentum vector $\underline{k}$, at our disposal for the construction of the wave function. This wave function must contain $\underline{e}_1$ and $\underline{e}_2$ linearly and must be invariant under $\underline{k} \leftrightarrow -\underline{k}$, along with $\underline{e}_1 \leftrightarrow \underline{e}_2$. Thus, we can construct the scalar $\underline{e}_1 \cdot \underline{e}_2$ and the pseudo-scalar $(\underline{e}_1 \times \underline{e}_2) \cdot \underline{k}$ where both expressions can be multiplied by an arbitrary function of $|\underline{k}|$. However, the possible vectors $(\underline{e}_1 \cdot \underline{e}_2)\underline{k}, ((\underline{e}_1 \times \underline{e}_2) \cdot \underline{k})\underline{k}, (\underline{e}_1 \cdot \underline{k})\underline{e}_2, (\underline{e}_2 \cdot \underline{k})\underline{e}_1$, and $\underline{e}_1 \times \underline{e}_2$ vanish either a) because $(\underline{e}_1 \cdot \underline{k}) = (\underline{e}_2 \cdot \underline{k}) = 0$ or b) on the $\underline{e}_1 \leftrightarrow \underline{e}_2$, $\underline{k} \leftrightarrow -\underline{k}$ symmetrization, which proves our assertion. This striking fact was of importance in the history of π-meson physics since the two-photon decay of the π^o proved that it cannot have spin one. Furthermore, it results in a considerable lengthening of the lifetime of the S-state of positronium, where the spins are parallel, since this state cannot decay into two photons.

Concluding this section we shall mention some remarkable selection rules which have some bearing on the two photon states with angular momentum zero. These selection rules stem from a constant of the motion which has its origin in an invariance property of the underlying space-time continuum which we have not exploited thus far.

We have seen that there are ten constant operators connected with the infinitesimal elements e_i and e_{ik} of the inhomogeneous Lorentz group. The existence of these operators might have been inferred by the following line of reasoning. If the laws of nature are the same in all systems connected by Lorentz transformations, the observables in the different systems must have the same eigenvalue spectrum. Therefore, we must be able to establish a one to one correspondence between the states belonging to identical eigenvalues of corresponding operators in the different systems. This defines a set of unitary transformations and their infinitesimal generators, whose commutation properties are dictated by the structure of the group.

We shall now consider in the same way the hypothesis that the laws of nature are invariant under the reflection of the spatial coordinates. This operation means $x_0 \rightarrow x_0$, $x_1 \rightarrow -x_1$, $x_2 \rightarrow -x_2$, and $x_3 \rightarrow -x_3$; and changes a right-handed coordinate system into a left-handed one. The above hypothesis assumes that empty space does not distinguish between clockwise and counterclockwise motion; i.e., it does not act like an optically active liquid. Whether a particular theory predicts such an invariance depends on whether the Lagrangian is unchanged by reflections. Reflection invariance is certainly present in the electric phenomena we are concerned with. However, there is evidence that it is not generally true. As in the case of the inhomogeneous Lorentz group reflection invariance will manifest itself in the existence of a unitary operator R. In this case, as in the case of charge conjugation, the group is not continuous, but consists only of 1 and R, if we assume, as it is natural to do, that $R^2 = 1$. (For spinors it has been proposed that $R^2 = \pm 1$, but this distinction is not relevant for our purposes.) Thus, there is no infinitesimal generator of the group and, correspondingly, we cannot use our general variational principle to construct R explicitly in terms of the field operators. Similarly, we cannot define a corresponding classical expression via generators of infinitesimal canonical transformations and Poisson brackets. This has the consequence that the selection rules at which we shall arrive cannot be explained by simple classical pictures and are a typical quantum mechanical effect, although the concept of reflection invariance is a classical one.

In a formal way the result of the transformation R on a scalar operator S, a tensor operator V_i, or tensors of higher rank will be

$$RS(\underline{x}, t)R^{-1} = S(-\underline{x}, t)$$
$$RV_0(\underline{x}, t)R^{-1} = V_0(-\underline{x}, t) \tag{2.75}$$
$$R\underline{V}(\underline{x}, t)R^{-1} = -\underline{V}(-\underline{x}, t).$$

For quantities integrated over a surface σ we are free to choose for σ the plane $t = $ constant in the frame in which R produces the space inversion. Then we find, for example, if $RL(\underline{x}, t)R^{-1} = L(-\underline{x}, t)$

$$RP_0R^{-1} = \int d\underline{x}^3 T_{00}(-\underline{x}, t) = P_0. \tag{2.76}$$

Analogously, we find that R anticommutes with the total momentum and commutes with the number of particles, charge, and angular momentum, if the latter refers to the same origin as R. (These statements are to be understood, of course, as referring to a particular Lorentz-frame defined by R.) This shows that we can construct eigenstates of R with states with a definite number of particles, energy, and angular momentum. If they are also eigenstates of the total momentum they must have eigenvalue zero.

A state with one Boson $|\ \rangle = \int d\sigma_\mu V(x) \overleftrightarrow{\partial^\mu} \Phi^-(x) |0\rangle$ is an eigenstate of R if $\underline{V}(\underline{x}, t) = \pm \underline{V}(-\underline{x}, t)$. Furthermore, we note that the states with two photons, considered above, are eigenstates of R. The scalar belongs to the eigenvalue $+1$ and the pseudo-scalar to the eigenvalue -1.

The effect of R on a spinor field ψ is a little more involved since $\psi(-\underline{x}, t)$ does not satisfy the same equation as $\psi(\underline{x}, t)$. Since R is not supposed to depend explicitly on $\underline{x}$, R cannot carry $\psi(\underline{x}, t)$ into $\psi(-\underline{x}, t)$. However, $\beta\psi(-\underline{x}, t)$ obeys the same equation as $\psi(\underline{x}, t)$ and it is consistent to put

$$R\psi(\underline{x}, t)R^{-1} = \beta\psi(-\underline{x}, t). \tag{2.77}$$

For the notation, see Eq. (A1.1). In the following we take the usual representation for the γ where $\beta = \gamma_0$. It is certainly possible to replace β here by $-\beta$ but the distinction is not important for our work.

We may examine the significance of R by considering states describing particles at rest. In this case, the positive or negative frequency of the Dirac equation belongs to the eigenvalue $+1$ or -1 of β. Thus we see that a positron at rest has the opposite parity to an electron. While the absolute parity of an electron, as mentioned above, is only a matter of convention, the relative parity between electron and positron has physical significance. This is related to the fact that electrons and positrons are created and annihilated in pairs, and one can observe the parity they leave behind but not the parity of a single electron. If the annihilation of a pair results in the creation of two photons and parity is conserved in this process they must have the same parity as the pair. Thus, an electron and a positron without momentum form an eigenstate of R with eigenvalue -1, which can decay only into the two photon pseudo-scalar state. This causes the polarization directions of the two photons to be perpendicular to each other. This striking consequence, which illustrates the power of such an apparently abstract invariance principle, has been experimentally verified for the ground state of positronium with angular momentum zero. Here the particles are not completely at rest, but the argument above can be extended to cover this case as well.

Reviewing this section, we may remark that the formalism of field quantization includes all of elementary wave mechanics, and exhibits some subtle features which do not follow intuitively from any classical concepts.

7. Fluctuation Phenomena

In concluding this part of the book, which has been about *free* fields, we shall investigate the expectation values of more complicated expressions. In particular, we shall be interested in how much the square of the expectation value of a given operator deviates from the expectation value of the square of the operator. In other words, we shall estimate typical quantum mechanical fluctuations from the point of view of the field theory formalism thus far developed.

The first case to consider is that in which the operator is a bilinear expression in the Dirac field. Now the $: \ldots :$ is defined in such a way that its vacuum expectation value vanishes. However, $\psi^+\bar\psi^-$ has a nonvanishing vacuum expectation value which can be computed from the commutation relations.

$$(0 \mid \psi_\alpha(x)\bar\psi_\beta(x') \mid 0) = (0 \mid \psi_\alpha{}^+(x)\bar\psi_\beta{}^-(x') \mid 0)$$

$$= (0 \mid \{\psi_\alpha{}^+(x), \bar\psi_\beta{}^-(x')\} \mid 0) = iS_{\alpha\beta}^+(x - x') \qquad (2.78)$$

$$= \frac{1}{(2\pi)^3} \int_{p_0>0} dp e^{-ip(x-x')}\delta(p^2 - m^2)(\mathbf{p} + m)_{\alpha\beta}.$$

One can express this result in a somewhat different way by thinking of $\bar\psi^-$ as the operator which takes the vacuum into the one electron state described by the Dirac function u, while ψ^+ leads back from this state to the vacuum. Hence, summing over all Dirac functions u, we may write

$$(0 \mid \psi^+(x)\bar\psi^-(x') \mid 0) = \sum(0 \mid \psi^+ \mid u)(u \mid \bar\psi^- \mid 0)$$
$$= \sum u(x)\bar u(x'). \qquad (2.79)$$

We may choose a plane wave representation for u, $e^{-ip\cdot x}$, and replace the sum over momenta by an integral over plane waves which satisfy the Dirac equation, so that $p^2 = m^2$. We shall now show that the sum over all spin states with momentum p gives the invariant $(\mathbf{p} + m)_{\alpha\beta}$. To this end we express iS^+, with the aid of the δ function identity in Eq. (N.1), as

$$\frac{1}{(2\pi)^3} \int_0^\infty dp_0 \frac{1}{2p_0} \delta(p_0 - \sqrt{\underline{p}^2 + m^2}) \int d\underline{p} e^{-ip(x-x')}(\mathbf{p} + m). \qquad (2.80)$$

77

(The p_0 integration may be performed, and after this is done p_0 can be taken as $\sqrt{\underline{p}^2 + m^2}$). The remaining integral may be done in a finite normalization volume so that $1/(2\pi)^3 \int d\underline{p} \to (1/\underline{V}) \sum$. By comparison with Eq. (2.78) it is now easy to see that

$$\sum_{\text{spin}} (0 \mid \psi_\alpha{}^+(x) \mid p)(p \mid \bar{\psi}_\beta{}^-(x') \mid 0) = \frac{e^{-ip(x-x')}}{2V\underline{p_0}} (\mathbf{p} + m)_{\alpha\beta}. \quad (2.81)$$

This expression will prove useful shortly when we want to sum over states with the same momentum but different spin.

This vacuum to vacuum calculation can be carried out for other fields as well. For the scalar field one finds that

$$(0 \mid \Phi(x)\Phi(x') \mid 0) = -i\Delta^+(x - x'). \quad (2.82)$$

However, in the case of the electromagnetic field the vacuum definition does not determine the expectation value of A^+A^-, for there remains the ambiguity of a gauge transformation. In fact,

$$(0 \mid A_j(x)A_k(x') \mid 0) = (0 \mid A_j{}^+(x)A_k{}^-(x') \mid 0)$$
$$= ig_{jk}D^+(x - x') + \lambda_{,j}(x)\lambda_{,k}(x'). \quad (2.83)$$

Because of the gauge invariance we can set $\lambda = 0$ in practical cases.

To compute the matrix elements of more complicated expressions it is useful to write them as sums of $: \ldots :$ products, which means that one must commute the operators so that all the absorption operators ψ^+ stand to the right of the emission operators $\bar{\psi}^-$. If one makes use of the commutation relations, then the product of two $: \bar{\psi}\psi :$ products can be written[1]

$$: \bar{\psi}(1)\psi(1) : : \bar{\psi}(2)\psi(2) : = : \bar{\psi}(1)\psi(1)\bar{\psi}(2)\psi(2):$$
$$+ i[\bar{\psi}^+(1)S^+(12)\psi^+(2) + \psi^+(1)S^-(21)\bar{\psi}^+(2)$$
$$- \psi^-(2)S^+(12)\bar{\psi}^+(1) - \bar{\psi}^-(2)S^-(21)\psi^+(1)$$
$$+ \bar{\psi}^-(1)S^+(12)\psi^+(2) + \bar{\psi}^-(1)S^+(12)\psi^-(2)$$
$$+ \psi^-(1)S^-(21)\bar{\psi}^+(2) + \psi^-(1)S^-(21)\bar{\psi}^-(2)$$
$$- S^+(12)S^-(21). \quad (2.84)$$

For the arguments x_1, x_2 we have just written the indices so that $\psi(1)$ means $\psi(x_1)$, etc.

---

[1] The dedicated reader is advised to study the order of the spin indices!

Thus we see that the vacuum expectation value of Eq. (2.84) does not vanish, but is equal to $-S^+(12)S^-(21)$. This means that the square fluctuation of the current $j(x)$ is not zero in the vacuum state, but

$$(\Delta j)^2 = (0 \mid \{j - (0 \mid j \mid 0)\}^2 \mid 0) = (0 \mid j^2 \mid 0) - (0 \mid j \mid 0)^2 \qquad (2.85)$$

is equal to the infinite quantity $\gamma S^+(0)\gamma S^-(0)$. Hence, it is suggested that we calculate the square fluctuation of the current over a finite space-time volume[2]

$$\left[\Delta \int_V dx j_k(x)\right]^2 = (0 \mid \int_V dx\, dx' j_k(x)j_k(x') \mid 0)$$

$$= -e^2 \int_V dx\, dx' T_r[\gamma_k S^+(x - x')\gamma_k S^-(x - x')]. \qquad (2.86)$$

(there is no sum over k here).

This fluctuation effect obviously has its origins in the fact that in the act of measurement the system is defined within a small volume, so that pairs are generated. In fact, if this volume is given one sharp boundary, then the mean square fluctuations become infinite. In particular, integrating over a space volume gives infinite fluctuations, as one easily sees by writing Eq. (2.86) in momentum space. Later we shall see that Eq. (2.84) corresponds, in fact, to pairs created by the electric field which is necessary to define the volume.

It is important to notice that the total charge has no mean square fluctuation. Physically this must be, since an induced polarization cannot change the total charge.

The next question we might ask is in what way the fluctuations of the charge current density are changed by the presence of a particle. To answer this we compute the expectation value of two j's for a state $\mid u)$, where one electron with a wave function u is present. For this purpose we use Eq. (2.84) to write the expression in the frequency-ordered form and find, after multiplying by the required γ matrices

$$(u \mid j_k(x)j_k(x') \mid u) = e^2[\bar{u}(x)\gamma_k i S^+(x - x')\gamma_k u(x')$$

$$- \bar{u}(x')\gamma_k i S^-(x' - x)\gamma_k u(x)] \qquad (2.87)$$

$$- e^2[\text{Tr}(\gamma_k S^+(x - x')\gamma_k S^-(x - x')].$$

[2] One notices that $(0 \mid j \mid 0) = 0$, and that the spin indices are

$$j_{\alpha\beta}j_{\delta\sigma}S^+_{\beta\,\delta}S^-_{\sigma\,\alpha}.$$

We recognize that this expression consists of a part that depends on the wave function u and a remainder independent of u, which is just what we had when there was no electron present. Thus, the first two terms represent what comes from the electron, whereas the last is the contribution from the vacuum fluctuations which always exist. In the following discussion we consider only the former. Let us first see what we get when we integrate j over a space volume which is large compared to the Compton wave length of the electron. The expressions simplify when we take for u a wave function which is also spread out, so that it does not contain momentum components of order m. Since S^+ and S^- decay in spacelike distances as e^{-mr}, they act in this case like a δ function. By integrating x and x' over the same volume we can combine the two expressions above into one, with $S^+ - S^- = S^1$ in the middle. Because

$$\int dV S^1_{\alpha\beta}(x) = -i\delta_{\alpha\beta} \tag{2.88}$$

for $x_0 = 0$, see Eqs. (A2.9) and (A2.19), we find for this case that

$$\int_V d\underline{V}\, d\underline{V}'(u \mid j_k(x)j_k(x') \mid u) \cong g_{kk}e^2 \int_V d\,\underline{V}u(x)u(x). \tag{2.89}$$

The term with S^+ always gives a positive contribution to Eq. (2.87), whereas the S^- term, which expresses a decrease of the vacuum-expectation value due to the presence of an electron and the effect of the exclusion principle,[3] can give a negative contribution. In fact, for $k = 1, 2, 3$, the S^- term dominates and makes the expression negative. The whole expression, Eq. (2.87), is, of course, always positive, since the negative electron contribution is always overcompensated by the vacuum term, which is in this case positive infinite. The former is, however, finite and of order e^2 times the probability of finding the electron in the volume considered. To see this we recall that the wave function u is not supposed to have any high momentum components so that $\bar{u}(x)u(x) \sim u^\dagger(x)u(x)$ is the particle density. We note Eq. (2.89) does not contain the velocity $\underline{v}$ of the electron.

This situation is rather surprising. One would expect for the square of the current something of order $e^2\underline{v}^2$, since $\int d\underline{V}(u \mid j(x) \mid u) \sim e\underline{v}$

---

[3] If *all* electron states are filled, then the current fluctuations are completely quenched.

The character of the result given above has its origins in the phenomenon which is usually called the "zitterbewegung of the electron" when it is mentioned in elementary discussions of the Dirac equation. There it is argued that the electron travels in any direction with the velocity of light since, say, $(i\gamma_x)^2 = 1$. However, it is not possible to regard the Dirac equation, like the Schrödinger equation, as the quantum mechanical description of a single particle, so that arguments made within this framework are not very significant. Since the Dirac equation can be interpreted consistently only within the theory of quantized fields or equivalent methods, we shall discuss the "zitterbewegung" a little further at this point.

If we introduce the "total current" $\underline{J} = \int d\underline{V}\underline{j}(x)$ we find

$$[J, \psi(x)] = -e\gamma_0\gamma\psi(x). \tag{2.90}$$

(One must keep in mind that $\underline{J}_k$ is not independent of x_0 and this equation holds only if ψ and $\underline{J}$ are taken at the same x_0.) As in the spin case, we conclude that the eigenvalues of $\underline{J}_k$ are $\pm e$, since $(\gamma_0\gamma)^2 = +1$. However, it is not possible to build the eigenstates of $\gamma_0\gamma$ from the positive frequency solution of the Dirac equation, so that the eigenstates of $\underline{J}$ cannot be one electron states. This can also be inferred from the failure of $\underline{J}$ to commute with N. Thus, a state in which the charge moves with the velocity of light is a rather complicated excited state of the Dirac equation with peculiar phase relations between positive and negative particles.

This is to say that the electron cannot be thought of as moving with the velocity of light, but the "zitterbewegung" affects it, inasmuch as it shows anomalous current fluctuations. In the elementary picture the "zitterbewegung" is a zigzag motion of the electron with an amplitude $\sim m^{-1}$. This is only partly borne out by the quantum field theory since in any case the electron shares the uncertainty in position of any relativistic particle, as we have discussed before. This is of the same order as the zigzag motion and cannot be distinguished clearly from it. However, it is true that the fluctuations of the current are different for spin ½ particles and spin zero particles, the difference being connected with the spin.

To show this difference, we use the decomposition of the current into an orbital and spin part; see Eq. A1.13. We shall see that the orbital part, like the current for scalar particles, shows only fluctuations of the order expected from the Schrödinger equation. In fact, using

$$j_k^{(\text{orb})} = \frac{ie}{2m} \bar{\psi} \overleftrightarrow{\partial_k} \psi \tag{2.91}$$

we get

$$\int (u \mid j^{\text{orb}}(x) j^{\text{orb}}(x') \mid u) \, dV \, dV'$$

$$= -\frac{ie^2}{4m^2} \int dV \, dV' \overline{\overleftrightarrow{u(x)} \partial_k} S^1(x - x') \overrightarrow{\partial_k}' u(x') \tag{2.92}$$

$$\cong \frac{e^2}{m^2} \int dV \, \frac{\partial \bar{u}}{\partial x} \frac{\partial u}{\partial x}.$$

In this calculation we have made use of the formula in Eq. (2.88)

$$\int dV \, S_{\alpha\beta}^1(x) = -i\delta_{\alpha\beta}.$$

See Eqs. (A2.9) and (A2.19).

For a scalar field we find for the corresponding quantity

$$+ \frac{ie^2}{4} \int dV \, dV' u^\dagger(x) \overleftrightarrow{\partial_k} \Delta^1(x - x') \overleftrightarrow{\partial_k}' u(x'). \tag{2.93}$$

The difference in sign from the spin ½ case is compensated by the difference in sign in the expression

$$\int dV \Delta^1(x) = i/m. \tag{2.94}$$

Hence, we obtain the same expression for the square orbital current fluctuation here as for the spinor field.

The magnitude of the integral over V depends on the extension of the wave packet u in momentum space and can be made as small as $e^2 v^2$. The anomalous term of order e^2 is due to the spin part and is missing for scalar particles. Thus, we can say that the spin of the electron, being far from the region of large quantum numbers and classical description, manifests itself in current fluctuations which are ordered to such an extent as to give the electron its intrinsic angular momentum and magnetic moment. The g factor 2 of the electron, which obtains only for systems where both signs of the charge are represented, also shows that the spin is tied up with virtual pair fluctuations in regions of order m^{-1}.

All the quantities discussed above, however, are not to be taken too seriously, since they are space integrals of local variables at a sharp time. We have seen that they have an infinite mean square fluctuation and should not, therefore, be called observables, since any measurement takes some time and one must consider local variables integrated over a space-time volume with diffuse boundaries. To make the vacuum fluctuations small we have to smear out the boundaries of the volume over a region greater than m^{-1}. In this case, however, one finds $(1 \mid \bar{j}^2 \mid 1) \sim e^2 v^2 \int dV \bar{u} u$ with $\bar{j} = \int dV j$. Thus, with the averaging over times greater than m^{-1}, the fluctuations due to the zitterbewegung disappear, as to be expected, since they have a frequency approximately equal to m.

Finally, we shall consider fluctuations in states where an arbitrary number of particles are present.

For states in which a given number of electrons, say u, with Dirac functions u_i, are present we may consider the following matrix elements

$$(\text{all } u \text{ except } u_k \mid \psi^+(x) \mid \text{all } u) = u_k(x)$$

$$(\text{all } u \text{ except } u_i \text{ and } u_k \mid \psi^+(1)\psi^+(2) \mid \text{all } u) \tag{2.95}$$

$$= u_i(1)u_k(2) - u_i(2)u_k(1)$$

and so forth. In this way we can compute the expectation value of Eq. (2.84) for a state in which n electrons with Dirac functions u_i are present.

$$
\begin{aligned}
(u_i \mid :\bar{\psi}(1)\psi(1)::\bar{\psi}(2)\psi(2): \mid u_i) &= (u_i \mid :\bar{\psi}(1)\psi(1)\bar{\psi}(2)\psi(2): \mid u_i) \\
&+ i(u_i \mid \bar{\psi}^-(1)S^+(12)\psi^+(2) - \bar{\psi}^-(2)S^-(21)\psi^+(1) \mid u_i) \\
&= \sum_{ik}(\bar{u}_i(1)u_i(1)\bar{u}_k(2)u_k(2) - \bar{u}_i(1)u_k(1)\bar{u}_k(2)u_i(2)) \\
&+ i\sum_{i}(\bar{u}_i(1)S^+(12)u_i(2) - \bar{u}_i(2)S^-(21)u_i(1)).
\end{aligned}
\tag{2.96}
$$

When we compute for such a state the square fluctuation

$$
\begin{aligned}
\left[\Delta \int dx g(x)\right]^2 &= (u_i \mid \int dx \, dx' g(x)g(x') \mid u_i) \\
&- (u_i \mid \int dx g(x) \mid u_i)(u_i \mid \int dx' g(x') \mid u_i)
\end{aligned}
\tag{2.97}
$$

with $g = :\bar{\psi}\psi:$, the first term on the right side of the last term of Eq. (2.96) compensates the last term in Eq. (2.97), so that the mean square fluctuations become the integral over the last three terms in Eq. (2.96). The second term in the first sum in Eq. (2.96) is the well-known exchange term which appears because of the antisymmetry of the wave functions. The terms in the second sum are a typical product of the quantization procedure, for they depend on the behavior of the S functions and disappear for commutative quantities. As we will now show, this part of the square fluctuation corresponds to the classical particle picture. As before, we shall suppose that u does not vary significantly in a region of order m^{-3}, and we shall integrate Eq. (2.96) over a volume $\underline{V}$ which is much larger than m^{-3}. As in Eqs. (2.88) and (2.89), we get

$$i \sum_i \int d\underline{V}_1 \, d\underline{V}_2 \bar{u}_i(1)\gamma_0 S^1(12)\gamma_0 u_i(2)$$

$$= \sum_i \int d\underline{V} \bar{u}_i(x) u_i(x) = n \frac{\underline{V}}{\underline{V}_0}. \tag{2.98}$$

In the last step of Eq. (2.98) we have assumed that $\underline{V}$ is imbedded in a large normalization volume $\underline{V}_0$, in which the particle density $\bar{u}u$ remains constant and in which the u's in Eq. (2.98) are given their nonrelativistic normalizations.

If one has n particles in a volume $\underline{V}_0$, then in the classical particle picture the average number of particles in a particle volume $\underline{V}$ equals $n\underline{V}/\underline{V}_0 = \bar{n}$ and the probability $w(m)$ that in the volume $\underline{V}$ one finds m particles is given by a Poisson distribution[4] $w(m) = e^{-\bar{n}}(\bar{n})^m/m!$. The mean square fluctuation in the number of particles in $\underline{V}$

$$(\Delta n)^2 = \sum_m w(m)m^2 - \left(\sum_m w(m)m\right)^2 = \bar{n}$$

agrees with Eq. (2.98).

The exchange term referred to earlier is usually proportional to the square of the number of particles in the volume. The mean square fluctuations which arise from a combination of the particle and wave properties are given essentially by $\bar{n} - \bar{n}^2 = \bar{n}(1 - \bar{n})$. For Bose statistics the computation proceeds in the same fashion, except that we must replace commutators by anticommutators and change the sign of the exchange term. This yields an expression of the form $\bar{n}(1 + \bar{n})$

[4] This holds only if the orbits of the particles are completely independent of one another; i.e., if they do not interact.

instead of the one above. Thus, for Fermi particles the fluctuations are reduced, and for Bose particles enhanced in comparison with classical particles. This difference is accounted for by the exchange term, which is an interference of waves belonging to different particles and manifests the wave aspect of the field.

We can relate these fluctuation effects back to the tendency, already discussed, of Bose particles to stick together, and for Fermi particles to stay apart. For Bosons, such as photons, collected in an intense beam, counting rates do not follow a Poisson distribution, as one might expect. Instead, they favor a clustering. The formulae for the mean square fluctuations were derived from thermodynamical principles before the invention of quantum field theory. It is interesting to note this connection of field theory with classical physics.

Finally, we wish to make intuitive the orders of magnitude of some of the phenomena to be examined. If one examines the mean square vacuum fluctuations of the mean value of the electric potentials over a space volume L^3, $\bar{A} = L^{-3} \int dV A(x)$, then one learns

$$(\Delta \bar{A})^2 = L^{-6} \int dV\, dV' \frac{1}{2i} D^1(x - x') \sim L^{-2} \qquad (2.99)$$

or

$$\Delta \bar{A} \sim L^{-1}.$$

This is the value we found in the opening section by an elementary consideration.

This result is not quite true for the longitudinal or timelike components, nor for a static potential, because these components satisfy the Lorentz condition and hence are not eigenfunctions of the photon number operator.

In computing the vacuum fluctuation of the current, we find, after some calculation, the time average over an interval T for the charge in a volume L^3 with a surface of thickness b to be

$$\Delta e = e \frac{L}{T(mb)^{1/2}}.$$

The fluctuations are not significantly larger than the elementary charge unless one wishes to define the surface more accurately than the Compton wave length and to measure the charge more quickly than it takes light to traverse the volume.

Since the energy and the electric field strength do not commute, any measurement of the field strengths is always correlated with a fluctuation in the energy and, therefore, the photon number. This makes the converse also true. If one has a large number of photons at one's disposal, then one can construct, from states with different numbers of photons, states in which the field strengths are sharply defined. In macroscopic electrical phenomena, this is always the case. For example, we may think of constructing an electric field in a cm^3 of 1 volt/cm out of waves of wave length $\frac{1}{10}$ cm long. This region will then contain 10^{10} photons. A sender who has a 100 kw source and a 100 meter wave length sends 10^{30} photons/sec, so that one maintains over 100 km a flux of about 10^{15} photons/sec cm^2. Only when we consider the radiation emitted from single atoms do photons begin to play more of a role. For macroscopic phenomena the field picture is relevant, while for microscopic phenomena one needs the particle concepts.

Part III

Fields with External Sources

8. General Formulae

The free fields considered so far are not, in themselves, physically interesting since they are not observable; particles manifest themselves only in interaction with other particles. Nevertheless, the properties of free fields will be the basis for the following material, since they provide an adequate framework for the description of the wave and particle properties of isolated particles. In particular we shall study in the next sections the effects of a mechanism which produces the particles under consideration; i.e., an external source of the fields, still neglecting the interactions of the particles themselves. By external, we mean that we consider the source as a prescribed function of space and time, and do not consider the back-reaction of the field upon the source. This is reasonable when, for example, the source is a macroscopic body, so that quantum effects are small or easily estimated. Mathematically we express this by representing the source $\rho(x)$ as an ordinary number, i.e., a multiple of the unit operator in Hilbert space. The introduction of a source for any Hermitian field ψ means adding a term, $eL' = e\rho(x)\psi$, to the "free" Lagrangian L_0. The e is an ordinary real number which characterizes the strength of the source. This addition results in the appearance of ρ as an inhomogeneous term in the field equations. In this simple case, it is even possible to solve the problem explicitly by finding operators which obey the new field equations and the commutation rules, as one does in the free field case. However, for many problems such a procedure will not be possible, so that we will now derive a general method for treating an interaction term.

To this end we shall assume that it is possible to expand the solution of the problem posed by $L = L_0 + eL'$ in powers of e. The expansion coefficients can be found by the use of the general variational principle, Eq. (1.54), which gives us the change of the transformation function for an infinitesimal change, $L \to L + \delta L$. By iteration we obtain an expansion in the powers of e. The formulae so arrived at will not depend on the assumption that L_0 is a free Lagrangian and L' is a source term. They are more general and will be used in the next part of the book as well. However, we shall confine ourselves to cases in which L' does not contain time derivatives of the fields. This has the consequence that the canonically conjugate field—and, therefore, the canonical commutation rules—has the same form for the problem with and without L'. Therefore, all quantities constructed from canonical quantities (the field and its canonical conjugate) at a certain time in the two problems will be connected by the same unitary transformation.

Applying the general variational principle, Eq. (1.54) for $\delta L = \delta e L'$ we get

$$\frac{\delta}{\delta e}\left(o'\sigma_1 \mid o''\sigma_2\right) = i\left(o'\sigma_1 \mid \int_{\sigma_2}^{\sigma_1} L'(x)\, dx \,\middle|\, o''\sigma_2\right)$$

$$= i\int_{\sigma_2}^{\sigma_1} dx \left(o'(\sigma_1) \mid o'''(\sigma_x)\right)\left(o'''(\sigma_x) \mid L'(x) \mid o''''(\sigma_x)\right) \tag{3.1}$$

$$\left(o''''(\sigma_x) \mid o''\,(\sigma_2)\right).$$

The σ_x is a spacelike surface through x, and the summation is to be taken over all states whose eigenvalue indices occur twice. We have rewritten Eq. (3.1) in order to facilitate taking the second variation of $(1 \mid 2)$ with respect to δe. In the second variation the middle expression on the right hand side of Eq. (3.1) is left invariant, since the unitary transformation generated by δL transforms the eigenstates and the operators equivalently.[1] Hence

$$\frac{\delta^2}{\delta e^2}\left(o'(\sigma_1) \mid o''(\sigma_2)\right) = i^2 \int_{\sigma_2}^{\sigma_1} dx \int_{\sigma_x}^{\sigma_1} dx'$$

$$\{\left(o'(\sigma_1) \mid L'(x') \mid o'''(\sigma_x)\right)\left(o'''(\sigma_x) \mid L'(x) \mid o''''(\sigma_x)\right)$$

$$\left(o''''(\sigma_x) \mid o''(\sigma_2)\right)\} + i^2 \int_{\sigma_2}^{\sigma_1} dx \int_{\sigma_2}^{\sigma_x} dx'$$

$$\{\left(o'(\sigma_1) \mid o'''(\sigma_x)\right)\left(o'''(\sigma_x) \mid L'(x) \mid o''''(\sigma_x)\right) \tag{3.2}$$

$$\left(o''''(\sigma_x) \mid L'(x') \mid o''(\sigma_2)\right)\}$$

$$= i^2\left(o'(\sigma_1) \mid P\int dx\, dx'\, L'(x)L'(x') \mid o''(\sigma_2)\right).$$

[1] The reader who has difficulties at this point is reminded that in elementary wave mechanics, too, a matrix element $(x' \mid f(x, P) \mid x'')$ in the Schrödinger representation does not depend on the form of the Hamiltonian. The latter comes in only when one considers the time dependent operators $x(t) = e^{-iHt}x e^{iHt}$. Similarly, we assume, of course, that $\mid o'$) does not depend explicitly on e. It may, for instance, refer to eigenstates of N, constructed from creation and destruction operators.

The symbol P which we have introduced here expresses the time-ordering[2] of the factors composing a product and is defined by

$$P(A(x)B(x')) = AB \qquad \text{for} \qquad x_0 > x_0'$$
$$\qquad\qquad\qquad = BA \qquad \text{for} \qquad x_0 < x_0'. \tag{3.3}$$

If we continue this process we generate a Taylor series for the transformation matrix U where the expansion is in terms of e, the coefficients being time-ordered products of free field operators.

$$U_{12} = \sum_{n=0}^{\infty} \frac{(ie)^n}{n!} \int_{\sigma_2}^{\sigma_1} dx_1 \cdots dx_n P(L'(x_1) \cdots L'(x_n)) \tag{3.4}$$

or, more compactly

$$U_{12} = P e^{ie\int_{\sigma_2}^{\sigma_1} dx L'(x)}. \tag{3.5}$$

Without using P this can be written

$$U_{12} = \sum_{n=0}^{\infty} (ie)^n \int_{\sigma_2}^{\sigma_1} dx_1 \int_{\sigma_2}^{\sigma_{x_1}} dx_2 \cdots \int_{\sigma_2}^{\sigma_{x_{n-1}}} dx_n (L'(x_1) \cdots L'(x_n)). \tag{3.6}$$

U describes the change in time of the eigenstates of operators under the influence of eL', as will be made precise below. Let us denote the eigenstates of operators obeying the field equations stemming from $L = L_0 + eL'$ by $\mid \mathbf{o}(\sigma))$. We write $\mid o(\sigma))$ for the eigenstates obtained by putting $e = 0$ in the Lagrangian above. These states will have different time-dependences since the two kinds of operators obey different field equations. If $\mid \mathbf{o}(\sigma))$ happens to coincide with $\mid o(\sigma))$ at a particular time, say σ_2, then they will differ at other times. This change is expressed by U_{12} through the following equation, which summarizes the content of Eqs. (3.2) and (3.4)

$$(\mathbf{o}'(\sigma_1) \mid \mathbf{o}''(\sigma_2)) = (o'(\sigma_1) \mid U_{12} \mid o''(\sigma_2)). \tag{3.7}$$

Therefore, the transition probability $\mid (\mathbf{o}'(\sigma_1)) \mid \mathbf{o}''(\sigma_2) \mid^2$ from an eigenstate $\mid \mathbf{o}'')$ of $\mathbf{O}$ at time σ_2 is given by the matrix element of U_{12} between corresponding eigenstates of free operators.[3]

---

[2] P has a relativistically invariant meaning when it is applied to operators which commute for spacelike points.

[3] Note that U_{12} is defined here somewhat differently from Eq. (1.45).

Using Eq. (3.5), for example, one may easily check that U is unitary and has the group property

$$U_{12}^{-1} = U_{21} = U_{12}^{\dagger}$$

$$U_{13} = U_{12} \, U_{23} \, .$$

If we adjust $O(x)$ in such a way that it coincides with $\mathbf{O}(x)$ at a particular time, say σ_2, then the unitary transformation which transforms $O(x)$ into $\mathbf{O}(x)$ is just U_{x2}, since it describes the change of the motion of the eigenvectors under the influence of L'

$$\mathbf{O}(x) \mid \mathbf{o}'(\sigma_x)) = U_{2x}O(x)U_{x2}U_{2x} \mid o'(\sigma_x)) = o' \mid \mathbf{o}'(\sigma_x)).$$

This enables us to obtain an explicit representation of the $\mathbf{O}(x)$ in the terms of free field operators between σ_2 and σ_x

$$\mathbf{O}(x) = U_{\sigma_2 x}O(x)U_{x\sigma_2} = O(x) + ie \int_{\sigma_2}^{\sigma_x} dx'[O(x), L'(x')]$$

$$+ \tfrac{1}{2}(ie)^2 \int_{\sigma_2}^{\sigma_x} dx' \int_{-\sigma_2}^{\sigma_x{}'} dx''[[O(x), L'(x')], L'(x'')]] + \cdots$$

(3.8)

One has to keep in mind that this holds only if $\mathbf{O}$ is constructed out of canonical quantities, e.g., A, ∂A, $\bar{\psi}$, ψ but not $\partial_0 \psi$. The difference stems from the time-dependence of U, which implies that

$$\partial/\partial x_0(U\psi U^{-1}) \neq U((\partial/\partial x_0)\psi)U^{-1}.$$

Having developed the relevant formulae for constructing representatives of the field operators in the presence of an interaction we turn now to the discussion of the physical meaning of this new situation. As a first difference between this and the last section we may note that the operator N, the number of particles, is now neither invariant nor constant in time. These two properties were peculiar to the linear form of the field equations. In addition, we must distinguish here between the case in which L' contains only field operators and that in which it contains prescribed space-time functions, such as those considered at the beginning of this section. We shall defer an investigation of the former case until the last part of the book. As for the latter, we recognize that a prescribed space-time function in L' excludes the possibility of having relativistic invariance and therefore an invariant and constant energy-momentum vector. This simply means that the external source will define a certain reference frame and may supply energy and momentum to the field.

As an aid to further discussion we shall now limit ourselves to linear couplings to external sources $\rho(x)$ which are such that they vanish[4] for $t \to \pm\infty$, and we shall take for L_0 the Lagrangian of the free fields. In this case, the field operator of, for example, a Bose field $\Phi(x)$ will be identical with the free operator $\Phi_0(x)$ for times before the source was switched on. This operator will be called $\Phi^{\text{in}}(x)$ for a reason which we will make clear in the next section. The operator

$$N^{\text{in}}(x) = i \int d\sigma_\mu (\Phi^{+\text{in}}(x),_\mu \Phi^{-\text{in}}(x) - \Phi^{+\text{in}}(x)\Phi^{-\text{in}}(x),_\mu) \quad (3.9)$$

is obviously to be interpreted as the number of Bosons which were present before the source was switched on. N^{in} and therefore its eigenstates

$$\left| {n \atop \text{in}} \right), \qquad N^{\text{in}} \left| {n \atop \text{in}} \right) = n \left| {n \atop \text{in}} \right)$$

are constants, so that $\left| {n \atop \text{in}} \right)$ describes the situation which develops from an initial state with n particles. On the other hand, if we were to form a particle number operator $N(t)$ from the field operators

$$\Phi(x) = U_{-\infty t}\Phi^{\text{in}}(x)U_{t-\infty}$$

then it would no longer be constant. As soon as the source is switched on, Φ will obey different equations than Φ^{in} and $N(t)$ will depart from N^{in}. This is clearly to be understood as a creation of particles by the source, so that the incoming particles do not account for all of the particles present.

However, not all of the particles created by the source will reach infinity and will be observed as free quanta. Some of them will be virtual, in the terminology of Section 1. We can distinguish the real particles when the source is finally switched off. Then $\Phi(x)$ will again equal a free field operator which will in general differ from Φ^{in} and will be called Φ^{out}. If we let S denote $U_{\infty,-\infty}$ we obtain the connection

$$S^{-1}\Phi^{\text{in}}(x)S = \Phi^{\text{out}}(x). \quad (3.10)$$

$N^{\text{out}} = S^{-1}N^{\text{in}}S$ constructed from Φ^{out} represents the number of par-

---

[4] This switching on and off of the source may seem objectionable in the case of the electric field with $L' = A_i j_i$ where the total charge must be conserved. In this case we may, for example, spread the charge out over all space as $t \to -\infty$ so that it becomes ineffective.

ticles which remain after the source has been switched off. It will be different from N^{in}, so that a state with n outgoing particles

$$\left(\begin{smallmatrix} n \\ out \end{smallmatrix}\right| = \left(\begin{smallmatrix} n \\ in \end{smallmatrix}\right| S$$

will not correspond to n incoming particles. The latter will be a mixture of outgoing states with different n, whose coefficients are given by

$$\left(\begin{smallmatrix} n' \\ out \end{smallmatrix}\middle| \begin{smallmatrix} n \\ in \end{smallmatrix}\right) = \left(\begin{smallmatrix} n' \\ in \end{smallmatrix}\middle| S \middle| \begin{smallmatrix} n \\ in \end{smallmatrix}\right).$$

Similarly, the energy-momentum vector P constructed from the field operators Φ will depend on time. The constant operators P^{in} and P^{out} will be different from P and from each other. It can, of course happen that $N^{in} = N^{out}$ while $P^{in} \neq P^{out}$. That is to say, the number of particles remains constant while their energy and momenta are changed. This means that the particles have been scattered by the external field. Since S gives the connection between the in and out fields and all operators connected with them it contains all information about the overall effect of the interaction. The in and out states are usually referred to as physical states, since they correspond to initial and final situations of actual experiments. In this context, infinite space and time intervals mean macroscopic intervals, whereas finite intervals refer to intervals on the atomic scale.

In contradistinction, the eigenstates of N, $|n)$ which have the properties

$$\Phi^+(x, t) \,|\, 0) = 0 \qquad |n) = \Phi^-(x_1) \cdots \Phi^-(x_n) \,|\, 0)_{t_1 = \cdots = t_n = t}$$

$$= U_{-\infty t} \,\middle|\, \begin{smallmatrix} n \\ in \end{smallmatrix}\right)$$

are states which are hard to prepare in reality. For instance, $|\,0)$ corresponds to a state in which all particles, real and virtual, which the source generates are extinguished at a certain time instant. Such states are referred to as the "bare" states and describe the "bare" source, with the dress of virtual particles removed.[5]

---

[5] The physical states are sometimes called the dressed states. One frequently finds the misconception that $\Phi(x)$, the Heisenberg operator, creates dressed particles whereas $\Phi^{in}(x)$, the interaction representation operator, creates bare particles. Actually, it is the other way around, unless the interaction representation is such that it coincides with the Heisenberg representation at a finite time. In the latter case, both kinds of operators produce bare particles. However, in the course of time, all bare particles dress themselves, so that in the next part of the book we shall be able to create physical states with the aid of $\Phi(x)$.

Hence, $U_{t-\infty}$ contains information which is not directly usable in present experiments, but which is of some academic interest. Generally, when one talks of particles one means physical particles. In this sense of "particle," the field operators Φ do not emit single particles but rather create that mixture of "particle" states which characterize the bare particle. However, conservation laws limit the possible mixtures. For instance, a complex field will always change the total charge by one unit, so that it will create a charged particle plus a pair of oppositely charged particles, and so forth.

We shall use these ideas in this part of the book to treat, first, the problem of an electromagnetic field with an external source and, secondly, an electron in an external electromagnetic field. The two problems are essentially different. The first is characterized by $L' = (Aj)$, which is linear in the field operators, and the second by $L' = A\bar{\psi}\gamma\psi$ (A, unquantized; ψ, quantized). The latter is bilinear in ψ. Higher powers of the field operators in L' correspond to interactions between the field quanta themselves and will be dealt with in the last part of the book.

9. Emission of Light

In this section we will analyze the problem defined by

$$L = -\tfrac{1}{2}:A_{i,k}A^{i,k}: - j_i(x)A^i(x) \qquad (3.11)$$

where $j_i(x)$ is a given function of space and time which satisfies the criteria outlined in the last section. The coupling constant we imagine to be included in j. There are many ways of solving this problem. However, we shall use the one which follows most immediately from our previous development. This involves formula (3.10) in which, for simplicity, we denote A^{in} by A. We begin by obtaining an explicit representation of S in terms of eigenstates of N^{in}.

To this end we write the general term of Eq. (3.4)

$$S = \sum_{m=0}^{\infty} \frac{(-i)^m}{m!} \int_{-\infty}^{\infty} dx_1 \cdots dx_m (j(1) \cdots j(m)P(A(1) \cdots A(m)) \qquad (3.12)$$

as an ordered product by commuting A^+ to the right. This is a process which is performed inductively, the elementary process being the same as the one used in deriving Eq. (2.96) in Section 7. Taking an arbitrary A, $A(k)$ and using the commutation rules we may derive the identity

$$P(A(1) \cdots (A^-(k) + A^+(k)) \cdots A(m))$$

$$= i \sum_{k \neq l} (D^+(kl)\theta(kl) + D^+(lk)\theta(lk)) \prod_{\substack{i \neq k \\ i \neq l}} P(A(i))$$

$$+ A^-(k)P \prod_{i \neq k}(A(i)) + P(\prod_{i \neq k}(A(i))A^+(k) \qquad (3.13)$$

with $\theta(kl) = \theta(x_k^{\,0} - x_l^{\,0})$. The $\theta(kl)$ expresses the fact that when we try to commute $A^-(k)$ to the left or $A^+(k)$ to the right we run into a given $A(l)$ only if it occurs later or earlier, respectively, in the time sequence in the P bracket. When we do run into some $A(l)$ with $A^+(k)$ or $A^-(k)$ the commutation relations produce a D^+ function.

Having performed this operation for a given $A(k)$ we may do it again for some other $A(m)$ in the P product and in the end we will have transformed the P bracket into a frequency-ordered product which will have a structure like

$$\sum \prod D_f : \prod A :. \tag{3.14}$$

The D_f function arises through the identity, Eq. (A2.7)

$$D_f(x) = D^+(x)\theta(x^0) + D^+(-x)\theta(-x^0).$$

A typical term in Eq. (3.14) will involve D_f, say, k times; A^-, r times; and A^+, $m - 2k - r$ times in a combination like

$$[D_f(12) \cdots D_f(2k - 1, 2k)][A^-(2k + 1) \cdots A^-(2k + r)]$$

$$[A^+(2k + r + 1) \cdots A^+(m)].$$

The coordinates $x_1 \cdots x_m$ can, of course, appear in the above arguments in any order and r and k can be any nonnegative integers such that $2k + r \leqslant m$. Each of these possibilities occurs exactly once in the ordered product. Thus, the sum of Eq. (3.14) goes over all permutations of the indices $l \cdots m$ which lead to a different term and over all permissible values of k and r.

Now we must observe that terms with equal k and r make the same contribution to Eq. (3.14), since they differ from one another only by the labeling of the integration variables. Hence, it is sufficient to sum over all possible values of k and r and to multiply each term by the number of terms equivalent to it. This number equals the number of permutations of the m coordinates divided by the number of those permutations which do not lead to anything new. The latter are inversions of arguments in D_f functions and the exchange of the arguments of two D_f functions or of A^+ or A^- factors. This gives us $m!/(2^k k! r!(m - 2k - r)!.)$ Thus, we arrive at the following expression for the S-matrix:

$$S = \sum_{m=0}^{\infty} \sum_{k=0}^{m/2} \frac{(m-1)}{2} \sum_{r=0}^{m-2k} \left(\frac{(-i)^m}{2^k k! r!(m - 2k - r)!} \right)$$

$$\cdot \int dx_1 \cdots dx_m \left[\prod_{j=1}^{m} j(j) \prod_{t=1}^{k} iD_f(2t - 1, 2t) \right. \tag{3.15}$$

$$\left. \prod_{i=2k+1}^{2k+r} A^-(i) \prod_{i=2k+r+1}^{m} A^+(i) \right].$$

The general term in Eq. (3.15) involves $m - 2k - r$ absorption operators and r emission operators. If we compute the transition element from the vacuum state to the state with n photons we are interested in picking out of the S matrix only those terms which involve no A^+ operators and nA^- operators

$$(n \mid S \mid 0) = \frac{(-i)^n}{n!} \int dx_1 \cdots dx_n \left[(n \left| \prod_{i=1}^{n} j(i)A^-(i) \right| 0) \right]$$

$$\cdot \sum_{k=0}^{\infty} \frac{(-)^k}{2^k k!} \cdot \int dx_1 \cdots dx_{2k} [j(1) \cdots j(2k)]$$

$$\cdot iD_f(12) \cdots iD_f(2k-1, 2k) = \frac{(-i)^n}{n!} e^{-1/2(\bar{n}+i\beta)} \tag{3.16}$$

$$\cdot \int dx_1 \cdots dx_n \; (n \left| \prod_{i=1}^{n} j(i)A^-(i) \right| 0) .$$

We have summed the series above into an exponential function where the exponent has real and imaginary parts. Note that $[iD^1(12)^\dagger = iD^1(12)]$:

$$\bar{n} + i\beta = \int dx_1 \, dx_2 j(1) \, j(2) iD_f(12)$$

$$= \int dx_1 \, dx_2 j(1) \, j(2) \left[\frac{i}{2} D^1(12) + i\bar{D}(12) \right]. \tag{3.17}$$

The imaginary part is of no interest here[1] since the transition probability is given by $\mid (n \mid S \mid 0) \mid^2 = w_n$, so that the imaginary exponential only contributes a unit multiplicative factor to w_n.

Eq. (3.16) just gives transitions to states with n photons having spacelike polarization directions. A_0^- is not an emission operator, but rather an absorption operator. To find the total emission probability for n photons, we must sum w over all momentum directions and over both states of polarization. To get a manifestly covariant expression for the emission probability we can extend the polarization sum so that it includes all four polarization directions. We shall prove below that the sum over the four polarization directions gives the same result for the probability as summing over just the two transverse ones. The former procedure has the advantage of exhibiting the Lorentz invariance of the expression immediately. That this extension does not change the probability is fundamentally a consequence of gauge invariance, which assures us that the emission probability for a photon whose polarization direction is along its

---

[1] However, for a pointcharge it turns out to be divergent and connected with the infinite self energy.

energy-momentum vector will vanish. Any such field can be transformed away by a gauge transformation. Formally, we note that the matrix element for photons can be written in the invariant form $e_i M^i$. (See Eq. (2.62). The vector index in M comes from the vector index of the corresponding current.) Gauge invariance imposes the condition $k_i M^i = 0$. One sees at once that, because of the continuity equation, $k_i j^i_{(k)} = 0$, this is actually satisfied. If the 1-direction is chosen to lie on the direction of the space part of k. Then, since $k^2 = 0$, we have $M^0 = M^1$, or

$$- |M^0|^2 + |M^1|^2 + |M^2|^2 + |M^3|^2 = |M^2|^2 + |M^3|^2.$$

That is, the summation of the squared transition elements over both transverse polarization directions 2 and 3 is equivalent to the formation of the scalar product $-(M^\dagger M)$. In the computation of w we were led to an expression of the form

$$\sum_f (0 \mid A^+(1) \cdots A^+(n) \mid f)(f \mid A^-(n+1) \cdots A^-(2n \mid 0) \quad (3.18)$$

where the sum runs over all states with n photons. Since we have shown that the sum can be made to include all polarization directions we have a sum over a complete set of states. Thus, the calculation of the total emission probability amounts to the calculation of a vacuum expectation value similar to Eq. (2.79) above;

$$w_n = \frac{e^{-\bar{n}}}{(n!)^2} \int dx_1 \cdots dx_n \, dx_1' \cdots dx_n' \left[\prod_{i=1}^n j(i) \prod_{i'=1}^n j(i') \right.$$
$$\left. (0 \mid \prod_{i=1}^n A^+(i) \prod_{i'=1}^n A^-(i') \mid 0) \right] = \frac{e^{-\bar{n}}}{n!} (\bar{n})^n. \quad (3.19)$$

The vacuum expectation value was computed by commuting the A^+ through to the right. In this way we obtain $n!$ products of nD^+ functions, corresponding to the $n!$ possible orderings of $i \leftrightarrow i'$. In this calculation each D^+ gives a factor of $\bar{n}$, since

$$i \int dx_1 \, dx_2 j(1) j(2) D^+(12) = \int dx_1 \, dx_2 \frac{i}{2} \underbrace{[D^+(12) - D^-(12)]}_{D^1(12).} \quad (3.20)$$

Eq. (3.19) shows that the photons are emitted with a Poisson distribution having a mean photon number $\bar{n}$.[2] The mean square fluctuation of the particle number $(\Delta n)^2$ is

$$(\Delta n)^2 = \bar{n}$$

so that the fluctuation of the emitted energy is proportional to $\bar{n}$. The Poisson distribution implies that the photons are emitted independently. This is no longer true if the recoil of the photon is accounted for. However, it is a good approximation in many situations and has been experimentally verified in the absorption of microwaves by electrons.

If one is not interested in the total probability that n photons are emitted, but only in the probability that n photons are emitted in the momentum interval Δk then, by analogy with Eq. (2.81), one must put the expression for $\bar{n}$ into momentum space; we use Eqs. (A2.8) and (N.4)

$$\bar{n} = \int i \, dx_1 \, dx_2 j(1) \, j(2) D^+(12) = -\frac{1}{(2\pi)^3} \int dk \, | \, j(k)|^2 \delta(k^2) \, dk^0 \quad (3.20)$$

and integrate only over a momentum interval $\Delta \underline{k}$. This gives, for the probability[3] of emitting n photons in the interval Δ

$$w_{n,\Delta} = e^{-\bar{n}} \frac{(\bar{n}_\Delta)^n}{n!}, \qquad \bar{n}_\Delta = -\int_\Delta \frac{dk}{(2\pi)^3} \, \delta(k^2) \, | \, j(k)|^2. \quad (3.21)$$

It is clear from the formalism that not only are photons within one momentum region emitted independently, but that photons in different momentum regions are also independent of each other. If we divide an interval into two subintervals $\Delta = \Delta_1 + \Delta_2$ then we obviously have $\bar{n}_\Delta = \bar{n}_{\Delta_1} + \bar{n}_{\Delta_2}$ and, from the addition theorems for the Poisson distribution

$$w_{n,\Delta} = e^{-\bar{n}} \frac{(\bar{n}_\Delta)^n}{n!} = \sum_{m=0}^{n} w_{m,\Delta_1} w_{n-m,\Delta_2}. \quad (3.22)$$

Similarly, if we divide the whole momentum space into two intervals and ask for the probability, $w_{1,n}$, for the emission of n photons into the first interval irrespective of what happens in the second interval, we get a Poisson distribution

$$w_{1,n} = \sum_{m=0}^{\infty} w_{1n} w_{2m} = e^{-\bar{n}_1} \frac{(\bar{n}_1)^n}{n!}. \quad (3.23)$$

---

[2] As must be the case, $\sum_{n=0}^{\infty} w_n = 1$. The notation $\bar{n}$ is justified by the statement that $\sum_{n=0}^{\infty} n w_n = \bar{n}$; $\bar{n}$ is just the average number of emitted photons.

[3] It will turn out that $j(k)$ is, in fact, spacelike, so that $\bar{n}$ and w are positive.

The probability for emission of photons with a definite polarization direction e has the same characteristics as the one for a definite momentum. Using the matrix element in Eq. (1.73) we see that in this case we have to replace $\sum_i |j_i(k)|^2$ by $|j_i(k)e^i|^2$. Calling the corresponding integral $\bar{n}_e$ we have

$$w_{n,e} = e^{-\bar{n}_e} \frac{(\bar{n}_e)^n}{n!}. \tag{3.24}$$

As for the mathematical structure of the solution we note that the expansion in powers of the coupling exists if $\bar{n} < \infty$ and has an infinite radius of convergence. But even if $\bar{n}$ diverges in some part of momentum space this part may be excluded and we may use Eq. (3.23) above to get finite answers for the other parts.

To illustrate the preceding development we shall compute $\bar{n}$ for a special $j(x)$. Let us consider the simplest nontrivial case in which we have a charged particle of mass M which moves with a constant four-velocity v_k up to a proper time $s = 0$, at which point its velocity is abruptly changed to $v_k{}'(v^2 = v'^2 = 1)$, after which it again moves uniformly with a velocity $v_k{}'$. The motion is easily expressible in terms of the θ function

$$z(s) = sv\theta(-s) + sv'\theta(s). \tag{3.25}$$

This sudden change in the motion is certainly meaningless physically. However, we regard Eq. (3.25) as an idealization for a change of motion which one does not wish to follow in detail. In reality, the transition from one velocity to the other will occur during a certain time interval Δt, which, because of the uncertainty relation, must be greater than $1/\Delta E$, where ΔE is the energy change. In the rest system of either velocity, i.e., in the system S or S' in which v or v' is equal to $(1, 0, 0, 0)$, we find

$$\Delta t > (\Delta E)^{-1} = (2WM)^{-1} \tag{3.26}$$

where $W = -(v - v')^2/4$. For either system S or S' this will equal $((1 - \beta^2)^{-1/2} - 1)/2$, where β is the magnitude of the spatial part of the velocities v or v' as measured in S or S', respectively. In the two limits $\beta \to 0$ or $\beta \to 1$ we have $W \cong \beta^2/4$ and $W \cong (1 - \beta^2)^{-1/2}/2$.

In such a motion the current will not contain frequencies greater than $1/\Delta t$. Therefore, the particles will not emit any photons with frequencies larger than ΔE. Thus, we will only ask for the probability for the emission of photons with a frequency less than a bound L, where L can have a maximum in the rest system of v' of $L_{\max} = 2WM$.

The Fourier representation of the current[4]

$$j(x) = e\left[\int_{-\infty}^{0} ds v \delta(x - vs) + \int_{0}^{\infty} ds v' \delta(x - v's)\right] \quad (3.27)$$

can be written (see notation section for the relevant formulae)

$$j_n(k) = e\left(\int_{-\infty}^{0} ds v_n e^{i(vk)s} + \int_{0}^{\infty} ds v_n' e^{i(v'k)s}\right) \quad (3.28)$$

and, using the formula

$$\int_{0}^{\infty} e^{isx} = iP\left(\frac{1}{x}\right) + \pi\delta(x)$$

where P stands for "principle part"

$$j_n(k) = ie\left(\frac{v_n'}{(v'k)} - \frac{v_n}{(vk)}\right) + e\pi[v_n'\delta(v'k) + v_n\delta(vk)]. \quad (3.29)$$

The term in the last bracket gives no contribution to Eqs. (3.27) and (3.28) since, save for the one point $k = 0$, k^2 and (vk)—note that $v^2 = 1$—have no common zero. Thus, we have[5] for $\bar{n}$

$$\bar{n} = -e^2(2\pi)^{-3}\int_{(v'k)<L} dk\left(\frac{v}{(vk)} - \frac{v'}{(v'k)}\right)^2 \delta(k^2)\theta(k_0). \quad (3.30)$$

To condense the k-dependence into an invariant expression it is best to make use of the identity

$$\left(\frac{v}{(vk)} - \frac{v'}{(v'k)}\right)^2 = -\int_{-1}^{+1} dx\left(2W - x\frac{\partial}{\partial x}\right)\frac{1}{(Nk)^2}$$

with

$$N = \frac{(v + v')}{2} + x\frac{(v - v')}{2} \qquad N^2 = 1 + W(1 - x^2). \quad (3.31)$$

One can easily do the integral over k in Eq. (3.30) by specializing to the rest system of the timelike vector N. We find

$$e^2(2\pi)^{-3}\frac{1}{2}\int_{\lambda}^{L} dk_0 k_0 d\Omega(k_0[N_0 - N\cos(\varphi)])^{-2} = \frac{\alpha}{\pi}N^{-2}\ln\left(\frac{L}{\lambda}\right). \quad (3.32)$$

[4] See Eq. (1.10).

[5] According to our earlier remarks, the integral evaluated in the rest system of V' is to be taken over frequencies smaller than L. We shall get about the same by using the rest system of N.

Since the integral diverges at the lower limit we have introduced a cut-off λ. In this case $\bar{n} \to \infty$ as the cut-off goes to zero, which simply means that the probability of emitting only a finite number of photons is zero, since there are always infinitely many zero frequency photons emitted. This is connected with the infinite range of the Coulomb field and shows that for very long wave lengths the photon picture is inadequate. Since the wave lengths where $\bar{n} > 1$ are $> e^{137} m^{-1} \gg$ diameter of the world, this phenomenon ("infra-red catastrophe") is just an academic curiosity. Hence, we shall continue to use the cut-off dependent $\bar{n}$. That is to say, we ask for emission probabilities of observable photons irrespective of the zero frequency photons; we use Eq. (3.21).

There is still the integration over the auxiliary variable x which we must carry out

$$\int_{-1}^{1} dx \left(2W - x \frac{\partial}{\partial x} \right) \frac{1}{1 + W(1 - x^2)} = 2 \int_{0}^{1} \frac{dx W(1 + x^2)}{1 + W(1 - x^2)}$$

$$= \frac{8}{3} W \quad \text{for} \quad W < 1 \tag{3.33}$$

$$= 2 \ln W \quad \text{for} \quad W > 1.$$

Large and small W correspond to large and small changes in the velocity (the extreme relativistic and nonrelativistic limits).

Collecting our results, we get for the mean number of photons with a frequency less than L and greater than λ

(N.R): $$\bar{n} = \frac{\alpha}{\pi} \frac{2}{3} \beta^2 \ln \left(\frac{L}{\lambda} \right)$$

(E.R.): $$\bar{n} = \frac{\alpha}{\pi} \ln (1 - \beta^2)^{-1/2} \ln \left(\frac{L}{\lambda} \right)$$

$$\tag{3.34}$$

For small velocity changes β we get the result estimated in the introductory chapter.[6] For $\beta \to 1$, $\bar{n}$ increases logarithmically. We have previously observed that for a realistic change in velocity, L cannot exceed $2\,MW$. That is to say, the probability for emission of photons restricted only by $k_0 > \lambda$ goes for $W \to \infty$ as $\alpha(\ln (W))^2$. Thus, for reasonable energies and frequencies the probability that a singly charged particle emits a photon when it is deflected becomes $\ll 1$. For macroscopic, multiply charged particles, however, there will

[6] See p. 7 of the General Introduction.

usually be an emission of many photons and the quantum structure of the electric field is unimportant. It only becomes apparent at all because of the smallness of α.

The calculation of $\bar{n}$ for other typical forms of $j(x)$ with our methods leads to familiar results and shall not be discussed further. We shall now turn to the calculation of $U_{t-\infty}$. We see at once that the operator

$$U_{t-\infty} = Pe^{-i\int_{-\infty}^{t} dx\, j(x)A(x)} \tag{3.35}$$

can be obtained from S if we replace $j(x')$ in S by $j(x')\theta(t - t')$, i.e., if we switch the current on at the time t. As a consequence, even if $j(x)$ is of such a form that it does not produce real photons (if $|j(k)|^2 \delta(k^2) = 0$), $U_{t-\infty}$ will contain matrix elements connecting states with different numbers of photons. This means that if for this case we analyze $|_{in}^{0}\rangle$ in terms of eigenstates of $N(t)$, we get a probability distribution for the presence of photons. These photons are the virtual photons mentioned in the introduction. They can be defined as the particles which are left over when the source is suddenly switched off. A current with $|j(k)|^2 \delta(k^2) = 0$ does not create a field in the wave zone. The virtual particles are all confined to the near zone. For photons the Lorentz condition requires some qualifications of the virtual particle concept which, however, do not seem interesting enough to warrant a detailed discussion.

To escape these complications we will consider for the moment a scalar field with a mass m. A static point source[7]

$$\rho(x) = e \int ds\delta(x - vs)$$

gives a mean number of particles

$$\bar{n}_{\text{virtual}} = (2\pi)^{-3}e^2 \int dk\delta(k^2 - m^2)\,\frac{1}{(vk)^2}. \tag{3.36}$$

Comparing this to Eq. 3.30 we see that the mean number of photons emitted in bremsstrahlung has the simple meaning mentioned in the introduction; that is, the average number of virtual particles contained in the difference of the fields before and after the deflection.

---

[7] In order to satisfy the conditions mentioned earlier, we imagine $\rho(x)$ to be switched on very slowly; i.e., $\rho(x) \xrightarrow[\alpha \to 0]{} e^{-\alpha|x_0|}\rho(x)$, which does not affect our calculations.

The integral for $\bar{n}_{\text{virtual}}$ again diverges, this time for large k_0. Thus, for a point source our expansion method fails, since the eigenstates of N are orthogonal to the ones of N^{in}. This difficulty again seems academic, since it occurs for $k_0 \sim e^{137}m$. It disappears when $\rho(x)$ has a finite extent.

It is instructive to compare $|\,{}^{o}_{\text{in}})$, analyzed using eigenstates of $N(t)$, with the state vector of a heavy atom with many electrons. The latter vector is an eigenstate of the number of particles, whereas $|\,{}^{o}_{\text{in}})$ is a mixture of n particle states with various n. Correspondingly, the n particle states contained in the mixture are not normalized to unity but to a number smaller than 1 which is the probability of finding n particles. This is an essential difference between elementary wave mechanics and quantum field theory. In the former the Schrödinger function is always normalized to unity, since one is sure to find the particle somewhere. In quantum field theory, however, we deal with systems of fluctuating particle numbers, so that particles suddenly appear and disappear. Otherwise, the wave function of the n-particle states in $|\,{}^{o}_{\text{in}})$ manifest a simple structure. They are just the product of one particle wave functions, as one would expect, since the particles are independent in this trivial problem.

Looking at Eq. (3.36), we note that the individual wave functions behave in momentum space like $k_0^{-3/2}$, as we guessed in the Introduction. Apart from this, the virtual particles have no familiar features. Since N is not an invariant, observers in different Lorentz systems would not agree about their number. Moreover, because the particles constitute the field of the near zone their wave function in x space behaves like e^{-mr}. There are no wave functions which would correspond to an orbit of large quantum numbers. This indicates that they do not have anything like a classical path, since they disappear before their change in position exceeds their uncertainty in position. Within those random fluctuations virtual particles disappear at one point and simultaneously reappear at another point, which prevents a Lorentz invariant definition of their number.

The explicit representation of the field operators A can easily be obtained with the aid of formula (3.8). Since the commutator of A with L' is an ordinary number, all the multiple commutators in Eq. (3.8) vanish, so that the infinite series terminates after the second term. Again taking A and calling it $A^{\text{in}}(x)$ we obtain

$$A_l(x) = A_l^{\text{in}}(x) + \int D^{\text{ret}}(x - x')j_l(x')\,dx'. \qquad (3.37)$$

$A_l(x)$ obviously satisfies the field equations $\Box^2 A_l(x) = j_l(x)$ which result from Eq. (3.11). Furthermore, it obeys the same commutation relations as the free field operator, since it differs from A^{in} only by an ordinary number and thus satisfies all requirements of the solution.

We note that A^{in} is actually the counterpart of the corresponding classical quantity in Eq. (1.14). Since A is an operator it is now not possible to put $A^{\text{in}}(x) \equiv 0$. However, in the state $\mid {}^{o}_{\text{in}}\rangle$, for example, the average value of A^{in} is zero, so that the expectation value of A is the same as in the classical calculation with $A^{\text{in}} = 0$. The same is true for P_k, since terms linear in A again drop out and terms quadratic in A^{in} are ordered so as to give a vanishing vacuum expectation value.

The energy-momentum vector fed into the system by j during its existence, $\langle P^{\text{out}}\rangle - \langle P^{\text{in}}\rangle$, can be verified to be the classical radiation loss integrated over all times. We find (problem 20)

$$\left({}^{o}_{\text{in}} \mid P^{\text{out}}_m \mid {}^{o}_{\text{in}} \right) = \left({}^{o}_{\text{in}} \mid P^{\text{rad}}_m \mid {}^{o}_{\text{in}} \right) = \left({}^{o}_{\text{in}} \mid \int dx\, j_l(x) f_{lm}(x) \mid {}^{o}_{\text{in}} \right)$$

$$= \left({}^{o}_{\text{in}} \mid \int dx\, j_l(x) f^{\text{rad}}_{lm}(x) \mid {}^{o}_{\text{in}} \right). \tag{3.38}$$

This can be cast into the suggestive form

$$\sum_n \left({}^{o}_{\text{in}} \mid {}^{n}_{\text{out}} \right) \left({}^{n}_{\text{out}} \mid P^{\text{out}}_m \mid {}^{n}_{\text{out}} \right) = (2\pi)^{-3} \int dk \delta(k^2) \mid j_i(k) \mid^2 k_m . \tag{3.39}$$

The summation in Eq. (3.39) goes over all outgoing states and yields exactly the mean number of photons per momentum interval multiplied by the corresponding energy-momentum vector and integrated over all momentum space. For the energy loss into a particular frequency interval we also get a formula of the above structure, where the k integration is extended only over the interval under consideration. For example, in the case of the special current in Eq. (3.27), we find

$$P_m(\Delta) = (2\pi)^{-3} \int_\Delta dk \delta(k^2) k_m \left(\frac{v}{(vk)} - \frac{v'}{(v'k)} \right)^2 \tag{3.40}$$

which shows that the bremsstrahlung reproduces the spectrum of the virtual photons in the difference field. Calculating the energy loss in the rest system of v or v' we find, with the same methods that we employed to calculate $\bar{n}$

(N.R.):
$$\Delta P_0 = \frac{\alpha}{\pi} \frac{2}{3} \beta^2 L$$

$$\tag{3.42}$$

(E.R.):
$$\Delta P_0 = \frac{\alpha}{\pi} \ln (1 - \beta^2)^{-1/2} L.$$

In this case there is no infinity connected with the long wave lengths. The energy loss increases linearly with the upper bound L of the frequency interval. This reflects the radiation spectrum $\sim d\nu/\nu$, which stems from the (wave function)^2 $\sim 1/k^3$ times the number of states per frequency interval $\sim k^2 \, dk$. As a consequence, every energy loss between zero and L_{max} has the same probability.

Although A^{in} does not contribute to the expectation value of A, it makes the mean square fluctuation of A different from zero. In a state in which the number of incoming particles is definite it equals the fluctuations of the free fields. This fluctuation of the electric fields around their classical values has been discussed in the introduction and will be looked at from a more formal point of view in a later section.

10. The Dirac Field in an External Electric Field

The problem of this section is characterized by a Lagrangian

$$L(x) = :\bar{\psi}(x)\,(\partial - m)\psi(x): - A_\mu(x)\,j^\mu(x) \qquad (3.43)$$

where $j^\mu(x) = e:\bar{\psi}(x)\gamma^\mu\psi(x):$. Here the $:\ :$ symbols take on their usual meaning when we expand the exact solutions in terms of free fields. $A_\mu(x)$ is a given (unquantized) function of space and time with the property that it vanishes for $t \to \pm\infty$. As in the previous section, we begin by examining S. To get explicit expressions, we again have to cast the time-ordered form of S

$$S = P\,e^{-i\int dx A_\mu(x)\,j^\mu(x)} \qquad (3.44)$$

into an ordered form. The corresponding rearrangements are a little more complicated than those of the preceding chapter. Before going into this for the nth order term $S^{(n)}$ we shall evaluate the terms of lowest order in A. A typical matrix element contained in S is one connecting a given electron state with a wave function v to another with a wave function u. Using the results of Section 6, this matrix element is immediately seen to be[1]

$$(1, u \mid S^{(1)} \mid 1, v) = -i \int dx A_k(x) e\bar{u}(x)\gamma^k v(x). \qquad (3.45)$$

Its square gives, in the lowest order in e, the probability for a transition of the electron from the state v to the state u under the influence of the field A. We shall not pursue this further, since Eq. (3.45) is the well-known Born approximation expression as derived from elementary methods and is not a typical feature of quantum field theory. We turn, therefore, to a process which is beyond elementary wave mechanics; namely, the creation of an electron-position pair by the electric field. In the corresponding matrix element between the vacuum and a state with a pair $(2 \mid$

$$(2 \mid S^{(1)} \mid 0) = -ie \int dx A_\mu(x)(2 \mid \bar{\psi}^-(x)\gamma^\mu\psi^-(x) \mid 0) \qquad (3.46)$$

[1] Here and in what follows, we omit the subscripts "in" of the state vectors.

109

we again have to replace $\bar{\psi}^-$ and ψ^- by the wave function of the electron and positron, respectively. The characteristic difference between Eqs. (3.45) and (3.46) is that the former contains a positive and a negative frequency wave function whereas, in the latter, both wave functions have only negative frequencies. To give something different from zero, A in Eq. (3.46) must contain frequencies greater than $2m$. Only such a field has, in this order in e, enough energy to produce a pair.

We shall now evaluate w, the total probability for pair creation, which is the square of Eq. (3.46) summed over all possible states of the pairs. Although it would be of considerable interest to study more detailed questions like the polarization of the electron and positron, we must go immediately to the problems which will turn out to be crucial for quantum field theory. Similar to the case of the emission of light, we find

$$w = \sum_2 |(2 \mid S^{(1)} \mid 0)|^2$$

$$= -e^2 \int dx\, dx' \{A_\mu(x) A_\nu(x')\, \mathrm{Tr}\, [\gamma^\mu S^+(x - x') \gamma^\nu S^-(x' - x)]\}. \tag{3.47}$$

Since the sum over two particle states can be extended to a sum over a complete set of states (the others do not contribute to the sum), we could reduce the expression to a vacuum expectation value, which we have evaluated with the aid of Eq. (2.43). The tensor

$$K_{\mu\nu}(x) = e^2 \mathrm{Tr}[\gamma_\mu S^+(x)\gamma_\nu S^-(-x)] \tag{3.48}$$

has, as a consequence of the conservation of the current j_μ and j_ν, the property

$$\frac{\partial}{\partial x_\mu} K_{\mu\nu} = \frac{\partial}{\partial x_\nu} K_{\mu\nu} = 0. \tag{3.49}$$

Because it is an invariant[2] function of x, it can contain only terms of the form $\delta_{\mu\nu}f(x)$ or $\partial/\partial x_\mu \partial/\partial x_\nu g(x)$. From Eq. (3.49) it then follows that

$$K_{\mu\nu}(x) = \left(\delta_{\mu\nu}\Box^2 - \frac{\partial}{\partial x_\mu}\frac{\partial}{\partial x_\nu}\right) K(x) \tag{3.50}$$

where $K(x)$ is an invariant function which has only positive frequencies. We can, therefore, represent it as a linear combination of

[2] Under the proper Lorentz group.

Δ^+ functions with different masses. The weighting function is obtained from Eq. (A2.23)

$$\tfrac{1}{3} K_\mu{}^\mu(x) = \square^2 K(x) = -i \int_{4m^2}^\infty dc^2 \sigma(c) c^4 \Delta^+(x, c) \qquad (3.51)$$

with

$$\sigma(c) = \frac{2ie^2}{3c^5} f_{ss}(m, m, c) = \frac{\alpha}{3\pi} \left(\frac{1}{c^2} + \frac{2m^2}{c^4} \right) \sqrt{1 - \frac{4m^2}{c^2}} \Theta(c^2 - 4m^2).$$

Inserting Eq. (3.50) into Eq. (3.45), we see by partial integration that the term $\partial/\partial x_\mu \partial/\partial_\nu K$ does not contribute, since A obeys the condition $A_{\mu,}{}^\mu = 0$. Thus we get

$$w = i \int dx\, dx'\, A_\mu(x) A^\mu(x') \int dc^2 \sigma(c) c^4 \Delta^+(x - x', c).$$

This expression becomes more suggestive in momentum space and, if we introduce a current $\mathcal{g}$ which is to be though of as the source of A, we have $\square^2 A = \mathcal{g}$ or $A(k) = -\mathcal{g}(k)/k^2$. Hence[3]

$$w = -\frac{\alpha}{3\pi} \int_{\substack{k^2 > 4m^2 \\ k_0 > o}} \frac{dk}{(2\pi)^3} \mid \mathcal{g}(k) \mid^2 \left(\frac{1}{k^2} + \frac{2m^2}{k^4} \right) \sqrt{1 - \frac{4m^2}{k^2}}. \qquad (3.52)$$

As we shall presently show, w, in this form, is an integral over the differential probabilities for creating a pair with a kinetic energy-momentum vector k. By the latter, we mean the expression in Eq. (2.38). This is not conserved, but it has the property that $[O(x) , P_\mu] = i(\partial O/\partial x_\mu)$ if $O(x)$ is constructed from the $\psi(x)$. Consequently,[4] the matrix element $(k \mid \mathcal{g}(x) \mid 0)$, where $\mid k)$ is an eigenstate of P with eigenvalue k, must have a space-time dependence $e^{kx}(k \mid \mathcal{g}(0) \mid 0)$. Comparing this with Eq. (3.46), we recognize that the Fourier vector k in Eq. (3.52) actually has the meaning of the eigenvalue of P in the pair state. For a source with a definite frequency, $\mid \mathcal{g}(k) \mid^2 \sim \delta(k_0 - \omega)$, the behavior for the differential probability for low energies, corresponding to ω, is of the familiar $\sqrt{\epsilon}$ form where ϵ is the energy above threshold. For high energies, w goes like $1/\epsilon^2$, which reflects the general decrease of electric interactions for energies greater than m. This arises because the electron is smeared out over a region $\sim 1/m$, due to the cloud of vitural pairs which it emits (see the remarks in the introduction).

[3] As in the previous chapter, $\mid \mathcal{g} \mid^2$ means $\mid \mathcal{g}_0 \mid^2 - \mid \mathcal{g}_1 \mid^2 - \mid \mathcal{g}_2 \mid^2 - \mid \mathcal{g}_3 \mid^2$.
[4] Evaluate $(k \mid [P_\mu , O(x)] \mid 0) = - i(\partial/\partial x_\mu) (k \mid O(x) \mid 0)$.

The expression in Eq. (2.86) for the mean square fluctuation of the charge in a volume V can be written in the form

$$-e^2 \int dx \, dx' a(x) a(x') \, \text{Tr} \left[\gamma S^+(x - x') \gamma S^-(x' - x) \right]$$

where $a(x) = 1$ if a is contained in V and is 0 if x is not contained in V. This resembles the formula for pair creation by a potential $a(x)$, which is plausible physically since the volume V can be defined by electromagnetic means only if we use a field of the same form. Since the $a(x)$ above contains arbitrarily high frequencies the fluctuation integral diverges. We obtain a finite result if the system is confined in a volume whose edges are not defined sharply. Similar infinities occur if U_{12} instead of S is calculated.

One can use Eq. (3.52) to learn how large the probability is for finding pairs in the energy which a charged particle loses in a scattering process. For this task we take for the current $\mathcal{g}(x)$ the same one that we used in Eq. (3.27), the only difference being that we shall suppose that the charge of the scattered particle is given by Ze. Furthermore, we specialize by limiting ourselves to the case in which $WM^2 > 4m^2$. The main contribution to Eq. (3.52) comes from k for which $k^2/4m^2 > 1$, so that in the k integration we take only that part of the integrand which goes as $(4m^2/k^2)$.

As the maximum effective frequency we again take $2WM$ and integrate Eq. (3.52) after inserting $\mathcal{g}(k)$ only over the range $(kv') < 2ML$. (The resulting calculation follows the same pattern as Eq. (3.27) and ff.) We take over the results of our earlier work in which the integral we are trying to compute was written as follows

$$w_P = \frac{\alpha}{8m^2} (2\pi)^{-4} \int_{\substack{k^2 > 4m^2 \\ (kv') < 2ML}} dk$$

$$\frac{8m^2}{3k^2} \int_{-1}^{1} dx \left(2W - x \frac{\partial}{\partial x} \right) Z^2 e^2 (Nk)^{-2} = \frac{\alpha Z^2}{6\pi} \int_{4m^2}^{4M^2L} d\lambda^2 e^2 \lambda^{-2}$$

$$\int_{(kv') < 2ML} dk (2\pi)^{-3} \delta(k^2 - \lambda^2) \int_{-1}^{1} dx \left(2W - x \frac{\partial}{\partial x} \right) (Nk)^{-2} \quad (3.53)$$

$$= \frac{Z^2}{3} \left(\frac{\alpha}{\pi} \right)^2 2 \int_{2m}^{2ML} \frac{d\lambda}{\lambda} \ln \left(\frac{L}{\lambda} \right) \int_{-1}^{1} dx \left(2W - x \frac{\partial}{\partial x} \right) N^{-2}$$

$$\left(\begin{matrix} \text{N. R.} \\ \text{E. R.} \end{matrix} \right) : w_P = 2 \frac{Z^2 \alpha^2}{3\pi^2} \ln \left(\frac{WM}{m} \right)^2 \left(\frac{4/3 \, W}{\ln W} \right).$$

The ratio of the probability for pair creation to the probability that in a collision a photon with an energy greater than $2m$ is generated is $2\alpha/3\pi \ln (WM/m)$. Because of the small value of α pair creation is in general, rather improbable, and only becomes significant when large energy transfers are involved in the collision. However, one can readily observe pair creation by studying cosmic ray tracks in photographic plates. One sees in the plate a single track suddenly become three tracks, an event which is known to experimental physicists as a trident. The statistics on these are not yet sufficiently good to constitute a detailed proof of Eq. (3.53), but this result certainly gives the correct orders of magnitude.

Another application of Eq. (3.52) is in the internal pair creation from nuclei. For a nuclear transition in which the total angular momentum of the initial and final states is zero one photon emission is forbidden and the available energy can only be given up as internal conversion of internal pair creation. Some transitions supply enough energy for the latter process, which has actually been observed. The most common means for pair production is by a photon in a Coulomb field. This process belongs to the next part of the book, however.

We shall now orient ourselves about the terms which are of higher order in the expansion of Eq. (3.44). To find the probability for scattering from a state u to a state v, we shall have to evaluate a matrix element which is closely related to Eq. (2.84)

$$(v \mid P\!:\!\bar{\psi}(1)\psi(1)\!:\!:\!\bar{\psi}(2)\psi(2)\!:\mid u)$$

$$= i(v \mid [\bar{\psi}(1)^- S^+(12)\psi^+(2) - \bar{\psi}^-(2)S^-(12)\psi^+(1)]\theta(12)$$

$$+ [\bar{\psi}^-(2)S^+(21)\psi^+(1) - \bar{\psi}^-(1)S^-(21)\psi^+(2)]\theta(21) \mid u)$$

$$= i[\bar{v}(1)S_f(12)u(2) + \bar{v}(2)S_f(21)u(1)].$$

In the last step we have used

$$S_f(x) = \theta(x)S^+(x) - \theta(-x)S^-(x).$$

Hence, we get

$$(v \mid S^{(2)} \mid u) = ie^2 \int dx_1 \, dx_2 \, \bar{v}(1)\gamma_\mu A^\mu(1)S_f(12)\gamma_\nu A^\nu(2)u(2). \quad (3.54)$$

Equation (3.54) corresponds to the second Born approximation for a scattering process. The matrix elements, Eqs. (3.45) and (3.54), can

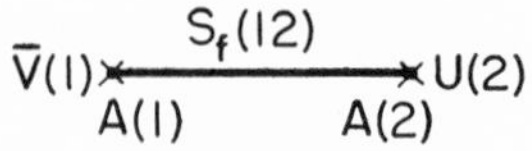

$$\overline{V}(1) \xleftarrow{\quad S_f(12) \quad} U(2)$$
$$A(1) \qquad A(2)$$

Fig. 7. This diagram illustrates a second-order scattering process.

be interpreted as the electron being scattered once or twice at the points x or x_1 and x_2. We may characterize these processes by a diagram like Fig. 7. As is characteristic in quantum mechanics, the matrix elements (amplitudes), and not the probabilities themselves, are summed over all coordinates where the scattering might take place. Furthermore, in $S^{(2)}$ the function relevant for the propagation of the electron between the two scatterings turns out to be S_f. We may write Eq. (3.54) as the sum over amplitudes where the electron propagates from 1 to 2 or 2 to 1, depending on the time ordering. S_f then includes the sum over all possible wave functions compatible with the positive definite character of the energy of the free electron. This restriction on the energy causes (as we have frequently mentioned) a spatial and temporal smearing of the extension of the S_f function, as is exemplified by its nonvanishing outside the light cone. We shall see later that propagation which is apparently faster than the velocity of light stays within the uncertainty relations for space-time and energy-momentum and hence is not observable.

After this orientation, we shall now examine the general structure of the expansion of Eq. (3.44). For this we shall concentrate on one matrix element; namely, $(0 \mid S \mid 0)$. All other matrix elements can be obtained by the same method or by differentiating $(0 \mid S \mid 0)$. However, these will not be needed later on. The task of evaluating

$$(0 \mid j(1) \cdots j(n) \mid 0)$$

can be done by our standard method of commuting absorption operators to the right. Proceeding stepwise as in the last section and suppressing spinor indices, we start this process with $\psi(1)$

$$(0 \mid P : \bar{\psi}(1)[\psi^-(1) + \psi^+(1)] : : \bar{\psi}(2)\psi(2) : : \cdots : : \bar{\psi}(n)\psi(n) : \mid 0)$$

$$= \sum_{l \neq 1} [\theta(1l)iS^+(1l) + \theta(l1)iS^-(l1)] \qquad (3.55)$$

$$\cdot (0 \mid P\bar{\psi}(1) : \bar{\psi}(2)\psi(2) : \cdots \psi(l) : \bar{\psi}(n)\psi(n) : \mid 0).$$

The part taken out under the expectation value we recognize as $\epsilon(1l)iS_f(1l)$. Proceeding with $\psi(2)$, etc., we arrive at

$$\sum_P \epsilon \prod_j \epsilon \, (jP_j) \prod_j iS_f(jP_j)$$

where $P_1 \cdots P_n$ is a permutation of $1 \cdots n$, and ϵ is a sign factor which stems from the anticommutivity of the ψ and which we shall determine immediately. The sum above goes over all permutations P corresponding to all possible pairings between the ψ's and the $\bar{\psi}$'s. To determine ϵ we notice that it is the sign we get by commuting the ψ^+ or ψ^- from the time-ordered sequence to its partner in the S-function. Depending on the time ordering, the partner is approached from the right or from the left. Putting all anticommutators equal to zero for the moment and starting from the time-ordered expression, we obtain ϵ as the sign of

$$\bar{\psi}^+(1)\psi^-(P_1) \cdots \psi^+(a)\bar{\psi}^-(Pa) \cdots \bar{\psi}^+(n)\psi^-(Pn)$$

where we have the order

$$\bar{\psi}^+(i)\psi^-(P_i) \qquad \text{for } \epsilon(iP_i) = 1$$

and

$$\psi^+(P_a)\bar{\psi}^-(Pa) \qquad \text{for } \epsilon(aP_a) = -1.$$

Thus $\epsilon \prod_j \epsilon \, (jP_j)$ is the sign of

$$\bar{\psi}(1)\psi(P_1)\bar{\psi}(2)\psi(P_2) \cdots \bar{\psi}(n)\psi(Pn)$$

$$= (-)^{\frac{(n(n-1))}{2}} \bar{\psi}(1) \cdots \bar{\psi}(n)\psi(P_1) \cdots \psi(Pn)$$

$$= (-)^{\frac{(n(n-1))}{2}} (-)^P \bar{\psi}(1)\bar{\psi}(n)\psi(1) \cdots \psi(n)$$

$$= (-)^P \bar{\psi}(1)\psi(1) \cdots \bar{\psi}(n)\psi(n)$$

which can be brought by even permutation (moving $\bar{\psi}\psi$ together) into the time-ordered sequence. Thus, Eq. (3.55) equals

$$i^n \sum_P (-)^P \prod_j S_f(j, P_j) = (i)^n \mid S_f(ij) \mid_{(n)}$$

where the subscript n on the determinant sign means that i and j go from 1 to n.

Restoring the missing factors, we get for the matrix element of order n

$$(0 \mid S^{(n)} \mid 0) = \frac{e^n}{n!} \int dx_1 \cdots dx_n \sum_{\mu_i \alpha_i \beta_i} A_{\mu_1}(1) \cdots A_{\mu_n}(n)$$

$$\times [\gamma^{\mu_1}_{\beta_1 \alpha_1} \cdots \gamma^{\mu_\alpha}_{\beta_n, \alpha_n}] \begin{vmatrix} 0 & S_f^{\alpha_1 \beta_2}(12) & \cdots & S_f^{\alpha_1 \beta_n}(1n) \\ S_f^{\alpha_2 \beta_1}(21) & 0 & \cdots\cdots\cdots \\ \vdots & & & \vdots \\ S_f^{\alpha_n \beta_1}(n1) & \cdots & & 0 \end{vmatrix} \qquad (3.56)$$

$$= \frac{1}{n!} \sum \mid K_{ij} \mid_n .$$

To ease the notation, we have introduced the shorthand

$$K_{ij} = eA_\mu(x_i)\gamma^\mu_{\beta_i\alpha}S_f^{\alpha\beta j}(x_i, x_j), \qquad K_{ii} = 0$$

and $\sum$ means summation over discrete and integration over continuous variables. Not all of the $n!$ terms in the determinant give different contributions. If a permutation contains c_l cycles with l elements, $c_1 + 2c_2 + \cdots nc_n = n$, then it will give a contribution

$$(-)^{c_2+c_4\cdots}(\operatorname{Tr} K)^{c_1}(\operatorname{Tr} K^2)^{c_2} \cdots (\operatorname{Tr} K^n)^{c_n}$$

where Tr includes integration over coordinates. Thus, all terms with the same c_i give identical contributions. The number of permutations of the class

$$\underbrace{(\cdot)(\cdot)\cdots(\cdot)}_{c_1} \quad \underbrace{(\cdot\cdot)\cdots(\cdot\cdot)}_{c_2} \quad \cdots \quad \underbrace{(\cdot\cdot\cdot\cdot)}_{c_n}$$

equals the number of all possible distributions of $1, 2 \cdots n$ into the above cycles divided by the number of those permutations which give nothing different

$$\frac{n!}{c_1!\, c_2!\, 2^{c_2} \cdots c_n!\, n^{c_n}}.$$

Thus, we may write

$$(0 \mid S^{(n)} \mid 0) = \sum_c \frac{(-\tfrac{1}{2}\operatorname{Tr} K^2)^{c_2}}{c_2!} \frac{(\tfrac{1}{3}\operatorname{Tr} K^3)^{c_3}}{c_3!} \cdots \frac{(1/n \operatorname{Tr} K^n)^{c_n}}{c_n!}$$

where the sum is to be extended over all possible values for the c_i and we have used $\operatorname{Tr} K = 0$. On summing over n, we obtain a product of exponentials

$$(0 \mid S \mid 0) = e^{\sum_{n=1}^{\infty} \frac{(-)^{n-1}}{n} \operatorname{Tr}(K^n)}. \tag{3.57}$$

The rearrangements leading from Eq. (3.56) to the final form are actually familiar from the theory of integral equations. There one shows that Eq. (3.56) is an expansion term of $\mid 1 + K \mid$, which one can write as $e^{\operatorname{Tr}[\ln(1+K)]}$ and, by expanding the exponent, arrive at Eq. (3.57).

Equation (3.57) can be further simplified by observing that terms with odd n's vanish, since generally the vacuum expectation value of a product of an odd number of currents vanishes because of the charge conjugation invariance of the vacuum

$$(0 \mid j(1) \cdots j(2n + 1) \mid 0) = (0 \mid U_c^{-1} j(1) \cdots j(2n + 1) U_c \mid 0)$$
$$= - (0 \mid j(1) \cdots j(2n + 1) \mid 0).$$

Introducing the square of K

$$(K^2)_{ij} = Q_{ij}$$
$$= e^2 \int dx A_{\mu_1}(x_i) \gamma^{\mu_1}_{\beta_i \alpha_1} S_f^{\alpha_1 \beta}(x_i x) A_{\mu_2}(x) \gamma^{\mu_2}_{\beta \alpha_2} S_f^{\alpha_2 \beta_j}(x x_j) \qquad (3.58)$$

we may write

$$(0 \mid S \mid 0) = e^{-1/2 \sum_{n=1}^{\infty} \mathrm{Tr}\, Q^n / n} = e^{1/2\, \mathrm{Tr}\, \ln\,(1-Q)}. \qquad (3.59)$$

The exponential form corresponds to what one gets for the emission of a photon. For pair creation one has the additional possibility that the pair is $n - 2$ times scattered by A between its creation and absorption. This is the significance of the series in the exponent of Eq. (3.58).

To investigate the analytic structure of Eq. (3.58) as a function of e^2 we note that the following upper bound is easily available

$$|(0 \mid S \mid 0) \mid^2 = e^{(1/2)\, \mathrm{Tr}\, \ln\,(1-Q-Q\dagger+QQ\dagger)} \le e^{-\mathrm{Re}\,(\mathrm{Tr}Q+1/2\, \mathrm{Tr}\, QQ\dagger)} \qquad (3.60)$$

since $\ln\,(1 + x) \le x$ for $(1 + x) > 0$ and $(1 - Q)(1 - Q^{\dagger})$ is positive definite. The term

$$\mathrm{Tr}\, Q = e^2 \int dx\, dx' A_{\mu}(x) A_{\nu}(x') \,\mathrm{Tr}\, [\gamma^{\mu} S_f(x - x') \gamma_{\nu} S_f(x' - x)]$$

can, with the aid of Eqs. (3.46) to (3.49), be written as

$$- i \int dx\, dx' A_{\mu}(x) A_{\nu}(x') \int_{4m^2}^{\infty} dc^2 c^2 \sigma(c) [\theta(x - x')$$
$$\cdot (g^{\mu\nu} \,\Box^2 - \partial^{\mu}\partial^{\nu}) \Delta^{+}(x - x', c) + \theta(x' - x) \qquad (3.61)$$
$$\cdot (g^{\mu\nu} \,\Box^2 - \partial^{\mu}\partial^{\nu}) \Delta^{+}(x' - x, c)].$$

Its real part is, because of

$$\mathrm{Re}\, i\Delta^{+}(x) = \frac{i}{2} \Delta^1(x) = \mathrm{Re}\, i\Delta^{+}(-x)$$

equal to

$$\mathrm{Re\,Tr}\,Q = -i\int dx\,dx'A_\mu(x)A^\mu(x')\int_{4m^2}^\infty dc^2c^4\sigma(c)\Delta^1(x-x',c) \quad (3.62)$$

which is identical with Eq. (3.52). This was to be expected due to the unitarity of S which tells us that $SS^\dagger = 1$ or

$$S^{(2)} + S^{\dagger(2)} + S^{(1)}S^{(1)\dagger} = 0$$

or

$$-2\,\mathrm{Re}\,(0\mid S^{(2)}\mid 0) = \sum_f \mid (f\mid S^{(1)}\mid 0)\mid^2. \quad (3.63)$$

Equation (3.62) is therefore finite for a large class of A's for which Eq. (3.52) converges. We shall see shortly, however, that the imaginary part of $\mathrm{Tr}\,Q$ diverges for all A. We defer to a problem the investigation of $\mathrm{Tr}\,QQ^\dagger$, which turns out to be finite for A's with finite total energy. For this class of fields the behavior of $|(0\mid S\mid 0)|^2$ can be stated as follows: It is finite (including zero) for real e as required by the unitarity of S. It does not exist for complex e since $\mathrm{Im}\,\mathrm{Tr}\,Qe^2 \to \infty$. After dividing out the divergent part, $(0\mid S\mid 0)e^{\mathrm{Tr}\,Q/2}$ is bounded from above by $e^{c\mid e\mid^2}$ with a finite c. Therefore, it has no infinities in the entire complex plane. By a more detailed analysis[5] one can exclude branch points and hence the expansion is an entire function and thus has an infinite radius of convergence.

The infinity in the imaginary part of $\ln\,(0\mid S\mid 0)$ has physical significance, as in the case of a Bose field with point sources. It results in an infinite charge induced by any external field. It will turn out that the vacuum expectation value of the current is not zero now as it was for the free fields. That is to say, even without having real particles the Dirac field will show a current, which is due to the virtual particles created by the external field. To calculate this induced current we use our general variational principle in Eq. (1.49), which we apply for a change δA in the external field[6]

$$\delta(^0_{\mathrm{out}}\mid^0_{\mathrm{in}}) = -i(^0_{\mathrm{out}}\mid j(x)\delta A(x)\mid^0_{\mathrm{in}}). \quad (3.64)$$

By introducing the functional derivative $\delta/\delta A_\mu$

$$\left[\frac{\delta}{\delta A(x)}A(x') = \delta(x-x')\right]$$

[5] See F. Smithies, *Duke Math. J.* **8**, 107 (1941).
[6] We now switch back to our old notation, $\mid 0) = \mid^0_{in})$.

we may rewrite Eq. (3.64) as

$$\left(^0_{\text{out}} \mid j_\mu(x) \mid ^0_{\text{in}}\right) = i \frac{\delta}{\delta A_\mu(x)} \left(^0_{\text{out}} \mid ^0_{\text{in}}\right). \tag{3.65}$$

We shall suppose that A is such that no real pairs are created. That is to say, the vacuum at $t \rightarrow -\infty$, $\mid ^0_{\text{in}})$ will differ from the vacuum at $t \rightarrow +\infty$, $\mid ^0_{\text{out}})$ only by a phase factor $(0 \mid S \mid 0)$. We can, therefore, express the vacuum expectation of the current as

$$(0 \mid j_\mu \mid 0) = \frac{i}{(0 \mid S \mid 0)} \frac{\delta}{\delta A_\mu(x)} (0 \mid S \mid 0)$$

$$= i \frac{\delta}{\delta A_\mu(x)} \ln (0 \mid S \mid 0) = i \sum_{n=1}^{\infty} (-)^n \, \text{Tr} \left(K^n \frac{\delta}{\delta A_\mu(x)} K \right) \tag{3.66}$$

by using Eq. (3.57). Of importance in this series is the first term. It is readily worked out by inserting for K its value, Eq. (3.56)

$$(0 \mid j_\mu^{(2)}(x) \mid 0) = \int dx' A^\nu(x') K_{f_{\mu\nu}}(x')$$

$$K_{f\mu\nu}(x - x') = -ie^2 \, \text{Tr} \, [\gamma_\mu S_f(x - x')\gamma_\nu S_f(x' - x)]. \tag{3.67}$$

The $j(x)$ can be interpreted as the sum of currents which are introduced by $A(x')$ at any point x' and propagate to x with the characteristic function S_f (Fig. 8). For the evaluation of $K_{f\mu\nu}$ we refer back to Eq. (3.61), where the real part of K_f has been worked out. Similarly, we obtain the imaginary part $x - x' = y$

$$\epsilon(y)(\square^2 \, \delta_{\mu\nu} - \partial_\mu\partial_\nu)\Delta(y).$$

Because of gauge invariance $A \rightarrow A + \partial\Lambda$ cannot change $(0 \mid j \mid 0)$ and current conservation demands $\partial^\nu K_{\mu\nu} = \partial^\mu K_{\mu\nu} = 0$. One can, in fact, check directly from Eq. (3.67) that these conditions are met. The conditions again require a representation of $K_f^{\mu\nu}(x)$ as $(\square^2\delta_{\mu\nu} - \partial_\mu\partial_\nu)K_f(x)$. This will be true if we can write $\epsilon(y)\partial_\mu\partial_\nu\Delta(y) = \partial_\mu\partial_\nu\epsilon(y)\Delta(y)$ under the integral in Eq. (3.67). Such a manipulation

FIG. 8. This diagram represents the process described by Eq. (3.67).

involves, however, some ambiguous expressions like $\delta(y_0)\partial_\mu\Delta(y)$ which gave rise to a considerable literature.[7] We shall not discuss this further, but we shall take gauge invariance as a guiding principle and assume that the above rearrangments are permissible. This gives us, with Eq. (3.51)

$$(0 \mid j_\mu^{(2)}(x) \mid 0) = -\int dx' A^\nu(x') \int_{4m^2}^\infty dc^2 c^2 \sigma(c) \tag{3.68}$$
$$\cdot (\Box^2 g_{\mu\nu} - \partial_\mu\partial_\nu)\Delta_f(x - x', c).$$

Again the term $\sim\partial_\mu\partial_\nu$ vanishes and $\Box^2$ produces, on partial integration, the current $\mathcal{J}$ which creates A. Going to momentum space we find

$$(0 \mid j_\mu^{(2)}(x) \mid 0) = -\int \frac{dk}{(2\pi)^4} \mathcal{J}_\mu(k)e^{-ikx} d(k) \tag{3.69}$$

where

$$d(k) = \frac{\alpha}{3\pi} \int_{4m^2}^\infty \frac{dc^2}{c^2 - k^2} \left(1 + \frac{2m^2}{c^2}\right) \sqrt{1 - \frac{4m^2}{c^2}}.$$

We remember that this was derived under the assumption that $j(k) = 0$ for $k^2 \geq 4m^2$. Otherwise, real pairs could be created. They would show up in an imaginary contribution to d stemming from a pole in $\int dc^2$. As we anticipated, $\int dc^2$ in $d(k)$ diverges, and we conclude that any external current induces an infinite current in the Dirac field. This infinity stems formally from the clash of the singularities of the S_f functions on the light cone and is related to the infinite charge fluctuation in sharply defined volumes. To be more explicit, we write half of it in a form similar to the expression for the charge fluctuation

$$\int dx' A(x')\theta(x - x') \, \text{Tr} \, [\gamma S^+(x - x')\gamma S^-(x' - x)].$$

This means that the pair propagates with positive frequencies if x' precedes x. The introduction here of sharp time limits brings with it infinite frequencies. Correspondingly, the integral for $d(k)$ diverges like the expressions for pair creation or for the charge fluctuation for A's with sharp edges. For purposes of further discussion, we

[7] See Pauli, W., and Villars, F., *Revs. Modern Phys.* **21**, 434 (1949).

assume that some mechanism modifies our formulae for small ($\ll m^{-1}$) space-time distances and puts an upper limit ($M^2 \gg m^2$) on $\int dc^2$. However, we shall see in the next part of the book that within the framework of field theory as developed so far, such a mechanism cannot exist.

Now we note that $d(k)$ is positive for permissible k. If we have a static charge,[8] $\mathcal{J}_0(x)$, then we can rewrite Eq. (3.68) in a more sug-

gestive form $\left(\int dx_0 \Delta_f(x) = e^{-m|x|}/4\pi |x| \right)$

$$(0 \mid j_0^{(2)}(x) \mid 0) = -\int dx' \mathcal{J}_0(x') \int_{4m^2}^{M^2} dc^2 \frac{e^{-|\underline{x}-\underline{x}'|c}}{4\pi |\underline{x} - \underline{x}'|} c^2 \sigma(c).$$

(3.70)

Therefore, the induced charge has the opposite sign from the original charge. This was partly to be expected, since by polarizing the virtual pairs of the Dirac field the external current will attract the oppositely charged member of the pair. The same happens in any dielectric, where a charge always induces a compensating charge, a surplus charge being left over at the surface of the dielectric. Since the Dirac field has no surface the surplus member of the pairs with the same charge as $\mathcal{J}_0$ are infinitely remote and do not show up in our formulae. This explains the apparent contradiction with charge conservation which is implied by an induced total charge.

Since jA is, as it must be, a Hermitian quantity, it commutes with Q and cannot, therefore, change $(0 \mid Q \mid 0) = 0$. To remove this contradiction one can limit the infinite range of the Coulomb field by introducing a mass μ in the photon field so that This gives a formula $(\Box^2 + \mu^2)A = \mathcal{J}$

$$(0 \mid j(x) \mid 0) = \int \frac{dk}{(2\pi)^4} e^{-ikx} \mathcal{J}(k) \frac{k^2 \epsilon(k)}{\mu^2 - k^2}.$$

(3.71)

In this case the total induced charge $\int dx(0 \mid j_0(x) \mid 0)$ vanishes for a static $\mathcal{J}_0$ $\left(\int d\underline{x} \text{ means } k \to 0 \right)$.

Equation (3.70) shows that the induced charge is essentially

[8] To comply with our general restrictions on A we may put $\mathcal{J} \sim \delta(x)e^{-\alpha|x_0|}$, $\alpha \ll m$.

proportional to $\mathcal{g}_0(x)$, save for the addition of an exponential tail with a range of $\tfrac{1}{2}m$ or smaller. It is conventional to lump the part of the induced current which is strictly proportional to $\mathcal{g}$ together with $\mathcal{g}$ to define the "renormalized" or observable charge since the two cannot be observed separately. This can be done by putting $1/(c^2 - k^2) = 1/c^2 + k^2/c^2(c^2 - k^2)$ in Eq. (3.69), which shows that the finite remainder, proportional to k^2, has total charge zero. For $\mathcal{g}(x)$ varying slowly over distances of approximately m^{-1}, for instance, we may expand $d(k)$ in powers of k^2

$$d(k) = \frac{\alpha}{3\pi} \ln \frac{M^2}{m^2} - \frac{k^2}{m^2} \frac{\alpha}{15\pi} \cdots$$

and get for the two terms

$$(0 \mid j_s^{(2)} \mid 0) = -\frac{\alpha}{3\pi} \ln \frac{M^2}{m^2} \, \mathcal{g}_s(x) + \frac{\alpha}{15\pi} \frac{\Box^2}{m^2} \, \mathcal{g}_s(x) + \cdots \quad (3.72)$$

It is important to recognize that the last term with total charge zero does not contribute to the asymptotic Coulomb field produced by the induced current. In fact, if we solve

$$\Box^2 A = \mathcal{g} + (0 \mid j \mid 0)$$

for $\mathcal{g}(x) = e_0 \delta(x)$ we get, for $r \to \infty$, $A_0 \sim (1 - c)e_0/4\pi r$ with $c = (\alpha/3\pi) \ln (M^2/m^2)$, since the other term contributes $A_0(x) \sim \mathcal{g}(x)$. Thus, by classical methods of observation, where one looks at the field at distances $\gg m^{-1}$ from the charge, one measures $e_0(1 - c)$ rather than the "bare charge" e_0, so that it is appropriate to call $e_0(1 - c)$ the charge e. In our investigation we did not consider the reaction of the field of the induced charge back on the Dirac field. This we can do consistently only in the last part of the book. We anticipate from the arguments above that the compensating charge attracts charges of the original sign. This means mathematically that

$$e = e_0(1 - c + c^2 - c^3 \cdots) = e_0/(1 + c)$$

so that the charge is completely quenched as in a substance with an infinite dielectric constant.

We consider the expression above as holding only to order α. To this order we have

$$A_0(x) = \frac{e}{4\pi r} + \frac{\alpha}{15\pi} \frac{e\delta(x)}{m^2}. \quad (3.73)$$

The second term, which is the only observable consequence of the vacuum polarization, has a range of approximately m^{-1} and gives an increase in the electric interaction at small distances. This comes, roughly, from the fact that after penetrating the cloud of virtual pairs, there is the stronger charge e. In more detail, the bare charge e_0 and the induced charge $\mathcal{J}$ combine to give a net charge as indicated in Fig. 9. The net charge we regard as consisting of a renor-

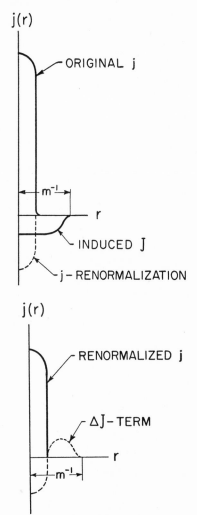

FIGS. 9 and 10. These diagrams illustrate charge renormalization.

malized charge which has the shape of $\mathcal{J}$ but which contains total charge e_0 and a remainder, Fig. 10. The latter goes with $-\Delta\mathcal{J}(x)$, i.e., is proportional to the excess of $\mathcal{J}$ over its local average. Thus, it increases the effect of the charge at small distances. This effect is appreciable only when charged particles come close together, as in μ-mesic atoms. It even has some effect on the P-wave proton-proton scattering around 1 Mev, although it is much weaker than the nuclear forces, since it has a much longer range.

The most precise measurement comes from the shift between the $2^2S_{1/2} - 2^2P_{1/2}$ levels in hydrogen. This effect is much smaller than the main contribution to the shift, which was discussed in the introduction and has the opposite sign. The experimental error in this measurement is only 1% of the vacuum polarization part. Hence, this experimental verification is an important check on the fundamental principles of quantum field theory, according to which the vacuum polarization is an unavoidable consequence of any theory which allows pair creation.

Referring back to the general expansion in Eq. (3.66), we note that the other terms are higher order in A and correspond to a dependence of ϵ on the field strength. These nonlinear processes give rise to the scattering of light by light or by a Coulomb field. They are very small and can barely be observed. We shall discuss them further later on.

Concluding this section, we remark that our treatment does not apply to certain types of electromagnetic fields. For instance, the important problem of scattering by a static field requires a separate discussion. We shall not go into that since it does not exhibit new features of quantum field theory.[9] We just mention an amusing result in a case of academic interest, namely, that of an electromagnetic field F_{ik} which is constant in space and time.

$$F^2 = -\tfrac{1}{2}F_{ik}F^{ik} > 0$$

(which means a sufficiently strong electric field). Here there is a continual production of pairs with a probability per unit space-time volume (Klein paradox) of approximately

$$\frac{\alpha^2}{\pi^2} F^2 \sum_{n=1}^{\infty} n^{-2} e^{-n\pi m^2/eF}.$$

[9] The reader interested in a treatment of this problem within the framework of quantum field theory is referred to J. Schwinger, *Phys. Rev.* **94**, 1352 (1954).

The exponential comes from the fact that energy conservation requires the pair to be separated by a distance greater than $2m/e \mid E \mid$, so that the gain in potential energy which equals the electric field strength $\mid E \mid$ times distance exceeds the rest energy of the pair $2m$. As we have indicated, the probability for finding a virtual pair at a distance d goes like e^{-dm} for $d > m^{-1}$. The exponential has the characteristic feature that it cannot be expanded in powers of e. If we were to calculate pair production by this field with our previous formula, we would get zero in every order. The constant field has no Fourier components for $k \neq 0$ and the condition for pair creation in first order is $k^2 > 4m^2$, while in second order it is $k^2 > 0$, etc. Thus, in this case, perturbation theory gives the asymptotic expansion of the exact solution. Here the expansion is identically zero, since $\lim_{e \to 0} e^{-n} e^{-(m^2/eF)} \to 0$. This shows that the expansion method is sometimes not very useful, although it may supply an asymptotic series.

11. The Limitations of Measurability

While commuting operators have common eigenvectors, operators which do not commute cannot be simultaneously diagonalized. Thus, the expectation value of two noncommuting operators cannot be an eigenvalue for both. For the fluctuations ΔA, ΔB of two quantities A and B in a state $\mid$) one has the general inequality

$$\Delta A \cdot \Delta B \geqslant \tfrac{1}{2} \left| (\langle [A, B] \rangle) \right|. \tag{3.74}$$

In order for our interpretation of the formalism to make sense, it is necessary to demand that the measurement of A with an accuracy ΔA generate an uncertainty in B which with ΔA satisfies the relation in Eq. (3.74). Hence, we must show that the formulae of the theory lead to commutator uncertainty relations which correspond to the possibilities of idealized physical measurements.

Naturally, a measurement always involves an interaction with a measuring apparatus. In order to confine ourselves to the development as presented thus far we restrict ourselves to the consideration of a system in interaction with an external field. Therefore, we shall ignore the interactions of the particles among themselves. Also, we shall consider only the general formal grounds for the consistency.

We begin by discussing the familiar example of the electromagnetic field. The electromagnetic field is defined, physically, by the force which it imparts to a charged body. Hence, the measurement of the electromagnetic field at a point x, in principle, involves bringing an electrically charged body to x and observing the acceleration which the field gives it. The limits in the accuracy of measurements of the field arise because of the uncertainties in the observation of the motion of the particle. For these test bodies we shall assume that the charge c (e is always reserved for the charge on the electron) and mass M can be arbitrarily chosen and that the uncertainty relations

$$\Delta x^i \Delta p_k = \delta_k{}^i, \qquad \Delta x^i \Delta x^k = \Delta p^i \Delta p^k = 0 \tag{3.75}$$

are the only limitations on the measurement. For the determination of the electric or electron fields these assumptions appear to be quite reasonable, because we may make the mass of the test charge large enough so that its wave packet becomes small enough for the validity of a description of the motion in terms of the classical equations, Eq. (1.11), etc.

The commutation relations in Eq. (1.70) imply that a field quantity f made up out of the A's has an uncertainty relation with the energy-momentum vector P of the form

$$\Delta P_i \Delta f(x) \geqslant |f_{,i}(x)|. \tag{3.76}$$

Here f stands for its expectation value. Also, in the classical equation of motion, A is to be understood as the expectation value of the quantized A.

We shall now briefly discuss how the uncertainties in Eq. (3.76) arise in an idealized experiment.

The attempt, by a measurement of $f(x)$, to localize the test body with an accuracy Δx must generate an uncertainty Δp in its momentum. This uncertainty in the momentum of the test charge has the consequence that its momentum change in an electric field and, hence, its momentum transfer to the field, has an uncertainty Δp. We shall now write, in a general form, how the uncertain knowledge of the position and momentum of the test charge generates an uncertainty in f.

$$\Delta f(x) = \Delta x^i f_{,i}(x) + \Delta p_i \frac{\delta}{\delta p_i} f(x) \tag{3.77}$$

where the last term symbolizes the uncertainty generated in f by Δp. This term naturally depends strongly on the nature of the test charge and the structure of the quantity f (see the discussion which follows). If one multiplies this equation with Δp_k, then one learns that

$$\Delta p_k \Delta f(x) = \Delta p_k \Delta x^i f_{,i}(x) + \Delta p_k \Delta p^i \frac{\delta}{\delta p^i} f(x). \tag{3.78}$$

According to our assumptions, the momentum uncertainty of the fields, ΔP, is due to the momentum uncertainty of the test particles alone. Hence, we may set ΔP equal to Δp. Further, one can, by an accurate momentum measurement, always make the second term on the right side arbitrarily small so that only the first term, because of the uncertainty relation in Eq. (3.75), cannot be made less than $f_{,i}$. This is the assertion of Eq. (3.76).

The commutation relations of the fields with the energy-momentum vector is therefore a direct logical consequence of the corresponding commutation relation of the particles. Since the eigenvectors of the number of quanta are equivalent to the eigenvectors of P, Eq. (3.76) shows that a simultaneous measurement of the field strength and the number of quanta is impossible. In particular, an eigenstate of the number of photons shows the characteristic fluctuations in the field strength which we discussed earlier, the wave and particle aspects being complementary features of a quantized field. Thus, quantum field theory gives a consistent description of the oft-noted paradox of the wave-particle duality.

Now we shall show in more detail how the uncertainty relations of A at different points corresponding to

$$[A(x), A(x')] = iD(x - x') \tag{3.79}$$

emerge in an idealized measurement. A is not directly measurable, for by measuring the motions of the particles one can only determine the derivatives of A. If the derivatives of A are known at a point x with an accuracy $\Delta A_{,i}^{k}(x)$, then the theory predicts that because of the commutation relation in Eq. (3.79), A at the point x' can only be known with an uncertainty $\Delta A^{j}(x')$, which is given by

$$\Delta A_{,i}^{k}(x) \Delta A^{j}(x') \geqslant |g^{kj}\partial_i D(x - x')|. \tag{3.80}$$

We shall suppose that x' is later in time than x. Otherwise, we must look for the influence on $A(x)$ by a measurement at the point x'. As must be the case, $D(x - x')$ vanishes for $(x - x')^2 < 0$, for a measurement at x induces a perturbation which cannot propagate faster than the velocity of light. The uncertainty of A and of the coordinate of the test charge are related by the equation

$$\Delta \dot{p}_i = c\dot{x}_k \Delta A_{,i}^{k} + cA_{,i}^{k} \Delta \dot{x}_k \tag{3.81}$$

as one finds by applying Δ to the equations of motion, Eq. (1.35). We are supposing that the uncertainty is small, so that Δ acts like a differential operator. In order to measure $A_{,i}^{k}(x)$, the test charge must remain in a region V around x a given time ds (Fig. 11).

The uncertainty of $\dot{p}$ due to the measurement is given by $\Delta \dot{p} = \Delta p/ds$, since the uncertainty of the difference of p's at different time points is certainly also of the order Δp, so that $\Delta \dot{p}$ decreases as $1/ds$. The $\Delta \dot{x} = (1/M)\Delta(p - cA)$ is, relative to Δp, of order $1/M$. Since we are free to choose the mass this term can play no role. Thus, we get for the uncertainty in the field strength

$$\dot{x}_k \Delta A_{,i}^{k} = \frac{\Delta p_i}{c} ds + O\left(\frac{1}{M}\right). \tag{3.82}$$

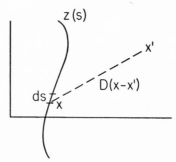

FIG. 11. This diagram represents the world line of the test charge.

The uncertainty in $A^j(x')$ rests on the uncertain knowledge of the motion of the test charges whose fields are therefore also not well-determined. We can express the field which the test charge generates by means of the Green's function D^{ret}, Eq. (A2.16)

$$A^j(x') = c \int ds\, D^{\text{ret}}(x' - x(s))\dot{x}^j(s). \qquad (3.83)$$

Hence, the uncertainty in $A^j(x')$ can be expressed by

$$\Delta A^j(x') = cds D^{\text{ret}}(x' - x)\Delta\dot{x}^j + eds\dot{x}^j\Delta x^k\partial_k D^{\text{ret}}(x' - x). \qquad (3.84)$$

The contributions to the integral expression for $A(x')$ come only from points at which the world line of the test charge cuts the light cone of x'. We have therefore replaced the integration by multiplication with ds and we have evaluated the integrand at the point x. Corresponding to the extension of the test charge one should actually integrate Eq. (3.84) over a finite region about x and over another finite region about x'. Since we have already supposed that the test charge can be made arbitrarily small we can forget this integration and use the result given above. If one multiplies Eq. (3.84) by Eq. (3.82), then one finds with the uncertainty relation for the test charge

$$\dot{x}_k \Delta A_{,i}^{k}(x) \Delta A^j(x') = \dot{x}^j \partial_i D^{\text{ret}}(x' - x) + O(M^{-1}, c). \qquad (3.85)$$

Only the term which explicitly appears in Eq. (3.85) above cannot be made arbitrarily small by an appropriate choice of M and c, the mass and charge of the test particle. Since the velocity $\dot{x}$ can be freely chosen and, further, since $D^{\text{ret}}(x' - x) = -D(x - x')$ for $x_0' > x_0$, one can reduce Eq. (3.85) to Eq. (3.80).

We may further note that in the expression for the uncertainty in the field strengths, Eq. (3.82), all of the terms involve M or c, so that a measurement of the field strengths alone can be made with arbitrary precision. This point was the subject of many discussions in which one raised the following objection: In order to measure the field strength accurately, one must make the charge on the test particle as large as possible. In this case, however, one cannot neglect the reaction of the field back on the test charge, and an observation of the motion of the particles does not constitute a measurement of the original field strength, since the motion of the test charges is influenced by the forces arising from their radiation as well as by the initial field. If one goes back over our calculation for this radiation force one will see that a term is introduced into the expression for the uncertainty in the field strength which increases with c so that one cannot find any value of the charge c which makes the total uncertainty disappear. The solution to this difficulty was found by Bohr and Rosenfeld.[1] They were able to show that the reaction back on the original field can be taken into account consistently if one keeps in mind the extended nature of test charges and hence seeks to measure the mean value of the field strengths over an extended space-time region. To be sure, the description of a suitable apparatus is rather intricate, which is why we have not entered into it here, and in the next part of this section we will assume that the self-reaction of the field can play no role. While our simple discussion shows that the theoretical uncertainty cannot be surpassed, it is difficult to show in detail how the optimal uncertainty is actually obtained.

The physical size of the measurement limit is naturally very small. If one writes the uncertainty relations in terms of the electric and magnetic field strength in a certain Lorentz frame one finds the following: Measurements of only the electric or only the magnetic field strengths at different points do not interfere with each other. However, mutual interference effects arise if one measures the electric field at one point and the magnetic field in a perpendicular direction at another point. This can be understood intuitively if one imagines the magnetic field produced by an accelerated test charge. In this case one calculates, from the general formula in Eq. (3.74), the uncertainty in the electric and magnetic field strengths E and H in

<hr />

[1] The reader is referred to the article by Bohr, N., and Rosenfeld, L., *Kgl. Danske Videnskab. Selskab. Biol. Medd.* **12**, 8 (1933), for the many elaborate details.

two volumes of dimension L during the time interval $T > L$ and in a distance R of the volumes $\Delta E_x \Delta H_y \sim 1/R^2 T^2$. If one takes $R = L = 1$ cm, $T = 1$ sec, and $\Delta E \sim \Delta H$, then one finds $\Delta E \sim 10^{-13}$ volts/cm. If, in a certain volume, one wishes to make ΔE essentially less than E, then we must have $E^3 L^3 T > 1$ $(R \sim L)$. Now the frequency ν of E must be larger than T^{-1}. Since the number of photons, n, must satisfy $E^2 L^3 = n\nu$, under the conditions above there must be a large number of photons. Unlike the electron case, there is for photons no expression for the particle density. If one wants to confine a photon in a space-time volume Δx, Δt, then one must have $\Delta x \gg 1/\omega$, $\Delta t \gg 1/\omega$, which means that the conditions for geometrical optics are satisfied. The possibility of localizing a photon is nothing more than the concept of rays in geometrical optics.

We now turn to the Dirac field. In this case from Eq. (2.40) the ψ do not commute at points separated by spacelike intervals but rather anticommute. However, the ψ are not observable; only bilinear quantities constructed from them are. The latter quantities commute for spacelike points because of the algebraic identity

$$[AB, CD] = -AC\{B, D\} + A\{B, C\}D - C\{A, D\}B$$
$$+ \{A, C\}DB.$$
(3.86)

This enables us to compute the commutators between j's at two different points, using Eqs. (2.38) and (2.40)

$$[j_i(x), j_k(x')] = ie^2[\bar{\psi}(x)\gamma_i S(x - x')\gamma_k \psi(x')$$
$$- \bar{\psi}(x')\gamma_k S(x' - x)\gamma_i \psi(x)].$$
(3.87)

The measurement of the charge amounts to the measurement of the electromagnetic field induced by the charge. Thus, the problem of the measurability of j can be reduced to the case previously discussed. For this purpose, we consider the charge confined in some arbitrary volume V, bounded by a surface σ. Then one has, with the help of Gauss's theorem, Eq. (N.5), and the field equations, $\Box^2 A_k = j_k(x)$

$$\int_V dx j_k(x) = \int_\sigma d\sigma^i A_{k,i}(x)$$
(3.88)

so that

$$\int_V dx \Delta j_k(x) = \int_\sigma d\sigma^i \Delta A_{k,i}(x).$$
(3.89)

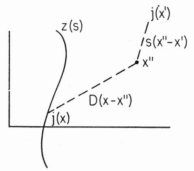

FIG. 12. This diagram illustrates the influence of a test charge at x'' on the current $j(x')$.

The uncertainty of $j(x)$ depends directly, therefore, on the uncertainty in $A(x)$. Since the electric field of the test charge is not exactly known, the change in the current cannot be precisely fixed. A test body which is used to measure $A(x)$ will create an electric field at x'' which will influence the current at x' (Fig. 12). The change of $\psi(x')$ due to an electromagnetic field was found in the last section. Applying it to the formula for the change in j in a one particle state we get

$$\Delta j_i(x') = e^2 \int dx'' K_{ik}(x', x'') \Delta A^k(x'')$$

$$= \dot{x}^k c e^2 \Delta x^i \, ds \int dx'' K_{ij}(x', x'') \partial_j D^{\mathrm{ret}}(x'' - x) \tag{3.90}$$

where

$$K^{kj}(x', x'') = \bar{\psi}(x'') \gamma^j S^{\mathrm{av}}(x'' - x) \gamma^k \psi(x')$$
$$+ \bar{\psi}(x') \gamma^k S^{\mathrm{ret}}(x' - x'') \gamma^j \psi(x''). \tag{3.91}$$

In the uncertainty relation for $j(x)$, there enters $A^k{}_{,i}$, which is not directly subject to measurement, since the equations of motion only involve $\dot{x}^k A_{k,i}$. We therefore multiply Eq. (3.89) with $\dot{x}^k$ and disregard, as before, terms of order $1/M$. From Eq. (3.82) we set $\dot{x}^k A_{k,i}$ equal to one. Now the whole expression can be multiplied by Eq. (3.90) to yield

$$\dot{x}^k \int dx \Delta j_k(x) \Delta j_i(x') = \int d\sigma^j \dot{x}^k \Delta A_{k,j} \Delta j_i(x')$$

$$= \frac{x^k e^2 \Delta x^j \, ds \Delta P^m}{ds} \int_\sigma d\sigma_m \int dx'' K_{ik}(x', x'') \partial_j D^{\mathrm{ret}}(x'' - x) \tag{3.92}$$

Substituting the uncertainty relation for the test charge and using

$$\int d\sigma^j \partial_j D^{\text{ret}}(x'' - x)$$

$$= \int_V dx \, \Box^2 \, D^{\text{ret}}(x'' - x) = \int_V dx \delta(x'' - x)$$

(3.93)

we learn that

$$\dot{x}^k \int_V dx \Delta j_k(x) \Delta j_i(x') = e^2 \dot{x}^k \int_V dx K_{ik}(x', x).$$

(3.94)

Since the velocity $\dot{x}$ as well as the volume V were arbitrary, and K is essentially given by the square brackets in Eq. (3.87), we have shown that the commutation relations given by the theory are physically necessary.

These examples show how the mathematical formalism and the physical interpretation join. We see that what is involved is not merely a manipulation of mathematical identities, but that the physical characteristics of the test charge enter in an essential way.[2] By the quantum theory of fields both the quantum theory and classical electrodynamics become unified into a logically complete system, in which the uncertainty relations for particles and the quantum nature of the fields are treated consistently.

---

[2] It may well be that in a future theory some idealizations of the test body, such as disregarding its atomic structure, will not be possible.

Part IV

INTERACTING FIELDS

12. General Orientation

In this last part of the book we shall deal with quantum fields in interaction. The case with which we shall be most concerned is that of a quantized electromagnetic field, the source of which is a quantized Dirac field. That is to say, for $\mathbf{j}$ in the interaction term $\mathbf{Aj}$ we insert the current operator of the Dirac field and thus obtain in the interaction the product of three field operators. Such a term describes elementary processes, such as the emission of a photon by an electron, or pair creation of an electron and positron by a photon. Taken together, these basic possibilities give rise to a wealth of phenomena.

The Lagrangian which governs this problem is[1]

$$L = \mathbf{L}^{\text{el}} + \mathbf{L}^{\text{phot}} + e\mathbf{L}', \qquad L' = -:\mathbf{A}_k\bar{\boldsymbol{\psi}}\gamma^k\boldsymbol{\psi}: \qquad (4.1)$$

where $\mathbf{L}^{\text{el}}$ and $\mathbf{L}^{\text{phot}}$ are the Lagrangians, Eqs. (2.37) and (2.27), of the electron and photon fields, respectively. Applying the general procedure of Section 3 to this case we find, first of all, that the field operators $\mathbf{A}$ and $\boldsymbol{\psi}$ obey the coupled Dirac-Maxwell equations

$$(\gamma^k(i\partial_k - e\mathbf{A}_k(x)) - m)\boldsymbol{\psi}(x) = 0$$
$$\Box^2\mathbf{A}_k(x) = e\bar{\boldsymbol{\psi}}(x)\gamma_k\boldsymbol{\psi}(x). \qquad (4.2)$$

These equations must be supplemented by the Lorentz condition $\mathbf{A}^k{}_{,k} \mid 0) = 0$ for the same reasons which we have given in the free field case. The canonical commutation rules for spacelike points

$$\int_{x'\text{co}} d\sigma_k\{\boldsymbol{\psi}(x'), \bar{\boldsymbol{\psi}}(x)\gamma^k\}f(x) = f(x')$$

$$\int d\sigma_k\{\boldsymbol{\psi}(x'), \boldsymbol{\psi}(x)\} = 0 \qquad (4.3)$$

---

[1] We again use bold face lettering $\mathbf{A}$, etc., for operators referring to the coupled fields in contradistinction to the free fields A, etc.

137

and

$$\int d\sigma_k[\mathbf{A}_i(x), \mathbf{A}^{j,k}(x')]f(x') = -i\delta_{ij}f(x)$$

$$\int d\sigma_k[\mathbf{A}^i(x'), \mathbf{A}^j(x)] = 0 \qquad (4.4)$$

remain unchanged, since $\mathbf{L}'$ does not contain derivatives. Furthermore we may take the variation of ψ to commute with $\mathbf{A}$ and vice versa and, therefore[2]

$$\int d\sigma_k[\mathbf{A}(x), \psi(x')] = 0. \qquad (4.5)$$

Working out the energy-momentum tensor we find (problem 22) that it is just the sum of the $\mathbf{T}$'s of the electrons, Eq. (2.38), and photons, Eq. (2.28), similar to the classical formula in Eq. (1.12).

$$\mathbf{T} = \mathbf{T}^{\mathrm{el}} + \mathbf{T}^{\mathrm{phot}}. \qquad (4.6)$$

That the coupling constant e does not occur in Eq. (4.6) is really apparent. It comes in when $\mathbf{T}$ is expressed in terms of canonical quantities, e.g., when we eliminate ψ with the aid of the Dirac equation. This means that because $\mathbf{T}$ is constructed from the interacting, rather than the free, field operators, it does not consist only of the kinetic energy, but includes the interaction. Since $\mathbf{L}'$ does not contain a prescribed space-time function all relations obtained in Section 3 on the basis of Lorentz invariance are valid.

Furthermore, one can check that $\mathbf{L}$ is invariant under a gauge transformation combined with a space-dependent phase transformation of the spinor-field

$$\mathbf{A}_i \to \mathbf{A}_i + \partial_i\lambda, \; \psi \to e^{ie\lambda}\psi, \; \overline{\psi} \to e^{-ie\lambda}\overline{\psi} \qquad (4.7)$$

where $\lambda(x)$ commutes with everything and obeys $\Box^2\lambda = 0$, that is to say, the relative phase of $\psi(x)$ at different space-time points loses its significance. Since Eq. (4.7) leaves $\mathbf{L}, \mathbf{T}, \mathbf{j}$, and the commutation rules invariant it can be represented by a canonical transformation. Its generators will be encountered later. We also note that $\mathbf{L}$ is in-

---

[2] It is not possible, however, to give a simple expression for the commutators at different times. In fact, $\mathbf{A}$ depends not only on A and $\dot{A}$ at a previous time, but also on ψ at an intermediate time. It turns out that the commutator at different times is not even a c-number.

variant under charge conjugation if we postulate that **A** changes sign under this operation—$\mathbf{A}_k \rightarrow -\mathbf{A}_k$, $\psi \rightarrow \psi'$, $\bar{\psi} \rightarrow \bar{\psi}'$.

Although the commutation rules of Section 3 between $\mathbf{P}_k$, $\mathbf{J}_{ik}$, **Q**, and the field operators are still valid one cannot base a complete discussion of the physical properties of the system upon them. They tell only that the eigenvalues of the momentum, angular-momentum, and charge are the same as for the free fields, but they tell nothing about the energy spectrum. The reason is that one cannot write down a solution of the nonlinear equations, Eq. (4.2), the time dependence of the field operators being nothing simple. Since the Fourier components of the field operators will not, in general, even be timelike, one cannot define invariantly positive and negative frequency components. Correspondingly, the introduction of the particle concept needs some discussion. In the attempt to obtain explicit results the only approach which has proved feasible is an expansion in powers of e which expresses everything in terms of the free field operators A and ψ. This will also give the $:\ldots:$ symbol in Eq. (4.1) a well-defined meaning.

The general formulae of Section 8 for expanding in powers of e meet a certain difficulty in this case. They give us the transition probabilities between states which are expressed in terms of bare particles. They do not, however, characterize the physical situation in which one is interested. It is clear from what we have learned in the last part of the book that as a consequence of $\mathbf{L}'$ in Eq. (4.1) an electron will surround itself with virtual photons. They will, in turn, create virtual pairs, and so on. Thus, $U_{t_1 t_2}$ will answer, as in Section 8, questions like the following, given a bare electron at $t = t_1$, what is the probability for finding at a bare photon and a bare electron $t = t_2$?

However, the particle one deals with in actual experiments is, of course, the physical particle with the cloud of virtual particles and not the bare particle at all. As we shall see, the mass of the "dressed" particle differs (by an infinite amount!) from m, so that a naive application of the methods of the previous part of the book even gives the wrong energies for the initial and final states. The difference between the previous problems and the one at hand is that in the former cases we were considering only external fields which were switched off for $t \rightarrow \pm \infty$, so that for such times **L** reduced to the free L. In the present problem, e must be considered a constant; otherwise Lorentz invariance and charge conservation are destroyed.

This means, physically, that we are not free to switch off the charge of an electron, and hence it is always in interaction with the surrounding cloud of virtual particles. What we can do is to separate the physical particles spatially, so that the interaction between them becomes negligible. These facts can be taken care of by regrouping the terms of the Lagrangian Eq. (4.1) and including terms in $\mathbf{L}'$ which, for instance, compensate the change in mass of the physical particle.

We will defer a detailed discussion of these questions until Section 14. For a first orientation we shall calculate transition probabilities in lowest order in e. The effects mentioned above appear only when one calculates higher order corrections in e and will not concern us for awhile.

Using the formulae of Section 8 we now proceed to express the field operators in terms of the free field operators with which we are so familiar. We shall assume that for $t \rightarrow -\infty$ both kinds of operators coincide and that the eigenstates of the free operators adjusted this way correspond to incoming particles as they are used in actual experiments. According to the preceding arguments this is justified to the order in e with which we are presently concerned. Thus, using Eq. (3.8), we have

$$
\begin{aligned}
\mathbf{O}(x) = O(x) &+ ie \int_{-\infty}^{\sigma_x} dx' [O(x), L'(x')] \\
&+ (ie)^2 \int_{-\infty}^{\sigma_x} dx' \int_{-\infty}^{\sigma_x'} dx'' [[O(x), L'(x')], L'(x'')] + \cdots
\end{aligned}
$$

(4.8)

Application of Eq. (4.8) to typical operators leads to similar though somewhat more complicated formulae than we had in the previous part. The total charge is again unchanged $\mathbf{Q} = Q$, since $\mathbf{L}'$ is Hermitian and, therefore, commutes with $\mathbf{Q}$. This is not true, however, for the charge contained in a finite volume, as we have already seen in Section 10. Expressing the energy-momentum vector in terms of the energy and momentum of the incoming particles requires more care, since $\mathbf{T}$ contains $\psi_{,i}$ and

$$
U_{x,-\infty} \psi_{,i}(x) U_{x,-\infty}^{-1} \neq \frac{\partial}{\partial x_i} U_{x,-\infty} \psi_i(x) U_{x,-\infty}^{-1}.
$$

Taking for σ the plane $t = $ constant, we find easily

$$
\int_{\sigma_x} d\sigma_i \mathbf{T}_{ik}(x) = U_{-\infty x} \int_{\sigma_x} d\sigma_i [T_{ik}^{\text{el}}(x) + T_{ik}^{\text{phot}}(x) - g_{ik} L'(x)] U_{x-\infty}.
$$

By applying Eq. (3.8) again and using

$$P_k = \int d\sigma_i(T_{ik}^{el} + T_{ik}^{phot}), \qquad [O(x), P_k] = iO(x)_{,k}$$

we obtain

$$\mathbf{P}_k = P_k - e \int_{\sigma=-\infty} d\sigma_k \mathbf{L}'(x). \tag{4.9}$$

This is consistent with the fact that $\mathbf{P}$ and P are constant.

To the extent that the last term vanishes the total energy equals the kinetic energy of the incoming particles. One might ask why the integral should vanish for $t \to -\infty$ since in a displacement invariant theory one time should be as good as any other. The idea is that wave packets which have a finite concentration at a finite time are completely thinned out for $t \to -\infty$. Thus the particles are, on the average, infinitely far away from each other, so that the interaction energy should be negligible. Once the self energy has been conpensated in $\mathbf{L}'$ one should expect no energy change due to the interaction.

States of a definite number of incoming particles are eigenstates of N, which is constructed from A and ψ in the way described in Section 4. There is, however, no operator $\mathbf{N}$ which has an invariant meaning like N. One can, of course, satisfy the commutation relations, Eqs. (4.3) and (4.4), by introducing creation and annihilation operators.[3] $\mathbf{N}$ constructed from these operators, which represent the number of bare particles, is not an invariant quantity. The number of particles has, therefore, only an invariant meaning in an asymptotic sense. One can talk about the number of physical particles if they are sufficiently separated so that there is no possibility of confusing one physical particle with the virtual particles of another.

The quantity we shall be most concerned with in the following is the S-matrix

$$S = \sum_{n=0}^{\infty} \frac{(-ie)^n}{n!} \int_{\nu} dx_1 \cdots dx_n A_{\nu_1}(x_1) \cdots A P_n(x_n)$$

$$:\bar{\psi}(x_1)\gamma^{\nu_1}\psi(x_1): \cdots :\bar{\psi}(x_n)\gamma^{\nu_n}\psi(x_n):. \tag{4.10}$$

Its matrix elements between eigenstates of N tells us with what probability one will find a certain configuration of physical particles at $t = +\infty$ when one knows the configuration of particles which have

---

[3] This is equivalent to letting the operators $\mathbf{A}$ and ψ coincide with free operators at a finite time.

been present at $t = -\infty$. Since the space integrals in Eq. (4.10) go over the infinite space-time, S will commute with the translation and rotation operators P and J. This means that if $|$ in$)$ is an eigenstate of J and P, $|$ out$) = S |$ in$)$ will be such an eigenstate and will in fact belong to the same eigenvalues. This does not, of course, mean that for $t = +\infty$ every particle has the same energy-momentum vector (or angular momentum) as for $t = -\infty$. Only the total energy-momentum vector (or angular momentum) is constant, and this is even compatible with a change in the number of particles. In fact, N does not commute with S and is not, therefore, conserved.

Conservation of P and J has been anticipated in the discussion of selection rules in Section 6. Such conservation rules reflect the invariance of the theory under the proper Lorentz group, and are characteristic of all Lorentz invariant theories. As a consequence, for example, in such a theory the number of spin $\frac{1}{2}$ particles can change only by an even number, as is required by angular momentum conservation. Generally, S will share the invariance properties of $\mathbf{L}'$ and translate these in terms of processes between physical particles. If $\mathbf{L}'$ is also invariant under space reflections S will commute with the parity operator. Similarly, the invariance of $\mathbf{L}'$ under rotation in the internal space of the electron field assures us that $\mathbf{Q}$ and U_c are conserved. This rotation may even be space dependent when combined with $\mathbf{A} \to \mathbf{A} + \partial\lambda$ (gauge transformation), in which case $U_{\sigma_1\sigma_2}$ is multiplied by the generator

$$E(\sigma) = \exp\left(-i \int d\sigma_k j^k(x)\lambda(x)\right)$$

of the phase transformation[4]

$$\psi(x) \to e^{-ie\lambda(x)}\psi(x)$$

$$U_{12} \to P \exp\left[-i\left(\int_{\sigma_2}^{\sigma_1} dx j_k(x)[A^k(x) + \partial^k\lambda(x)]\right)\right] = E(\sigma_1) U_{12} E(\sigma_2).$$

If $\lambda(x)$ goes to zero for $t \to \pm\infty$ S is invariant under this operation. To display the matrix elements of S with respect to the eigen-

---

[4] A series development shows

$$e^{iG}\psi e^{-iG} = \psi + i[G,\psi] - \frac{1}{2!}[G,[G,\psi]] + \cdots$$

$$= \psi - ie\lambda\psi + \frac{(-ie\lambda)^2}{2!}\psi + \cdots = \psi^{-ie\lambda}.$$

states of N we have to rearrange S in such a way that the annihilation operators are on the right-hand side of the creation operators. The corresponding rearrangements of $PA(x_1)\ldots A(x_n)$ and $P:\bar{\psi}(x_1)\psi(x_1):$ $\ldots:\bar{\psi}(x_n)\psi(x_n):$ have been performed in Sections 9 and 10 respectively. Since the nth order term $S^{(n)}$ in Eq. (4.10) is the product of the two expressions above, the rearrangements yield the products of the results of Sections 9 and 10.

We mention some of the simplest terms. $S^{(1)}$ is identically zero. This can be seen by writing it in momentum space

$$S^{(1)} = -ie \int d^4x A_j(x)\bar{\psi}(x)\gamma^j\psi(x)$$

$$= -ie(2\pi)^{-8} \int dk\, dp_1\, dp_2 A_j(k)\bar{\psi}(p_1)\gamma^j\psi(p_2)\delta(k-p_1-p_2) \tag{4.11}$$

The δ-function in Eq. (4.11) comes from the integration over all space-time and expresses energy-momentum conservation for the physical particles. As a consequence $S^{(1)}$ is identically zero, since the integrand is different from zero only for $k^2 = 0$, $p_1^2 = p_2^2 = m^2$, and $k - p_1 + p_2 = 0$. These conditions are never simultaneously satisfied (save for the one point $k \equiv 0$), which expresses the well-known fact that a free electron cannot emit a photon nor can a photon create a pair in free space. Processes of this kind only occur virtually and are contained in $U\sigma_1\sigma_2$, where the δ-function is replaced by a function with a broader width. $S^{(2)}$ gives transitions between two incoming and two outgoing particles. These are typical scattering processes like the scattering of photons by electrons or electrons by electrons. In the former case, for instance, the conditions for energy-momentum vectors are $k_1^2 = k_2^2 = 0$, $p_1^2 = p_2^2 = m^2$, and $k_1 - k_2 + p_1 - p_2 = 0$. Such relations are compatible in a finite interval in momentum space and yield finite transition probabilities. They will be worked out in the next section.

Concluding this section we shall discuss some aspects of an even more extended problem where, in addition to the Lagrangian, there are also external sources present. This problem has practical importance if, for instance, one considers situations in which, along with the electrons and photons, the electric fields of atomic nuclei are present. Furthermore, external sources will serve as test bodies for exploring the physical significance of the theory in our discussion in Section 14. In cases similar to the problems discussed in Part III the external fields distinguish between different Lorentz frames and supply energy and momentum to the field. This changes the energy-momentum relations and leads to the important process of the emission of a photon by a bound electron. The conventional treatment of this problem (to lowest order in e) consists of grouping $\mathbf{L}$ into

$$\mathbf{L}^0 = \mathbf{L}^{\text{el}} + \mathbf{L}^{\text{phot}} + \frac{e^2}{4\pi r} : \psi^\dagger \psi :$$

and   (4.12)

$$\mathbf{L}' = -e\mathbf{A}(x) : \bar{\psi}(x)\gamma\psi(x) :.$$

By expanding ψ in Coulomb wave functions one obtains eigenstates of P^0 and can work out transition probabilities between bound states from U constructed with L'. Here the first term

$$U^{(1)} = -ie \int_{\sigma_2}^{\sigma_1} dx A(x) \bar{\psi}\gamma\psi \qquad (4.13)$$

does not vanish identically. Taking the matrix element between a state with wave functions u_m and u_n means replacing $\psi(x)$ by $u_m(x)$ and $\bar{\psi}(x)$ by $\bar{u}_n(x)$.

Thus, in the same say as in Section 9, we get, for the transition probability from u_m to u_n associated with the emission of one photon

$$\sum_j | (j, n \mid U^{(1)} \mid m) |^2$$

$$= -e^2 \int dx\, dx'\, j_{nm}^\dagger D^+(x - x')\, j_{mn}(x') \qquad (4.14)$$

where the transition current $j_{nm}(x)$ is given by $\bar{u}_n(x)\gamma u_m(x)$. Its time dependence is $e^{it(E_n - E_m)}$ and picks out from the integral the contributions from those photons which satisfy the Bohr frequency condition. Equation (4.14) shows the elementary result that the emission probability of photons by atoms corresponds to the one of a classical current with a periodic time dependence and a space distribution going with the overlap of the wave functions. We give as a problem the reduction of Eq. (4.14) to the familiar form for dipole radiation (problem 23).

As a final point we shall discuss a problem which illustrates peculiar properties of the D_f function. We consider two well-separated atoms and ask for the probability of a transition in the first atom with a transition current $j^{(\text{I})}$ and a transition in the second atom with a current $j^{(\text{II})}$ without emission of a photon. The probability for this energy transfer from one atom to the other is

$$-e^2 \int dx \, dx' \, j^{(\mathrm{I})}(x) \, j^{(\mathrm{II})}(x') D_f(x - x'). \qquad (4.15)$$

The characteristics of the D_f function show up here in the way in which we choose to go around the pole in the k-plane. The pole in the D functions corresponds to real photons. In fact, bound particles can also transfer energy-momentum by the exchange of real photons. If one can localize the emission and absorption acts sufficiently in space-time, then one must naturally demand that emission shall precede absorption. Since the free field has positive energy, this means that, loosely speaking, we cannot get an energy loan from the electromagnetic field.

D_f has only positive frequencies for positive times and only negative frequencies for negative times. We shall see immediately that, because of this property, D_f actually satisfies the above-mentioned causality requirement. However, one has to keep in mind that energy and time are complementary. It is therefore necessary to investigate how a temporal localization of the emission act is compatible with the specification of the sign of the energy. Let us suppose that the photon spectrum, denoted by f_{k_0}, contains only positive frequencies, and that the distribution has a width $\Delta\omega$ about a mean value ω. Then, obviously, $\omega > \Delta\omega$ or, from the uncertainty relation, $\Delta\omega\Delta T \sim 1$, we must also have $\omega\Delta T > 1$, where ΔT measures the length of time of the emission process (see Fig. 13).

Our formulation of the causality requirement presupposes that the time T between emission and absorption processes is large compared

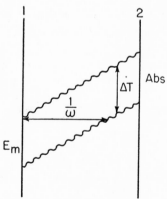

FIG. 13. This diagram illustrates the emission process.

with ΔT. This implies that the spatial separation of the emission and absorption acts must be greater than $1/\omega$. Therefore, the second particle must lie in the wave zone of the first. One easily sees that the field in the wave zone comes from the poles of the D_f function corresponding to real particles, while the field in the near zone comes from virtual photons. Thus, the causality requirement does not apply to virtual photons.

We shall now prove formally that if $j^{\mathrm{I}}(x)$ contains only positive frequencies then one can get a contribution to Eq. (4.15) only if (roughly speaking) $j^{\mathrm{II}}(x')$ is later than j^{I}. For simplicity we shall let the current of the first particle be represented by $j_s(x) = v_s\delta(x)f(t)$, where $f(t)$ is the Fourier transform of f_{k_0}. Then we must compute

$$\int dx\, j_s(x)D_f(x - x') = v_s \int dk e^{-ikx'} f_{k_0} k^{-2}.$$

Because[5]

$$\frac{1}{(2\pi)^3} \int d^3k\, e^{ik\cdot x}(k^2 + i\epsilon)^{-1} = -\frac{e^{i|k_0|r}}{4\pi r}$$

we have

$$\frac{1}{(2\pi)} \int dk_0 f_{k_0} e^{-ik_0(t - r\epsilon(k_0))} = f(t - r)$$

since f is supposed to contain no negative frequencies. If f has only negative frequencies, then the result becomes $f(t + r)$. This shows that, in fact, the signal propagates in the upper light cone. Although D_f does not vanish outside the upper light cone, the real photons are spread out in the light cone with a width ΔT of $f(t)$. That is to say, there is no propagation with a velocity greater than that of light outside the uncertainty ΔT in the time of the emission process.

[5] To characterize the integration path we add to the denominator a small negative imaginary part, which we set equal to zero in the final answer.

13. Scattering Processes

In this section we shall indicate the method by which scattering cross sections are calculated to lowest order in e. For this purpose we shall study the matrix elements of S between two particle states. As a typical example we may first consider the scattering of light by an electron. The question we wish to answer is what the probability is for a transition from an incident state $| \, ekp)$ in which there is a photon with a polarization vector e and a momentum vector k and an electron with momentum vector p to a state $(p'k'e' \, |$ with a photon with polarization vector e' and momentum vector k' and an electron with momentum vector p'.

The spin polarization of the electron is hard to observe. Hence, we shall average the transition probability over the spin polarization of the initial electron and sum over such spin states of the final electron. The second term in S describes this transition to lowest order in e

$$S^{(2)} = -\frac{1}{2} \int dx_1 \, dx_2 P j_i(x_1) j_k(x_2) A^i(x_1) A^k(x_2). \qquad (4.16)$$

To exhibit the matrix element in the best way we must arrange $j(1)j(2)$ and $A(1)A(2)$ into an ordered product, as we did in Eq. (2.84). First, one carries out the time ordering as in Eq. (3.14). This gives for the matrix element

$(p'k'e' \, | \, S^{(2)} \, | \, ekp) =$

$$-\frac{ie^2}{2} \int dx_1 \, dx_2 (p'k'e' \, | \, [\bar{\psi}^-(1)\gamma_i S_f(12)\gamma_k \psi^+(2)$$

$$+ \bar{\psi}^-(2)\gamma_k S_f(21)\gamma_i \psi^+(1)][A^{-i}(1)A^{+k}(2) + A^{-k}(2)A^{+i}(1)] \, | \, ekp)$$

$$= -ie^2 \int dx_1 \, dx_2 (p' \, | \, \bar{\psi}^-(1) \, | \, 0)\gamma_i S_f(21)\gamma_k (0 \, | \, \psi^+(2) \, | \, p)$$

$$[(k'e' \, | \, A^{-i}(1) \, | \, 0)(0 \, | \, A^{+k}(2) \, | \, ke)$$

$$+ (k'e' \, | \, A^{-k}(2) \, | \, 0)(0 \, | \, A^{+i}(1) \, | \, ke)]$$

$$(4.17)$$

since the state in which there is an electron and a photon can be

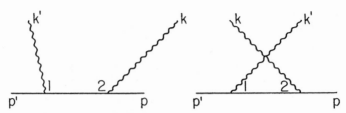

FIG. 14. The scattering diagrams represent Eq. (4.17).

represented in this order as simply the product of the free electron and photon states. One can interpret Eq. (4.17) to say intuitively that the electron at point 2 absorbs the initial photon after the electron at point 1 has emitted the final photon or conversely. Finally, one takes the probability amplitude for the process to occur at any two points x_1 and x_2 and integrates over all x_1 and x_2. As we have mentioned in Section 10, $S_f(12)$ represents the capacity of electrons to propagate between the two space-time points 1 and 2. Graphically, one may represent both terms of Eq. (4.17) in the intuitive fashion[1] shown in Fig. 14. The path of the electrons is traced by heavy lines and that of the photons by waved lines.

In order to compute the transition probability we must multiply Eq. (4.17) by its complex conjugate, which produces the following structure

$$| (p'k'e' \mid S^{(2)} \mid ekp) |^2 = e^4 \int dx_1 \, dx_2 \, dx_3 \, dx_4$$

$$\{ (p' \mid \psi^-(1) \mid 0)\gamma^i S_f(12)\gamma^k(0 \mid \psi^+(2) \mid p)$$

$$(p \mid \psi^-(3) \mid 0)\gamma^m S_f(34)\gamma^n(0 \mid \psi^+(4) \mid p') \, [(k'e' \mid A_i^-(1) \mid 0)$$

$$(0 \mid A_k^+(2) \mid ke) \, (ke \mid A_m^-(3) \mid 0) \, (0 \mid A_n^+(4) \mid k'e')$$

$$+ \, (k'e' \mid A_i^-(1) \mid 0) \, (0 \mid A_k^+(2) \mid ke) \, (ke \mid A_n^-(4) \mid 0)$$

$$(0 \mid A_m^+(3) \mid k'e')$$

$$+ \, (k'e' \mid A_k^-(2) \mid 0) \, (0 \mid A_i^+(1) \mid ke) \, (ke \mid A_m^-(3) \mid 0)$$

$$(0 \mid A_n^+(4) \mid k'e')$$

$$+ \, (k'e' \mid A_k^-(2) \mid 0) \, (0 \mid A_i^+(1) \mid ke) \, (ke \mid A_n^-(4) \mid 0)$$

$$(0 \mid A_m^+(3) \mid k'e')]\}.$$

(4.18)

[1] In each graph one must choose the appropriate integration path for the S_f function. However, as long as the contribution from the pole plays no role, this does not make any difference.

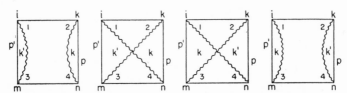

FIG. 15. These diagrams represent the scattering probability.

Multiplication by the complex conjugate means that we adjoin to each graph the mirror image of itself and the other graph with which we began. In this way we get four terms which contribute to the transition probability; see Fig. 15.

For further computation it is useful to go over into momentum space. The matrix elements of the incoming electron and photon are given by Eqs. (2.81) and (2.62), in which we choose the normalization in such a way that in the total space volume V there is one electron and one photon per unit volume before the collision. Furthermore, we integrate the transition probability over a finite interval in momentum space in the neighborhood of k' and p'. Thus, we can represent the final particles by the expressions (2.78) and (2.33), in which we integrate the Fourier representation of the S^+ and D^+ functions over only the selected region about p' and k'. If one inserts the Fourier representation of the S_f function then the space-time integral can be done, since the integrand depends only on the exponential of the coordinates.

Denoting the integration variable of $S_f(12)$ by p'' the whole dependence on x_2 is contained in the exponential factor $e^{-ix_2(p+k-p'')}$. Integration over x_2, using Eq. (N.4), leads simply to

$$(2\pi)^4 \delta(p + k - p'')$$

or

$$(2\pi)^4 \delta(p - k' - p'').$$

The integration over p'' means then that we replace p'' by $p + k$ or $p - k'$. In a similar fashion the integration over x_1 yields analogous relations. Combining these we find that $p + k = p' + k'$, which is the energy-momentum conservation law for the entire process. The integration over x_4 defines the energy-momentum vector of the other virtual electrons in the graph, while integration over x_3 multiplies the term by the total space-time volume, since after the integration over x_4 the integrand no longer depends on x_3. Each energy-momentum vector occurs in the exponent once with a positive sign and

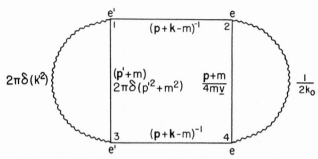

Fɪɢ. 16. The first term of Eq. (4.18) gives rise to this diagram.

once with a negative sign, so that the sum of the energy-momentum vectors in the exponent is identically zero. Through the foregoing integrations the factors involving x_1, x_2, and x_4 are set equal to zero and the factor involving x_3 disappears automatically. From the first term of Eq. (4.18) we have the contributions[2] illustrated by Fig. 16. The three other graphs give analogous expressions and we find for the whole transition probability the following expression in momentum space

$$w = \frac{e^4 V/\underline{V}}{2(p_0 k_0)} \int dk'(2\pi)^{-4}(2\pi)^2 \delta(k'^2)\delta((p + k - k')^2 - m^2)\tfrac{1}{4}\text{Tr}\{[e(\mathbf{p}$$
$$+ \mathbf{k} - m)^{-1}\mathbf{e}' + \mathbf{e}'(\mathbf{p} - \mathbf{k}' - m)^{-1}\mathbf{e}] (\mathbf{p} + \mathbf{k} - \mathbf{k}' + m) \qquad (4.19)$$
$$[\mathbf{e}'(\mathbf{p} + \mathbf{k} - m)^{-1}\mathbf{e} + \mathbf{e}(\mathbf{p} - \mathbf{k}' - m)^{-1}\mathbf{e}'] (\mathbf{p} + m)\}.$$

If one had inserted the spin indices explicitly, then one would be led to taking the trace along electron lines, as we have written in Eq. (4.19). As is quite reasonable, the transition probability is proportional to the total time $T = V/\underline{V}$.

The scattering cross section for the process is given in the rest system of the incident electron by the expression

scattering cross section

$$= \frac{\text{transition probability/unit time}}{\text{the number of incident photons per unit time and unit area}}.$$

Due to our normalization there is, per unit time, one photon going

---

[2] One should recall Eq. (N.2), where $\mathbf{e} = (\gamma e)$, etc. In the matrix element, Eq. (2.8), one has summed over both spin states. Hence, in order to compare, one must divide by a factor of 2.

through the unit cross section ($c = 1!$), so that one can find the cross section from the transition probability, Eq. (4.19), simply by dividing this equation by the total time. In order to define the cross section in any system it is useful to redefine the cross section in the rest system in a relativistically invariant way. In this system the quantity $1/mk_0$ characteristic of the incident particles can be rewritten in the invariant form $1/(pk)$. The invariant formula for the cross section valid in any system is obtained by replacing in Eq. (4.19) $V/\underline{V}/(p_0k_0)$ by $1/(pk)$.[3]

We may now state the general recipe for forming the cross section:[4]

a. Draw all graphs for the process and join them with all possible image graphs. Each graph of nth order has n vertices where a vertex is a point in which an electron line enters and another leaves and a photon line enters or leaves. The element of S is the sum of all topologically inequivalent graphs which have the same incident and outgoing lines.

b. Replace the incoming lines by the correctly normalized matrix elements of the absorption operators. The inner electron lines are replaced by the S_f and D_f functions and the outgoing lines by the S^+ or D^+ functions.

c. To each vertex corresponds a γ multiplied by the polarization vector of the photon times the charge e. One sums over polarization vectors of the inner photon lines.

d. In momentum space the invariant functions are replaced by their Fourier representations. The sum of energy-momentum vectors of lines entering a vertex is equal to the sum of energy-momentum vectors of lines leaving a vertex. Any energy-momentum vectors not fixed by this rule are to be integrated over.

e. If one does not measure the spin polarization direction of the electron, which is what is already implied by inserting S^+ for the

---

[3] If both particles have rest mass, then the corresponding quantity is

$$\sqrt{(pk)^2 - p^2k^2}.$$

[4] The factor of $n!$ usually disappears in the S matrix, since one has $n!$ terms which correspond to the same graph and there are only $n!$ distinct permutations of the variables $x_1 \cdots x_n$. For closed inner electron lines a situation can occur in which the graphs are not equivalent under permutation, so that the $n!$ does not disappear, see Section 10. When one adds the terms arising from the different orders of integration the relative phase factors are essential. Here each vertex gives $-i$, each internal or external line gives i, and each closed electron line gives -1.

final electron, then one has to replace the initial electron line by $(\mathbf{p} + m)/4m$ and to take the trace along the electron lines.

With these rules cross sections can be calculated quickly without going through all the complicated rearrangements. However, the graphs must always be thought of as an aid to computation and one (not, in fact, the only one) convenient way of summarizing the relevant matrix elements. They do not have any sort of deeper physical significance.

The most tedious[5] part of evaluating Eq. (4.19) is the taking of the traces. In this enterprise the identity $\mathbf{ab} = -\mathbf{ba} + 2(ab)$ and the following relations between the vectors we have introduced above are of great use

$$k^2 = k'^2 = 0, \quad p^2 = m^2, \quad (pk) - (pk') - (kk') = 0. \quad (4.20)$$

Furthermore, the polarization vectors are spacelike, $e^2 = e'^2 = -1$, and obey the orthogonality conditions $(ek) = (e'k') = 0$. Finally, one can make $(pe) = (pe') = 0$ by a gauge transformation $e \rightarrow e + \beta k$.

With this choice of gauge, $\mathbf{p}$ anticommutes with $\mathbf{e}$ and $\mathbf{e}'$. One may make use of this fact and the relations

$$(-\mathbf{p} + m)\,(\mathbf{p} + \mathbf{k} - m)^{-1} = (-\mathbf{p} + m)\mathbf{k}/2(pk)$$

and

$$(\mathbf{p} + \mathbf{k} + m)^{-1}(-\mathbf{p} + m) = \mathbf{k}/2(pk)\,(-\mathbf{p} + m)$$

(the same holds true for k replaced by $-k'$) to simplify[6] the square brackets in Eq. (4.19). It is convenient to split the trace into a non-relativistic part, which corresponds to using $\mathbf{p} + m$ in the term following the first bracket (this means neglecting the electron's recoil), and the recoil correction, which corresponds to $\mathbf{k} - \mathbf{k}'$ in the bracket.

The no recoil part gives

$$\frac{1}{4}\,\mathrm{Tr}\left\{(\mathbf{p} + m)\left[\frac{\mathbf{eke}'}{2(pk)} + \frac{\mathbf{e}'\mathbf{k}\mathbf{e}}{2(pk')}\right](\mathbf{p} + m)\left[\frac{\mathbf{e}'\mathbf{ke}}{2(pk)} + \frac{\mathbf{ek}'\mathbf{e}'}{2(pk')}\right]\right\}$$

$$= -2(ee')\,\frac{1}{4}\,\mathrm{Tr}\left\{(\mathbf{p} + m)\left[\frac{\mathbf{e}'\mathbf{ke}}{2(pk)} + \frac{\mathbf{ek}'\mathbf{e}'}{2(pk')}\right]\right\} = 2(ee')^2$$

---

[5] A thoughtless application of Eq. (A1.17) can generate over 1,000 terms, which then reduce to 3.

[6] Since $\mathrm{Tr}\,AB = \mathrm{Tr}\,BA$, $(\mathbf{p} + m)$ can be put at the beginning or the end of the trace.

as one finds by commuting $\mathbf{p} + m$ to the right and to the left and making use of Eq. (4.20).

In the expression for the relativistic correction[7]

$$\frac{1}{4}\operatorname{Tr}\left\{\mathbf{p}\left[\frac{\mathbf{eke'}}{(2pk)} + \frac{\mathbf{e'k'e}}{2(pk')}\right](\mathbf{k} - \mathbf{k'})\left[\frac{\mathbf{e'ke}}{2(pk)} + \frac{\mathbf{ek'e'}}{2(pk')}\right]\right\}$$

we take only the trace of the terms which are linked together as indicated by the joining lines. The other six terms, of which three involve k and three k', exactly compensate each other. The surviving terms give

$$\tfrac{1}{4}\operatorname{Tr}\{[2(pk')]^{-2}\mathbf{pe'k'ekek'e'} - [2(pk)]^{-2}\mathbf{peke'k'e'ke}\}$$

$$= \tfrac{1}{4}\operatorname{Tr}\{[2(pk')]^{-2}\mathbf{pk'kk'} - [2(pk)]^{-2}\mathbf{pkk'k}\}$$

$$= \frac{1}{2}\left[\frac{(pk)}{(pk')} + \frac{(pk')}{(pk)} - 2\right].$$

When everything is put together we arrive at the following invariant expression for the cross section

$$\sigma = \frac{\alpha^2}{(pk)}\int dk'\delta(k'^2)\delta((p + k - k')^2 - m^2)$$
$$\left[\frac{(pk)}{(pk')} + \frac{(pk')}{(pk)} - 2 + 4(ee')^2\right]. \qquad (4.21)$$

If one asks for the probability that the photon be scattered into a given solid angle then one must specialize Eq. (4.21) to the Lorentz frame in which the solid angle is specified. When we compute the probability that the photon scatters through a certain angle θ in the rest system of the initial electron we set $p = (m, 0, 0, 0)$. By making use of Eq. (N.1) both δ-functions can be put into a convenient form for the integration over k_0' and $|\underline{k}'|$

$$\delta(k'^2) = \frac{1}{2k_0'}\,\delta(k_0' - |\underline{k}'|)$$

(we do not need to integrate over the other zero point)

$$\delta((p + k - k')^2 - m^2) = \tfrac{1}{2}\delta((pk) - (pk') - (kk'))$$
$$= \tfrac{1}{2}\delta(m(k_0 - k_0') - k_0k_0'(1 - \cos\theta))$$
$$= \frac{k_0'}{2mk_0}\,\delta\left(|k'| - \frac{mk_0}{m + k_0(1 - \cos\theta)}\right).$$

---

[7] One remembers that the trace of an odd number of γ's disappears, Eq. (A1.15).

The first δ-function tells us that k_0' is to be regarded as an abbreviation for $|\underline{k}'|$ and the second δ-function obviously leads to the Compton relation between the incident and the scattered frequencies. With the functions written in this way one can immediately do the integrations and one only has the integration over the space angle in k' space left. We shall designate the angle between the polarization vectors in our system by ϕ. Then from Eq. (4.21) we obtain the quantity

$$\sigma = \left(\frac{\alpha}{2m}\right)^2 \int d\Omega \left(\frac{k_0'}{k_0}\right)^2 \left(\frac{k_0}{k_0'} + \frac{k_0'}{k_0} - 2 + 4 \cos^2 \phi\right) \quad (4.22)$$

which is called the Klein-Nishina formula, after its progenitors. Its experimental verification was one of the first successes of the Dirac equation.

The integrand of Eq. (4.22) is the differential cross section and gives the probability for scattering into a definite solid angle between the polarization directions. If one wishes to sum over the polarization vectors of the final photons then the sum over the two transverse directions can be replaced by a sum over all four directions, as in Eq. (3.18).

To compute the averaged cross section all we need to do is to replace the **e** in the matrix element and the conjugate, Eq. (4.19), by γ_j and γ^j. The process is similar for **e**'. This introduces a simplification in practical calculations, for one can then apply Eq. (A1.18). In our case, this leads to

$$\sigma = \frac{2\alpha^2}{(pk)} \int dk' \delta(k'^2) \delta((p + k - k')^2 - m^2)$$

$$\left\{\frac{(pk)}{(pk')} + \frac{(pk')}{(pk)} + \frac{m^2(kk')}{(pk)(pk')}\left[\frac{m^2(kk')}{(pk)(pk')} - 2\right]\right\}$$

or, in the rest system of the electron

$$\sigma = \frac{\alpha^2}{2m^2} \int d\Omega \left(\frac{k^{0'}}{k^0}\right)^2 \left(\frac{k^0}{k^{0'}} + \frac{k^{0'}}{k^0} - \sin^2 \theta\right). \quad (4.23)$$

If one is interested in the total scattering probability, then one must integrate Eq. (4.23) over the total k' space with $k^{0'} > 0$, $(p + k - k')^0 > 0$. This integral is the same as the one used for combining a D^+ and an S^+ function in (A2). To perform it most easily, one goes into the center of mass system, where the total energy-momentum vector $p + k$ has no time component, and finds that

$$\sigma = 2\pi\left(\frac{\alpha}{m}\right)^2\left[\left(\frac{1}{2\beta} - \frac{1}{\beta^2} - \frac{1}{\beta^3}\right)\ln\,(1 + 2\beta) + \frac{(1 + \beta)}{(1 + 2\beta)^2} + \frac{2}{\beta^2}\right] \quad (4.24)$$

with $\beta = (pk)/m^2$.

For small energies ($\beta \ll 1$) the total cross section is a constant, $8\pi/3(\alpha/m)^2$, and goes for large energies as $((\alpha/m)^2/\beta)\,\ln(2\beta)$. For small energies the cross section is identical to that which one would find for the scattering of light from a classical electron, the scattered radiation being that of the radiation from an oscillator in the direction e with the frequency k_0. The decrease in the cross section for large energies is a typical effect of the relativistic quantum theory. It comes from the fact that for wave lengths smaller than the Compton wave length the spatial extension of the S_f function must be considered. This one sees if in the matrix element

$$\int A(1)\bar{\psi}(1)S_f(12)A(2)\psi(2)$$

one introduces the relative coordinate $y = x_1 - x_2$, causing the expression to become essentially

$$\int dy S_f(y)e^{-iy(p+k)}.$$

Since $S(y)$ goes spatially as e^{-my} we get destructive interference for $k \gg m$ when the wave length is smaller than the relativistic spreading of the electron. This results in a decrease in the total cross section and in a peaking of the angular distribution in the forward direction. The latter shows that the electron does not have a sharp edge which would give a strong reflection even at high energies.

Needless to say, $S^{(2)}$ contains the matrix elements for several other processes which can be worked out according to the same pattern. We shall not go into more arithmetic details. However, we shall discuss the essential features of the results.

The same graphs which have been evaluated for Compton scattering can also be used for calculating pair production by two photons or for calculating the inverse process of pair annihilation. For this purpose one does not need to evaluate the trace afresh. It suffices simply to use different lines as incoming or outgoing (problem 24). For the limiting cases in the total cross section for pair annihilation one finds (taking $m = 1$ and giving all cross sections in the center of mass system)

$$\sigma_A = \frac{\pi\alpha^2}{p} \qquad \text{for } p \ll 1$$

$$= \frac{\pi\alpha^2}{p^2} \ln (p^2) \qquad \text{for } p \gg 1 \tag{4.25}$$

where p is the relative momentum of the pair. The cross section for $p \ll 1$ shows the usual $1/v$ law and is what one would expect on the basis of a simple probability argument. The relativistic decrease again shows the spreading of the charge over a region $\sim m^{-1}$.

The scattering of two charged fermions corresponds to the exchange of a virtual photon and is given by the graph in Fig. 17. According to our general prescription one has to sum the matrix elements over all four polarization directions of the photon. However, the number of timelike and longitudinal photons is fixed by the Lorentz condition, so that strictly speaking one cannot consider the exchange of such photons. Their contribution to the matrix element exactly corresponds to a static Coulomb field, as we are going to show. The exchange of a photon with polarization in the direction $k = p - p'$ does not give any scattering, naturally. Indeed, the Dirac equation

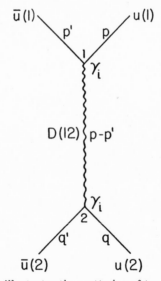

Fig. 17. This graph illustrates the scattering of two charged fermions.

immediately gives us

$$\bar{u}(2)\mathbf{k}u(1) = 0. \tag{4.26}$$

Putting the 1-axis in the direction of the space part of k, Eq. (4.26), tells us that

$$\bar{u}(2)\gamma_1 u(1) = \bar{u}(2)\gamma_0 u(1) \frac{k_0}{|k|}.$$

Thus, the sum of the matrix elements with the photon polarization in the direction 0 and 1 gives

$$\bar{u}(p)\gamma_0 u(p')\bar{u}(q)\gamma_0 u(q') \frac{i}{k_0^2 - |k^2|} \left(1 - \frac{|k_0|^2}{|k|^2}\right)$$

$$= u^\dagger(p)u(p')u^\dagger(q)u(q') \frac{-i}{|k|^2}$$

which is exactly the matrix element for scattering by a Coulomb field. In fact, one can eliminate the longitudinal and the timelike fields and replace them by the Coulomb interaction. However, this process cannot be done without reference to a particular timelike direction and therefore is not very rewarding for our purposes.

For two identical particles there are two graphs in this order for scattering; see Fig. 18. One must notice that the contributions of the second graph have to be subtracted for fermions because

$$(p'q' \mid \bar{\psi}^-(2)\bar{\psi}^-(1) \mid 0) (0 \mid \psi^+(2)\psi^+(1) \mid pq)$$

$$= \{[\bar{u}_{p'}(2)\bar{u}_{q'}(1) - \bar{u}_{q'}(2)\bar{u}_{p'}(1)] [u_p(2)u_q(1) - u_q(2)u_p(1)]\}$$

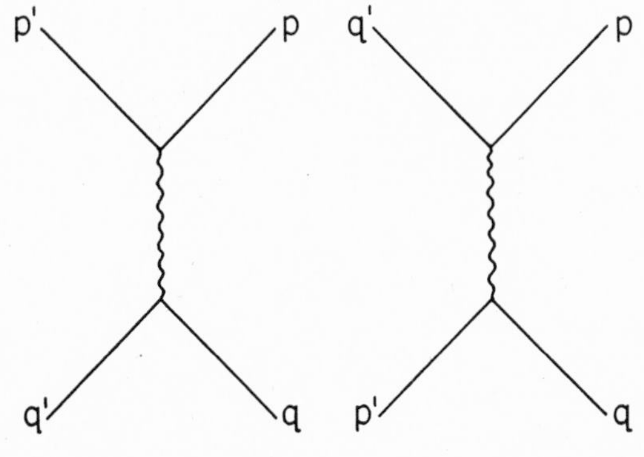

FIG. 18. These diagrams illustrate the scattering of identical particles.

which corresponds to antisymmetrized wave functions. As a result, the classical Rutherford formula must be modified for low energies to read

$$\frac{d\sigma}{d\Omega} = \frac{\alpha^2}{16p^4} \left[\sin^{-4}(\theta/2) + \cos^{-4}(\theta/2) - \sin^2(\theta/2)\cos^2(\theta/2)\right].$$

Its famous feature is that it is not the simple sum of the distributions for the two possible wave function orderings. It contains an interference term which maintains the Pauli exclusion principle. This prevents 75 % of the electrons (those with spin parallel) from scattering by 90°. At high energies the contributions from the transverse photons appear, corresponding to magnetic interactions. They are more singular than the Coulomb interactions and scatter more isotropically. Altogether one finds in this limit

$$\frac{d\sigma}{d\Omega} = \frac{\alpha^2}{4p^2} \left[1 + \sin^{-4}(\theta/2) + \cos^{-4}(\theta/2)\right].$$

There are also two graphs which represent the scattering of an electron by a positron (Fig. 19). The most interesting of the two corresponds to the annihilation of the pair into one photon, which then recreates the pair. This yields a short range force whose magnitude has been estimated in the introduction. Against naive expectation it turns out to be repulsive and thus interferes destructively with the Coulomb scattering. It does not, of course, contribute to the low energy limit, which is simply given by the Rutherford formula. For

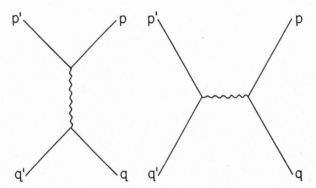

Fig. 19. These diagrams represent the scattering of an electron by a positron.

high energies we get

$$\frac{d\sigma}{d\Omega} = \frac{\alpha^2}{4p^2} \left\{ \frac{[1 + \cos^4 (\theta/2)]}{\sin^4 (\theta/2)} - \frac{\cos^4 (\theta/2)}{\sin^2 (\theta/2)} + 1 + \cos^2 \theta \right\}.$$

The first term is the Coulomb scattering, including magnetic effects; the last is the annihilation scattering; and the negative term is the interference between the two. Owing to its short range the annihilation scattering shows a fairly flat angular distribution.

14. Renormalization Theory

After having examined some consequences of the theory calculated to lowest order in e we turn to a discussion of its physical content without taking recourse to any expansion in terms of the interaction strength. Since it is impossible to get an exact solution of the field equations we shall proceed semi-empirically. Let us assume that the solution of our system of equations (keeping in mind that the existence of such a solution is very dubious) reflects some basic properties of systems of particles as we find them in nature.

First of all, we shall suppose that the system has a state of lowest energy $| 0 \rangle$ which corresponds to the vacuum. If we imagine, for the sake of simplicity, that we deal with a theory that describes only one kind of particle with a finite rest mass, then the state with the next greatest energy value over that of the vacuum will be a one-particle state. Its energy will be separated by a finite gap m from that of the vacuum. Such one-particle states, being eigenstates of $\mathbf{P}_\mu$, correspond to "dressed" particles. If we express $\mathbf{P}_\mu$ in terms of creation and annihilation operators of bare particles it will then connect states with different numbers of these. Hence, the eigenstates of $\mathbf{P}_\mu$ are states having clouds of virtual particles. After another finite gap the states of even higher energy appear. We shall, for the time being, leave as an open question whether there will be bound states between particles or just states belonging to the continuum. These will be states of particles scattering each other at a finite time while having been infinitely separated for $t \to \pm \infty$. Their energy will therefore start at $2m$.

Our assumptions about the mass spectrum are schematized in Fig. 20. In fact, they have far-reaching consequences for the vacuum expectation value of the product of two field operators. We shall see shortly that such quantities can be directly related to fields produced by external sources. As the simplest case we shall study a Hermitian scalar field ϕ. Let us consider the expression

$$\Delta^{+\prime}(x - x') = i(0 \mid \phi(x)\phi(x') \mid 0). \qquad (4.26)$$

The state $\phi(x') \mid 0)$ will neither represent simply one dressed nor one bare particle. Below we shall see that this would imply that ϕ has

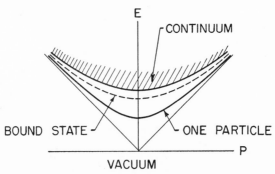

FIG. 20. This diagram represents the mass spectrum.

only Fourier components with $p^2 = m^2$. Thus, ϕ would obey the free field equation and not the interacting field equation which we wish to examine. The fact that $\phi(x') \mid 0)$ cannot be simply a state with one bare particle follows also from the fact that $\mid 0)$ is not an eigenstate of the annihilation operators having eigenvalue zero. One can even show that $\mathbf{P}_\mu$ will have terms which contain only creation operators.[1] We will call $\phi(x) \mid 0)$ an undressed particle at x and we will see that this is what is created by a weak external source in the vacuum. $\Delta^{+\prime}$ describes the propagation properties of undressed particles. It is the relative probability amplitude (because $\phi \mid 0)$ is not normalized) for finding an undressed particle at x' once it is known that there is one at x. For working out $\Delta^{+\prime}$ we expand $\phi(x) \mid 0)$ in terms of eigenstates $(p \mid$ of the energy-momentum vector $\mathbf{P}_\mu$. From the relation

$$(p \mid [\phi(x), \mathbf{P}_\mu] \mid 0) = i \frac{\partial}{\partial x_\mu} (p \mid \phi(x) \mid 0) = -p_\mu(p \mid \phi(x) \mid 0) \quad (4.27)$$

we conclude that its x dependence is of the form

$$(p \mid \phi(x) \mid 0) = e^{+ipx}(p \mid \phi(0) \mid 0).$$

This gives us

$$\Delta^{+\prime}(x - x') = i \sum_p (0 \mid \phi(x) \mid p)(p \mid \phi(x') \mid 0)$$
$$= i \sum_p e^{-ip(x-x')} \mid (p \mid \phi(0) \mid 0)\mid^2. \quad (4.28)$$

[1] The state $\mid 0)$ is not the state with no bare particles but rather that with no dressed particles. We use the terminology dressed particle $\equiv$ physical particle. Incoming particles will be used for specifying boundary conditions for physical particles.

From Lorentz invariance it follows that $| (p \mid \phi(0) \mid 0) |^2$ summed over all states with the same p can only depend on p^2, and we will call it $\rho(p^2)$. Thus we get

$$\Delta^{+\prime}(x - x') = i \sum_{p'} e^{-ip'(x-x')} \sum_{p} |(p \mid \phi(0)\mid 0)|^2 \delta(p - p')$$

$$= \frac{i}{(2\pi)^3} \int_0^\infty da^2 \rho(a^2) \int_{p_0'>0} dp' e^{-ip'(x-x')} \delta(p^2 - a^2) \quad (4.29)$$

$$= \int_0^\infty da^2 \rho(a^2) \Delta^+(x - x', a).$$

Here we have made use of the assumption about the mass spectrum which implies that p only goes over timelike vectors with $p_0 > 0$.

Remembering its definition we realize that $\rho(a^2)$ is the probability for finding the undressed particle in a state with total mass a and hence is always positive. Equation (4.29) shows us that propagation properties are a purely kinematical affair. The propagator for the undressed particle is a superposition of propagators with mass a weighted with the appropriate probability distribution. For free fields $\rho(a^2) = \delta(a^2 - m^2)$. That is to say, the undressed particle is already the physical particle. An interaction gives an admixture of other states which will have higher mass than a if the vacuum expectation value of ϕ vanishes. This is the case when, for example, ϕ anticommutes with some multiplicative invariance operation of the theory like parity or charge conjugation. This would be the case for a pseudo-scalar or an electric field.

Under these assumptions about ϕ we find

$$\rho(a^2) = Z\delta(a^2 - m^2) + \sigma(a^2) \tag{4.30}$$

where $\sigma(a^2) = 0$ for $a^2 < m^2 + \delta$, $\delta > 0$, and $Z > 0$ is a constant. It turns out to be related to the integral over σ if ϕ obeys the canonical commutation rules

$$[\phi(\underline{x}, t), \dot{\phi}(\underline{x}', t)] = i\delta(\underline{x} - \underline{x}').$$

Taking the vacuum expectation value of this relation we find

$$(0 \mid [\phi(\underline{x}, t), \dot{\phi}(\underline{x}', t)] \mid 0) = i\delta(\underline{x} - \underline{x}') = \frac{\partial}{\partial t'} \int_0^\infty da^2 \rho(a^2) \Delta(x - x', a)$$

$$= i\delta(\underline{x} - \underline{x}') \int_0^\infty da^2 \rho(a^2)$$

that is to say, in this case $\rho(a^2)$ has a continuum normalization condition

$$\int_0^\infty da^2 \rho(a^2) = 1$$

or

$$Z = 1 - \int_{m^2+\delta}^\infty da^2 \sigma(a^2) < 1. \tag{4.31}$$

Relations (4.29) to (4.31) comprise all the general statements that one can make about the propagator. The detailed form of σ depends on the dynamical properties of the system. Let us suppose that ϕ will obey a field equation of the form

$$(\Box + m_0^2)\phi(x) = j(x). \tag{4.32}$$

In anticipation of the electromagnetic case we have written $j(x)$ for the right-hand side of Eq. (4.32) which is defined by this equation. Since the interaction changes the mass of the particle, m_0 will be different from m. If the vacuum expectation value of $[\dot\phi(x, t), j(x', t)]$ vanishes one can derive a suggestive formula for m_0. We find

$$0 = (0 \mid [\dot\phi(x, t), (\Box^2 + m_0^2)\phi(x', t) \mid 0)$$

$$= i\delta(x - x')\left[m_0^2 - \int_0^\infty da^2 a^2 \rho(a^2) \right]$$

which gives

$$m_0^2 = \int_0^\infty da^2 a^2 \rho(a^2). \tag{4.33}$$

Thus m_0^2 is the average of a^2 weighted with ρ. This means that an undressed particle is not an eigenstate of the mass operator $\mathbf{P}^2$, m_0^2 being the expectation value of $\mathbf{P}^2$ for an undressed particle state. This shows, by the way, that under the circumstances above, the interaction reduces the mass.

Having determined the general form of the propagator by kinematical considerations, we are now prepared to explore the physical content of the theory by switching on external sources. That is to say, we shall now study the consequence of introducing a term $\mathbf{L}' = \phi(x)\mathcal{g}(x)$ into the Lagrangian, where $\mathcal{g}(x)$ is a c-number which we can treat classically. Furthermore, we want to disturb the system as little as possible. Hence, we make $\mathcal{g}(x)$ so weak that we may take only the first term in an expansion in powers of $\mathbf{L'}$.[2] We can now ask questions like the probability of the emission of particles by $\mathcal{g}(x)$ if the system was in its ground state before $\mathcal{g}(x)$ was switched on, or we may ask about the change of the energy or the expectation value of $\phi(x)$ under these circumstances.

All of these problems can easily be solved with the formulae derived in Section 8. The formula for the probability for creating a state $(\overset{p}{\text{out}}|$ with outgoing particles with energy-momentum p is

$$w_p = |\,(\overset{p}{\text{out}}\,|\int_{-\infty}^{\infty} dx \phi(x)\mathcal{g}(x)|\,0)\,|^2. \tag{4.34}$$

Using the previous expressions, the total emission probability in momentum space becomes

$$w = \sum_p w_p = \int_0^{\infty} da^2 \rho(a^2) \int \frac{dk}{(2\pi)^3} |\,\mathcal{g}(k)|^2 \,\delta(k^2 - a^2) \tag{4.35}$$

or the radiated energy-momentum is

$$\Delta \mathbf{P}_i = \int_0^{\infty} da^2 \rho(a^2) \int \frac{dk}{(2\pi)^3} |\,\mathcal{g}(k)|^2 \,\delta(k^2 - a^2)k_i. \tag{4.36}$$

For the change in $(0\,|\,\phi(x)\,|\,0)$ we get

$$\delta(0\,|\,\phi(x)\,|\,0) = i\,(0\,|\int_{-\infty}^{\sigma x} dx'[\phi(x),\,\phi(x')]\mathcal{g}(x')\,|\,0) \tag{4.37}$$

or

$$\frac{\delta}{\delta\mathcal{g}(x)}\,(0\,|\,\phi(x)|\,0) = i\theta(x - x')\Delta'(x - x') \tag{4.38}$$

or

$$\delta(0\,|\,\phi(x)\,|\,0) = \int_0^{\infty} da^2 \rho(a^2)\Delta^{\text{ret}}(x - x',\,a)\mathcal{g}(x')\,dx'$$
$$= \int_0^{\infty} da^2 \rho(a^2) \int \frac{dk}{(2\pi)^4} e^{ikx} \frac{\mathcal{g}(k)}{a^2 - k^2}. \tag{4.39}$$

[2] We do not assume, of course, any expansion in powers of internal coupling constants, but suppose that we have an exact solution of the interacting system available.

Since $(0 \mid \phi \mid 0) = 0$, only the second-order term contributes in the expression for the change in energy at time zero.

$$\delta \mathbf{P}_0 = \frac{1}{2} \int_{-\infty}^{0} dx \, dx'(0 \mid [[P_0, \phi(x)], \phi(x')] \mid 0) \mathcal{g}(x) \mathcal{g}(x')$$

$$= \frac{1}{2} \int_{-\infty}^{0} dx \, dx'(0 \mid [\dot{\phi}(x), \phi(x')] \mid 0) \mathcal{g}(x) \mathcal{g}(x'). \qquad (4.40)$$

Assuming the source to be switched on adiabatically

$$\mathcal{g}(\underline{x}, t) = \lim_{\alpha \to 0} [e^{\alpha t} \mathcal{g}(\underline{x})]$$

we get

$$\delta \mathbf{P}_0 = -\frac{1}{2} \int d^3 \underline{x} \, d^3 \underline{x}' \mathcal{g}(\underline{x}) \mathcal{g}(\underline{x}') \int_0^{\infty} da^2 \rho(a^2) \frac{e^{-a|\underline{x} - \underline{x}'|}}{4\pi \mid \underline{x} - \underline{x}' \mid}. \qquad (4.41)$$

All of these formulae are very similar to those we found for a source introduced into a free field. This shows that they are dominated by the kinematics, the dynamic properties of the system being condensed into $\rho(a)$. In particular, when we consider the macroscopic limit of the theory, that is to say, large distances (compared with m^{-1}) and low energies, then the effect of the internal interactions is only a renormalization factor Z. To see this take $\mathcal{g}$ such that it differs from zero only for the first mass level, e.g., $\mathcal{g}(k) = 0$ for $k^2 \geqslant m^2 + \delta$. In this case $\sigma(a)$ does not contribute to $\rho(a^2)$ and we get, for Eq. (4.35)

$$w = Z \int \frac{dk}{(2\pi)^3} \delta(k^2 - m^2) \mid \mathcal{g}(k) \mid^2. \qquad (4.42)$$

Similarly, for

$$\mathcal{g}(\underline{x}, t) = e\delta(x) \qquad (4.43)$$

$$\lim_{|\underline{x}| \gg m^{-1}} \delta(0 \mid \phi(x) \mid 0) = Ze \frac{e^{-m|\underline{x}|}}{4\pi \mid \underline{x} \mid} \qquad (4.44)$$

or, for δP_0 with two sources, $\mathcal{g}(x) = e[\delta(0) + \delta(\underline{x})]$ after subtraction gives the self energy E_0

$$\lim_{|x| \gg m^{-1}} (\delta P_0 - 2E_0) = -Ze^2 \frac{e^{-m|\underline{x}|}}{4\pi \mid \underline{x} \mid}. \qquad (4.45)$$

The obvious interpretation of these results is as follows. $\mathcal{g}(x)$ is primarily coupled to the undressed particle. If the energy is just sufficient to produce a dressed particle then this part of the undressed particle will be created as a real process. Therefore, the emission probability is the same as for free fields, but is multiplied by the probability of finding a dressed particle in the states which compose the undressed particle. Similarly, the dressed particle, being the state of lowest energy contained in the undressed particle, will get farthest away in the cloud of virtual particles of a source. The other states come into play only at higher energies or smaller distances.

It is interesting to note that they all contribute with the same sign. The self energy of a static source is given, for example, by

$$
- \left(Z \int \frac{d^3k}{(2\pi)^3} \frac{|\, \mathcal{J}(k)\,|^2}{k^2 + m^2} + \int_{m^2+\delta}^{\infty} da^2 \sigma(a^2) \int \frac{d^3k}{(2\pi)^3} \frac{|\, \mathcal{J}(k)\,|^2}{k^2 + a^2} \right).
$$

Hence, it goes to infinity for a point source. This is true in general and not just for the first term in an expansion in powers of the internal coupling constant. On the other hand, in the limit of high energies or small distances our results reduce to the high energy limits for the corresponding problem for free fields without the probability factor Z. For instance, for $\mathcal{J}(k) = \delta(k_0 - E)$ we get, with Eq. (4.31)

$$
\lim_{E \to \infty} W = \frac{Te^2}{4\pi^2} \lim_{E \to \infty} \int_0^E da^2 \rho(a^2) \sqrt{E^2 - a^2} = \frac{Te^2 E}{4\pi^2} \qquad (4.46)
$$

or, for the interaction energy at small distances

$$
\lim_{|x| \to 0} (2E_0 - \delta E) = \lim_{|x| \to 0} \int_0^{\infty} da^2 \frac{e^{-a|x|}}{4\pi|x|} \rho(a^2) = \frac{e^2}{4\pi|x|}. \qquad (4.47)
$$

That is to say, for sufficiently high energies or short times the mass spreading of the undressed particle becomes insignificant and it acts like one physical particle. We have already observed this behavior in Section 10 and we now see that it follows from general kinematical arguments.

In the conventional terminology fields and source strengths are defined with the aid of macroscopic aspects of the field. The strength of the current e in Eq. (4.43), however, measures the ability of $\mathcal{J}$ to create an undressed rather than a dressed particle. In order to tie on to familiar concepts we have to introduce parameters referring to the dressed particle rather than e. For this purpose we introduce a renormalized charge e_r in such a way that the low energy limits of processes are given by the usual formulae, which ignore the internal interaction and, hence, the cloud of virtual particles around the dressed particle. Similarly, we define the renormalized field ϕ_r so that its expectation value reduces at large distances from the source to the classical result (e.g., $e_r/4\pi \mid x \mid$ for $m = 0$)

$$Ze^2 = e_r^{\,2} \qquad \phi_r \xrightarrow{} \frac{e_r}{4\pi|x|} \xrightarrow{} \frac{1}{\sqrt{Z}}\,\phi. \qquad (4.48)$$

This leads to the definition

$$e_r = \sqrt{Z}e \qquad \phi_r = \frac{1}{\sqrt{Z}}\,\phi$$

which does not change $\phi \mathcal{J}$. Moreover, we find for the interaction energy at large distances (for $m = 0$, let us say) $e_r^{\,2}/4\pi \mid x \mid$, which could also have been taken as the defining expression for e_r. Rewriting previous formulae in terms of the new quantities and defining ρ_r through ϕ_r we get

$$[\phi_r(x, t), \dot{\phi}_r(x', t)] = \frac{i\delta(x - x')}{Z}$$

$$\rho_r = \delta(a^2 - m^2) + \sigma_r(a^2) \qquad (4.49)$$

$$\frac{1}{Z} = 1 + \int_{m^2+\delta}^{\infty} da^2\, \sigma_r(a^2).$$

Having studied the significance of renormalization with a scalar field we turn to the case of primary interest, namely, quantum electrodynamics. We assume that the system characterized by Eq. (4.1) has one state of zero energy and zero charge, which we interpret as the vacuum. The state with charge one we call the one-electron state. Charge conjugation tells us that there must be a state with the same mass and opposite charge, which we call the positron. The state with lowest mass and no charge is the photon.

For the coming analysis it is better not to assume at once the degenerate case of photon mass zero. Thus, for the moment we shall assume that the photon state is separated by a finite gap μ_0 from the vacuum,[3] which means that we have to start from the field equations

$$(\Box^2 + u_0^{\,2})\mathbf{A}_i = e\bar{\psi}\gamma_i\psi. \qquad (4.50)$$

In this case one cannot require that $\mathbf{A}^i{}_{,i} \mid 0) = 0$,[4] which seems seri-

---

[3] For a detailed discussion of the many ways to deal with the electromagnetic case, see J. M. Jauch and F. Rohrlich, "Theory of Photons and Electrons," Chapter 6, Addison-Wesley, Reading, Massachusetts, 1955.

[4] Even for $e = 0$, $[A_l, A_m] = ig_{lm}\Delta$ insures $(0 \mid [A^l{}_{,l}A^m{}_{,m}] \mid 0) = i\mu_0^{\,2}\Delta$.

ous, since this theory then contains negative energies. They turn out, however, to be rather harmless. By splitting A as follows

$$\mathbf{A}_i = \mathbf{U}_i + \frac{1}{\mu_0}\mathbf{B}_{,i}$$

with

$$\mathbf{U}^i{}_{,i} = 0$$

and demanding

$$(\Box^2 + \mu_0{}^2)\mathbf{B} = 0 \qquad [\mathbf{B}(x), \mathbf{B}(x')] = i\Delta(x - x') \qquad [\mathbf{B}(x), \mathbf{U}(x')] = 0$$

all negative energies are contained in the $\mathbf{B}$-field. It turns out that this field is, in effect, uncoupled. It can be gotten rid of by gauge transformation in which one changes the phase of ψ. Thus, the particles of negative energy are not created in any physical process and will not bother us for the moment. The dynamically relevant field is the $\mathbf{U}$-field, which obeys the Lorentz condition. We shall now determine the renormalization constant by following the same pattern as in the scalar case.

In constructing the kinematically permissible form of $(0 \mid \mathbf{U}_i\mathbf{U}_j \mid 0)$ we note that since $\mathbf{U}^i{}_{,i} = 0$ the indices i and j must occur in momentum space in the combination $g_{ij}k^2 - k_ik_j$. Thus we put

$$(0 \mid \mathbf{U}_i(x)\mathbf{U}_j(x') \mid 0) = -(2\pi)^3 \int_{k_0>0} dk e^{-ik(x-x')}$$

$$\cdot \int_0^\infty da^2\delta(k^2 - a^2)\Pi(a^2)(g_{ij}k^2 - k_ik_j). \tag{4.51}$$

Since for $i = j$ and $k^2 > 0$ one easily sees $k^2g_{ij} - k_ik_j < 0$ we conclude that $\Pi(a^2) > 0$. To use the canonical commutation rules for the $\mathbf{A}$-field, as in the scalar case, we have to add the contribution from the $\mathbf{B}$-field, which gives

$$(0 \mid [\mathbf{A}_i(x), \mathbf{A}_j(x')] \mid 0) = -(2\pi)^3 \int dk e^{-ik(x-x')}\epsilon(k) \int_0^\infty da^2$$

$$\cdot \left[\delta(k^2 - a^2)[\Pi(a^2)(a^2g_{ij} - k_ik_j)] + \frac{k_ik_j}{m_0{}^2}\delta(a^2 - m_0{}^2) \right]. \tag{4.52}$$

For $t = t'$ we conclude from

$$[A_i(x), A_j(x')] = 0$$

that

$$\int_0^\infty da \Pi(a) = \frac{1}{m_0^2}$$

and from

$$[A_i(x), \dot{A}_j(x')] = -ig_{ij}\delta(\underline{x} - \underline{x}')$$

that

$$\int_0^\infty da \Pi(a)a^2 = 1.$$

By introducing an external current $\mathcal{J}_i(x)$ we produce an electric field with the Green's function

$$\theta(x - x')(0 \mid [\mathbf{A}_i(x), \mathbf{A}_j(x')] \mid 0).$$

Performing the ambiguous rearrangement as in Section 10 we can rewrite this as a superposition of Δ^{ret} functions with the same weighting functions as for Δ. We demand, of course, that the external current satisfy $\mathcal{J}^i_{,i} = 0$. In this case the terms $k_i k_j$ do not contribute and we get

$$\delta(0 \mid \mathbf{A}^i(x) \mid 0) = \int \frac{dk}{(2\pi)^3} e^{-ikx} \int_0^\infty da^2 \frac{\Pi(a^2)a^2}{a^2 - k^2} \mathcal{J}^i(k). \quad (4.53)$$

This is quite analogous to what we had in the scalar case. The $\Pi(a^2)a^2$ replaces $\rho(a^2)$ here. In order to learn more detailed features of $\Pi(a^2)$ we assume the "empirical" mass spectrum and keep in mind that $(0 \mid \mathbf{A}_i \mid 0)$ must be zero because of Lorentz invariance and invariance under charge conjugation.[5] The first contribution to $\Pi(a^2)$ will therefore come from the one photon state, the mass of which we called μ. Furthermore, we assume that there are no bound states between photons, so that the next states will be the continuum of the two photon states, starting at 2μ. However, these states do not contribute since, by charge conjugation invariance, $\mathbf{A} \mid 0)$ must contain an odd number of photons. Thus we have

$$\Pi(a^2)a^2 = Z\delta(a^2 - \mu^2) + \sigma(a^2).$$

The fact that $\sigma(a^2) = 0$ for $a < 3\,\mu$, and $\int_0^\infty \Pi(a^2)a^2 = 1$ tells us

$$Z + \int_{(3\mu)^2}^\infty da^2 \sigma(a^2) = 1. \quad (4.54)$$

[5] For $\mu_0 = 0$ one has the freedom of gauge transformations and

$(0 \mid A \mid 0) = 0$ fixes the gauge.

Again the theory shows the same behavior with respect to the macroscopic (low energy) and the microscopic (high energy) limits as did the scalar field. To obtain the quantities usually referred to as the electric field strength we have to introduce the renormalized quantities as before

$$\mathbf{A}_r = \frac{\mathbf{A}}{\sqrt{Z}} \qquad e_r = e\sqrt{Z} \qquad \mathcal{g}_r = \mathcal{g}\sqrt{Z}.$$

In fact, we shall henceforth deal with the renormalized quantities exclusively and therefore in our notation we shall drop the subscript r. Some care is required in the definition of the total observable current J. It will consist of the external current $\mathcal{g}$ and the induced current $\mathbf{j}$. For a static source $\mathbf{A}$ behaves asymptotically like $e(e^{-\mu r}/4\pi r)$, which suggests defining $\mathbf{J}$ by $(\Box^2 + \mu^2)\mathbf{A} = \mathbf{J}$. Thus we get

$$\mathbf{J}_i(x) = (\Box^2 + \mu^2)\mathbf{A}_i = \frac{1}{Z}\mathcal{g}_i(x) + \mathbf{j}_i(x) \qquad (4.55)$$

where

$$\mathbf{j}_i(x) = \frac{e}{Z}\bar{\psi}\gamma_i\psi + (\mu^2 - \mu_0{}^2)\mathbf{A}_i \, .$$

In momentum space this gives the following connection between the external and the total current for a vacuum state in first order

$$(0 \mid \mathbf{J}_i(x) \mid 0) = \int \frac{dk}{(2\pi)^4}\, e^{-ikx}\, d(k)\mathcal{g}_i(k) \qquad (4.56)$$

where $d(k)$ is given by

$$d(k) = \int_0^\infty da^2 a^2 \Pi(a^2)\, \frac{\mu^2 - k^2}{a^2 - k^2}. \qquad (4.57)$$

It is normalized so that $d(\mu) = 1$. As a consequence, for an external charge of the form $\mathcal{g}^0 = e\delta(x)$ we have for the limit $\mu \to 0$

$$\int dV \mathcal{g}^0(x) = ed(0) = e. \qquad (4.58)$$

Thus, by our renormalization procedure we have realized the goal put forth in Section 10. The vacuum polarization does not change the total charge. The formal consistency of this statement requires

$$\int d\sigma^i\, (0 \mid \mathbf{j}^i \mid 0) = e\left(1 - \frac{1}{Z}\right). \qquad (4.59)$$

This is not a contradiction with charge conservation since **j** does not only contain $\bar{\psi}\gamma\psi$. The contribution comes from the other term for which we find with our previous formula

$$\int d\sigma_i \, (0 \mid \mathbf{A}^i(x) \mid 0) \, (\mu^2 - \mu_0^2) = e \int_0 da^2 \Pi(a^2)(\mu^2 - \mu_0^2)$$

$$= e \left[1 + \mu^2 \int_{(3\mu)^2}^{\infty} da^2 \sigma(a^2)/a^2 - \frac{1}{Z} \right]. \tag{4.60}$$

This checks with Eq. (4.57) if

$$\lim_{\mu \to 0} \mu^2 \int_{(3\mu)^2}^{\infty} da^2 \sigma(a^2)/a^2 = 0.$$

The first term of $\sigma(a^2)$, when expanded in powers of e^2, has been calculated in Section 10. It corresponds to an intermediate state of a pair and is, therefore, zero for $a < 2m$. Furthermore, we noted that

$$\int_{4m^2}^{\infty} dc^2 \sigma(c^2) \to \infty$$

implies $Z \to 0$. That is to say, in second order the bare charge has to be infinite and, correspondingly, the high energy limits diverge. Similarly, **L** and quantities like the canonical commutators contain infinite quantities. Nevertheless, quantities at finite energies or $(0 \mid [\mathbf{A}, \dot{\mathbf{A}}] \mid 0)$ smoothed out in space-time regions[6] are finite to this order in e. In Section 16 we shall discuss the question of whether one can forget the diverging limit in a fundamental sense. It has occasionally been assumed that by coupling several fields together the infinities might cancel. Since $\Pi(a^2)$ is greater than zero, we see that, within the framework we considered, their contributions will add and make the situation worse. A cancellation can be obtained only at the expense of introducing negative probabilities or negative energies.

The connection between $\mathscr{J}$ and **J** given in Eq. (4.56) is similar to the connection between div**P** and div**E** in a dielectric. The condition that light does not propagate faster than c implies that the dielectric

[6] Like

$$\left(0 \left| \left[\int dx A(x), \int dx' A(x') \right] \right| 0 \right)$$

rather than

$$(0 \mid [A(x), A(x')] \mid 0).$$

constant is an analytic function in one half plane in k-space.[7] We note that $d(k^2)$ is an analytic function except on the positive real axis. This corresponds in x-space to the fact that $(0 \mid \mathbf{A} \mid 0)$ is created from $\mathcal{J}$ with a superposition of Δ^{ret} functions which express the same state of affairs. In a manner similar to that used in the dielectric problem, the imaginary part of $d(k^2)$ is directly related to $\Pi(k^2)$ and hence to absorptive processes. The analyticity condition also requires a non-vanishing real part of $d(k^2)$, so that vacuum polarization is an inevitable part of any theory which gives pair creation.

Finally, we will construct the propagator for the Dirac field. Here, the coupling with the vector field causes the difficulty that ψ, being gauge variant, can give rise to states of negative energy. Postponing the discussion of this point we recognize, using arguments similar to those used before, that for a theory with positive energies we must get the general form

$$(0 \mid \psi_\alpha(x)\bar{\psi}_\beta(x') \mid 0)$$

$$= (2\pi)^{-3} \int_{-\infty}^{\infty} dar(a) \int_{k_0 > 0} dk e^{-ik(x-x')} \delta(k^2 - a^2)(\gamma k + a). \tag{4.61}$$

The expression for $(\bar{\psi}\psi)$ can then be obtained by charge conjugation. Using $U_c\psi U_c^{-1} = c\bar{\psi}$, $U_c\bar{\psi}U_c^{-1} = -\psi c^{-1}$, and $U_c \mid 0) = \mid 0)$, we find

$$(0 \mid \bar{\psi}_\beta(x')\psi_\alpha(x) \mid 0)$$

$$= -(2\pi)^{-3} \int_{-\infty}^{\infty} dar(a) \int_{k_0 < 0} dk e^{-ik(x-x')} \delta(k^2 - a^2)(\gamma k + a)$$

which gives us

$$S'(x - x')$$

$$= (0 \mid \{\psi_\alpha(x), \bar{\psi}_\beta(x')\} \mid 0) = \int_{-\infty}^{\infty} dar(a) iS(x - x', a). \tag{4.62}$$

The canonical commutation rules tell us that

$$\int_{-\infty}^{\infty} dar(a) = 1.$$

If the field equations are of the form

$$(\partial + m_0)\psi(x) = \mathbf{f}(x)$$

[7] See, for instance, J. Toll, *Phys. Rev.* **104**, 1760 (1956).

and

$$(0 \mid \{\mathbf{f}(x), \bar{\psi}(x')\}_{t=t'} \mid 0) = 0$$

we get, in the same way as in the scalar case

$$m_0 = \int_{-\infty}^{\infty} da\, a r(a). \tag{4.63}$$

It turns out that all these relations are also valid in quantum electrodynamics in spite of the negative energies. By introducing an indefinite metric in Hilbert space they can be reinterpreted as states with positive energies but negative probabilities.[8] In such a formulation the arguments above go through all right except that (|) is no longer greater than zero. As a consequence $r(a)$ is not positive any more in quantum electrodynamics. However, the reader may check that in our manipulations this relation has not, in fact, been used.

Since ψ changes the charge of a state by one unit, the state of lowest energy contained in $\psi \mid 0)$ will be the one electron state with a mass m. The next state is asymptotically an electron and a photon and comes at $m + \mu$. Hence we get

$$r(a) = N\delta(a - m) + s(a) \qquad s(a) = 0$$

for $\mid a \mid < m + \mu$.

The renormalization of the spinor originates from the familiar requirement that the part of $(0 \mid \bar{\psi}\psi \mid 0)$ which propagates the physical particle equals the free field propagator. This gives

$$\psi_r = \frac{1}{\sqrt{N}} \psi. \tag{4.64}$$

Henceforth, we shall use only the renormalized field and drop the subscript r. This gives us the renormalized equations

$$L^{el} = \frac{1}{N} \bar{\psi}(\partial - m_0)\psi$$

$$\{\psi(x), \psi^{+}(x')\}_{t=t'} = \frac{1}{N} \delta(x - x')$$

$$\frac{1}{N} = 1 + \int_{-\infty}^{\infty} da\, \sigma(a)$$

[8] See J. M. Jauch and F. Rohrlich, "Theory of Photons and Electrons," Chapter 6, Addison-Wesley, Reading, Massachusetts, 1955.

$$(0 \mid \psi(x)\bar{\psi}(x') \mid 0\rangle = \int_{-\infty}^{\infty} dar(a)iS^+(x - x', a)$$

$$r(a) = \delta(a - m) + \sigma$$

with m_0 again the mass effective for propagation over short time intervals. To see this we expand

$$\lim_{p \to \infty} S_F'(p) = \lim_{p \to \infty} \int_{-\infty}^{\infty} \frac{dar(a)}{\mathbf{p} - a} \simeq \frac{1}{\mathbf{p}} \frac{1}{N} + \frac{m_0}{p^2 N} \simeq \frac{1}{N} \frac{1}{\mathbf{p} - m_0}.$$

However, again these formal manipulations are only legitimate if $\int_{-\infty}^{\infty} dar(a)$ exists. We shall now see that this is not the case in the sense of an expansion in powers of e. Using the Dirac equation we find

$$e^2(0 \mid \psi(x)\gamma A(x)\bar{\psi}(x')\gamma A(x') \mid 0)$$

$$= -e^2\gamma_i S^+(x - x')\gamma^i D^+(x - x') \qquad (4.65)$$

$$= \int_{-\infty}^{\infty} dar(a)(a - m)^2 iS^+(x - x', a).$$

Now if we apply the combination formulae given in Appendix 2 we find in second order

$$r(a) = \delta(a - m) + \frac{\alpha}{4\pi} \frac{(a^2 - 4am + m^2)}{|a|^3 (a - m)} (a + m)\theta(a^2 - m^2).$$

Thus the expression for $1/N$ diverges logarithmically for the electric field. So does the integral $\int_{-\infty}^{\infty} dar(a)a$ which defines m_0, since the linear divergence cancels out. Replacing $\int_{-\infty}^{\infty} da$ by $\int_{-M}^{M} da$ we see that for $M \gg m$

$$m_0 = m \left[1 - \frac{2\alpha}{\pi} \ln \left(\frac{M}{m} \right) \right] \qquad (4.66)$$

that is to say, apparently the interaction with the electric field makes the particle heavier, as one would find by calculating the classical self energy. A closer examination, however, shows[9] that the two expressions have essential differences. First of all, the electrostatic self energy

[9] See K. Huang, *Phys. Rev.* **101**, 1173 (1956).

diverges only logarithmically in field theory because of the spread' of the charge due to virtual pairs. Furthermore, the recoil virtual photons increases the kinetic energy of the electron effect increases the mass and diverges quadratically. Finally, there a magnetic self energy which decreases the mass (parallel current. attract each other) and also diverges quadratically. It is just due to the g-value of the electron, which is 2 in this order, that the last mentioned contributions cancel exactly and one obtains the result given above.

15. Higher Order Corrections

In the last section we introduced the definitions of the various renormalized quantities which enter into quantum electrodynamics. This was done in such a way that the definitions connect these objects to the usual macroscopic measurements. Our program was to investigate the effect of introducing macroscopic test bodies into the coupled fields. We shall now see what the theory predicts about the behavior of the field quanta themselves (for example, scattering corrections) when it is expressed in terms of renormalized entities. The system under consideration will always be the coupled Maxwell-Dirac fields, but now without external sources. It will turn out that the first approximation to the various cross sections which we obtained in Section 13 is already very good, the effects of the higher order terms being mainly to substitute the renormalized for the unrenormalized quantities. There are only a few instances in which we will find observable departures from our previous expressions.

The first question we will ask concerns the current associated with one electron. Expressing everything in terms of renormalized objects and physical states we shall be interested in studying the expectation value of $\mathbf{j} = eN^2/Z : \bar{\psi}\gamma\psi : + \delta\mu^2\mathbf{A}$. In order to learn something about this quantity it is useful to express the one particle state as the product of an emission operator and the vacuum. This is what we did in the case of the free fields. We have seen above that the part of the Fourier transform of ψ for which $p^2 = m^2$ connects the vacuum with the one electron states. Therefore, we have to project this part out of ψ and apply it to the vacuum. This projection is most conveniently done by a limiting procedure. We define

$$\lim_{t \to {+\infty \atop -\infty}} e^{i\alpha t} = 1 \quad \text{for } \alpha = 0$$
$$= 0 \quad \text{for } \alpha \neq 0$$

where the limit is taken in an average sense. With this definition we assert

$$| 1) = \lim_{\sigma \to \pm\infty} \int d\sigma_\mu \bar{\psi}_\alpha(x) | 0) \, \gamma^\mu_{\alpha\beta} v_\beta(x) \tag{4.67}$$

177

where v is a solution of the Dirac equation $(\partial - m)v = 0$ which contains only positive frequencies. For a plane wave, for instance, $\int d\sigma$ selects the part of ψ which behaves like e^{ipx} and the limiting operation leaves only those frequencies for which $p_0 = \sqrt{m^2 + p^2}$. If v is a negative frequency solution, v^-, then we must require that

$$\lim_{t \to \pm\infty} \int d\sigma_\mu \bar{\psi}(x) \mid 0)\gamma^\mu v^-(x) = 0. \qquad (4.68)$$

Otherwise, this state would have lower energy than the vacuum. Thus $\lim \int d\sigma \bar{\psi}\gamma v^\mp$ has the properties of the emission and absorption operators $\psi^\mp$ for the free fields. The emission operator creates a state with one dressed electron having a wave function v. This means physically that although $\bar{\psi}(x)$ creates an undressed particle initially, after a sufficiently long time the particle dresses itself. Such a description corresponds to the actual experimental situation if, for example, one uses radioactive nuclei as the source of β rays. The decay process yields a bare electron which very soon develops a Coulomb field. Use of the renormalized ψ in Eq. (4.67) guarantees that $\mid 1)$ is correctly normalized, provided that v is a wave packet which has been normalized in the standard way.

With this expression for a one electron state we can write the matrix element of an operator as follows[1]

$$(0 \mid O(x) \mid 1) = i \int dx' P(0 \mid O(x)\bar{\psi}(x') \mid 0)(\overleftarrow{\partial}' + m)v(x') \qquad (4.69)$$

where $\overleftarrow{\partial}'$ means that it acts to the left. By partial integration $(\overleftarrow{\partial}' + m)$ becomes $(-\partial' + m)$, which gives zero when applied to v. The only contribution comes from the surface term where the upper limit

$$\lim_{\sigma' \to \infty} \int d\sigma_\mu \, (0 \mid \bar{\psi}(x')O(x) \mid 0)\gamma^\mu v(x')$$

gives zero since $\lim_{\sigma' \to \infty} \int \bar{\psi}\gamma v$ acts like an absorption operator on the left. Thus, Eq. (4.69) actually reduces to

$$\lim_{\sigma \to -\infty} \int d\sigma_\mu{}' (0 \mid O(x)\bar{\psi}(x') \mid 0)\gamma^\mu v(x').$$

---

[1] For anticommuting quantities we define P as follows: $2P \, \psi(1) \, \psi(2) = [\psi(1), \psi(2)] + \epsilon(1, 2) \{\psi(1), \psi(2)\}$.

A similar consideration shows that for $(1 \mid \mathbf{O}(x) \mid 1)$ we have

$$(1 \mid \mathbf{O}(x) \mid 1) = \int dx' \, dx'' \bar{v}(x')(\partial' - m)$$

$$\cdot P(0 \mid \psi(x')\mathbf{O}(x)\bar{\psi}(x'') \mid 0)(\overleftarrow{\partial}'' + m)v(x''). \tag{4.70}$$

We shall now apply these formulae to the study of $(1 \mid \mathbf{j}_\mu(x) \mid 1)$. We have kept the $\delta\mu^2$ term in $\mathbf{j}_\mu$ since we first want to check whether the electron has the correct charge, i.e., whether

$$\int d\sigma_\mu (1 \mid \mathbf{j}_\mu(x) \mid 1) = e$$

holds. Without this term we encounter the same contradictions with respect to charge conservation as we encountered at this point in the discussion of the external sources. In fact, it follows immediately from the commutation relations that

$$\int (1 \mid \frac{eN^2}{Z} : \bar{\psi}\gamma^\mu\psi : \mid 1) \, d\sigma_\mu = \frac{e}{Z}$$

if we use the $::$ symbols to mean

$$:\bar{\psi}\gamma\psi: \ = \ \bar{\psi}\gamma\psi - (0 \mid \bar{\psi}\gamma\psi \mid 0).$$

As in the external field case the $\delta\mu^2$ term can be used to give this the correct value for, as before, we integrate the field equation

$$(\Box^2 + \mu_0{}^2)\mathbf{A}_k = \frac{eN^2}{Z} \bar{\psi}\gamma_k\psi$$

and get

$$\int d\sigma_k (1 \mid \mathbf{A}^k \mid 1) = \frac{e}{Z\mu_0{}^2}$$

which gives us

$$\int d\sigma_k (1 \mid \mathbf{j}^k \mid 1) = \frac{e}{Z} \frac{\mu^2}{\mu_0{}^2}.$$

Under the circumstances mentioned in the previous chapter the last expression actually approaches e for $\mu \to 0$. By now the idea of a charge at infinity in the limit $\mu \to 0$ should be familiar. Hence, in the sequel we shall always go to this limit whenever it is possible.

Having seen that the charge of an electron is the renormalized e, we shall now see how the current distribution is changed by the interaction of the fields. For this program we must manipulate Eq. (4.70), making use of the renormalized field equations (which define $\mathbf{f}$)

$$(\partial - m)\psi(x) = \mathbf{f}(x) = e\mathbf{A}\gamma\psi + \delta m\psi$$

$$\Box^2 \mathbf{A}(x) = \mathbf{J}(x) = \frac{eN^2}{Z} : \bar{\psi}\gamma\psi : \tag{4.71}$$

$$\bar{\psi}(\partial + m) = \bar{\mathbf{f}}(x) = -\bar{\psi}\gamma\mathbf{A}e - \delta m\bar{\psi}$$

and the commutation relations

$$\{\psi(x), \psi^\dagger(x')\}_{t=t'} = \frac{\delta(x - x')}{N^2} \qquad [\dot{\mathbf{A}}(x), \mathbf{A}(x')] = \frac{i\delta(x - x')}{Z} . \tag{4.72}$$

Remembering the definition of the P symbol we get

$$(1 \mid : \bar{\psi}(x)\gamma_j\psi(x): \mid 1) = i \int dx'' P(1 \mid : \bar{\psi}(x)\gamma_j\psi(x): \bar{\psi}(x'') \mid 0)$$

$$\cdot(\overleftarrow{\partial}'' + m)v(x'') = i \int dx'' P(1 \mid : \bar{\psi}(x)\gamma_j\psi(x): \bar{\mathbf{f}}(x'') \mid 0)v(x'')$$

$$+ \frac{1}{N^2} (1 \mid \bar{\psi}(x) \mid 0)\gamma_j v(x) = \frac{\bar{v}(x)\gamma_j v(x)}{N^2} \tag{4.73}$$

$$+ \int dx' \, dx'' \bar{v}(x')(\partial' - m)P(0 \mid \psi(x'): \bar{\psi}(x)\gamma\psi(x): \bar{\mathbf{f}}(x'') \mid 0)v(x'').$$

We may apply the ∂' operator in the P bracket. In this way we learn that N^2/Z times the second term is (the spinor subscripts have been written out)

$$= i \int dx'' \bar{v}_\alpha(x)\gamma^j_{\alpha\beta} \frac{1}{Z} P(0 \mid \psi_\beta(x)\bar{\mathbf{f}}_\lambda(x'') \mid 0)v_\lambda(x'')$$

$$- i \int dx'' \bar{v}_\alpha(x'') \frac{1}{Z} P(0 \mid : \bar{\psi}_\sigma(x)\gamma^j_{\sigma\tau}\psi_\tau(x): e\mathbf{A}_k(x'')\gamma^k_{\alpha\beta} \mid 0)v_\beta(x'') \tag{4.74}$$

$$+ N^2/Z \int dx'' \, dx' \bar{v}_\alpha(x')P(0 \mid \mathbf{f}_\alpha(x'): \bar{\psi}_\sigma(x)\gamma^j_{\sigma\tau}\psi(x)_\tau: \bar{\mathbf{f}}_\beta(x'') \mid 0)v_\beta(x'').$$

Since the use of the $::$ redefines $\mathbf{j}$ only by an ordinary number, no change is made in the commutator of $\mathbf{j}$ with ψ. The first two terms in in Eq. (4.74) above can be further simplified by the following observations

$$P(0 \mid \psi(x)\bar{\psi}(x'') \mid 0)(\overleftarrow{\partial}'' + m) = iS_f'(x - x'')(\overleftarrow{\partial}'' + m)$$

$$= P0(\mid \psi(x)\bar{\mathbf{f}}(x'') \mid 0) - \frac{i}{N^2}\,\delta(x - x''). \qquad (4.75)$$

Hence, the first term in Eq. (4.74) becomes $\bar{v}(x)\gamma v(x)1/Z(1 - N^{-2})$. Similarly, we conclude from

$$\square^2 P(0 \mid \mathbf{A}_j(x)\mathbf{A}_k(x'') \mid 0) = \frac{eN^2}{Z}\,P(0 \mid \bar{\psi}(x)\gamma_j\psi(x)\mathbf{A}_k(x'') \mid 0)$$

$$+ i\,\frac{g_{jk}}{Z}\,\delta(x - x'')$$

that the second term of Eq. (4.74) equals

$$- \bar{v}(x)\gamma v(x)\,\frac{1}{ZN^2} + \int dx''\bar{v}(x'')\gamma v(x'')\,\square^2\,D'(x - x'')\,\frac{1}{N^2}.$$

Adding everything together we get

$$(1 \mid \mathbf{j}_j(x) \mid 1) = \frac{N^2e}{Z}\,(1 \mid \bar{\psi}(x)\gamma_j\psi(x) \mid 1)$$

$$= e\int dx''\bar{v}(x'')\gamma_j v(x'')\square^2 D'(x - x'') + \left(\frac{1}{N^2} - 1\right)$$

$$\cdot e\int dx''\bar{v}(x'')\gamma_j v(x'')\left[\square^2 D'(x - x'') - 2\frac{\delta(x - x'')}{Z}\right] \qquad (4.76)$$

$$+ \frac{N^2}{Z}\,e\int dx'\,dx''\bar{v}(x')P(0 \mid \mathbf{f}(x') : \bar{\psi}(x)\gamma_j\psi(x) : \bar{\mathbf{f}}(x'') \mid 0)v(x'').$$

Here the first term on the right-hand side is the effect of the vacuum polarization. It is the observable current which results when the external current $\bar{v}\gamma v$ is introduced into the vacuum. The remaining terms contain other higher order effects which we shall now study in the lowest order in e for which they do not vanish. This amounts to replacing the field operators in the last term by the free fields which produce to order e^3: (Graphically this term is represented by Fig. 21.)

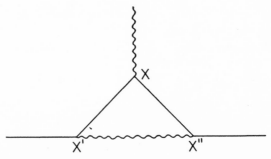

Fig. 21. This diagram represents the last term on the right-hand side of Eq. (4.76) graphically.

$$-e^3 \int dx' \, dx'' \bar{v}(x')(0 \mid A_s(x')\gamma^s\psi(x') : \bar{\psi}(x)\gamma_j\psi(x)$$

$$: \bar{\psi}(x'')\gamma^t A_t(x'') \mid 0)v(x'')$$

$$= ie^3 \int dx' \, dx'' \bar{v}(x')\gamma^s S_f(x' - x)\gamma_j S_f(x - x'')\gamma_s v(x'') \qquad (4.77)$$

$$\cdot D_f(x' - x'')$$

$$= \frac{e}{(2\pi)^8} \int dp' \, dp'' e^{ix(p'-p'')} \bar{v}(p')\Lambda_j(p', p'')v(p'')$$

where

$$\Lambda_j = -ie^2 \int \frac{dk^4}{(2\pi)^4} \gamma^s \frac{\mathbf{p}' - \mathbf{k} + m}{(p' - k)^2 - m^2} \gamma_j \frac{\mathbf{p}'' - \mathbf{k} + m}{(p'' - k)^2 - m^2} \gamma_s \frac{1}{k^2}.$$

This last form was obtained by using the Fourier transform of the propagation functions. In order to carry out the k-integrations it is convenient to combine the denominators by making use of the identity

$$\frac{1}{abc} = 2 \int_0^1 dx \int_0^x dy[ay + b(x - y) + c(1 - x)]^{-3}.$$

Such a combination of denominators produces one denominator of the form (remember $p'^2 = p''^2 = m^2$)

$$[k - p''x + (p'' - p')y]^2 - m^2 x^2 - (p' - p'')^2 y(x - y).$$

By the shift $k - p''x + (p'' - p')y \to k$ it becomes purely quadratic in k. With the abbreviation $\Delta = p' - p''$ we get

$$\Lambda_j = -ie^2 2 \int_0^1 dx \int_0^x dy \int \frac{dk}{(2\pi)^4} \frac{\gamma^s(\mathbf{q}' + m)\gamma_j(\mathbf{q}'' + m)\gamma_s}{[k^2 - m^2x^2 - \Delta^2 y(x - y)]^3} \quad (4.78)$$

where

$$q' = p'(1 - y) - p''(x - y) - k, \quad q'' = p''(1 - x + y) - p'y - k.$$

The numerator can be further simplified by applying Eq. (A1.18)

$$\gamma^s(\mathbf{q}' + m)\gamma_j(\mathbf{q}'' + m)\gamma_s = -2(\gamma_j m^2 + \mathbf{q}''\gamma_j\mathbf{q}') \\ + 4m(q_j' + q_j''). \quad (4.79)$$

We must now remember that this expression is to be taken between $\bar{v}(p')$ and $v(p'')$. Thus $\mathbf{p}''$ on the extreme right and $\mathbf{p}'$ on the extreme left can be replaced by m. Therefore, in the term $\mathbf{q}''\gamma_j\mathbf{q}'$ we shall commute all the $\mathbf{p}''$ to the right and all the $\mathbf{p}'$ to the left. Terms with p_j' and p_j'' can be evaluated by writing

$$p_j' = \tfrac{1}{2}(p_j' + p_j'') + \tfrac{1}{2}\Delta_j, \quad p_j'' = \tfrac{1}{2}(p_j' + p_j'') - \tfrac{1}{2}\Delta_j.$$

A contribution $\sim\Delta_j$ yields a current $\sim\partial/\partial x_j$ which does not interact with an electromagnetic potential obeying $A^i{}_{,i} = 0$. We may make use of the decomposition, Eq. (A1.13), to write

$$(p' + p'')_j = 2m\gamma_j + i\sigma_{j\mu}\Delta_\mu + (\mathbf{p}' - m)\gamma_j + \gamma_j(\mathbf{p}'' - m)$$

and hence we can effectively substitute

$$p_j', p_j'' \to m\gamma_j + \frac{i}{2}\sigma_{j\mu}\Delta_\mu.$$

Thus we make the replacements

$$\mathbf{p}''\gamma_j\mathbf{p}' \to \gamma_j(\Delta^2 + m^2) + i2m\sigma_{j\mu}\Delta_\mu \quad (4.80)$$

$$\mathbf{p}'\gamma_j\mathbf{p}' \to \gamma_j m^2 + mi\sigma_{j\mu}\Delta_\mu.$$

Since the denominator contains only even powers of k we can drop terms linear in k and replace $k_s k_t$ by $(1/4k^2)\delta_{st}$. With these simplifications we find

$$\mathbf{q}''\gamma_j\mathbf{q}' \to \gamma_j\left[-\frac{k^2}{2} + m^2(1 - x)^2 + \Delta^2(1 - x + y)(1 - y)\right] \\ + im\sigma\Delta[2 - 3x + x^2]$$

$$q_j' + q_j'' \to (2m\gamma + i\sigma\Delta)(1 - x)$$

and hence the numerator of Eq. (4.78) becomes

$$\gamma_j[k^2 + 4m^2(1 - x - x^2/2) - 2\Delta^2(1 - x + y)(1 - y)]$$

$$+ 2mi\sigma_{j\mu}\Delta_\mu x(1 - x).$$

If we insert this in Eq. (4.78) we see that it still contains a contribution proportional to $\bar{v}\gamma v$. To separate this term off we decompose Λ into $\Lambda(\Delta = 0) + [\Lambda(\Delta) - \Lambda(\Delta = 0)]$. The last term will be at least of order Δ and therefore proportional to derivatives of $\bar{v}\gamma v$ or $\bar{v}\sigma v$. Correspondingly, it does not contain any net charge. This decomposition can be effected with the aid of the identity

$$\frac{1}{[k^2 - m^2 x^2 - \Delta^2 y(x - y)]^3} = \frac{1}{[k^2 - m^2 x^2]^3}$$

$$- 3\Delta^2 \int_0^1 \frac{dz y(x - y)}{[k^2 - m^2 x^2 - \Delta^2 z(x - y)]^4} \qquad (4.81)$$

which we apply to those terms which do not contain Δ in the numerator. The k-integration is performed by noticing that the standard integral

$$\int \frac{dk}{[k^2 - L]^3}$$

can be written

$$- \lim_{x \to 0} \frac{(2\pi)^4}{2} \frac{\partial^2}{\partial L^2} \Delta_f(x, \sqrt{L}).$$

Using Eq. (A2.14) this becomes[2]

$$\int \frac{dk}{[k^2 - L]^3} = -\frac{i\pi^2}{2L}. \qquad (4.82)$$

Furthermore, we may deduce by differentiation

$$\int \frac{dk}{[k^2 - L]^4} = \frac{i\pi^2}{6L^2}, \qquad \int \frac{dk k^2}{[k^2 - L]^4} = -\frac{i\pi^2}{3L}. \qquad (4.83)$$

[2] It can also be integrated in k-space by observing the appropriate path around the singularities.

When all of these observations are put together we find

$$\bar{v}(p')\Lambda_j(p', p'')v(p'') = \bar{v}(p')\gamma_k v(p'') \left\{ B + \frac{\alpha}{2\pi} \frac{\Delta^2}{m^2} \int_0^1 dx \int_0^x dy \right.$$

$$\left[\frac{(1 - x + y)(1 - y)}{x^2 + y(x - y)\frac{\Delta^2}{m^2}} + \int_0^1 \frac{dz\, y(x - y)}{x^2 + zy(x - y)\frac{\Delta^2}{m^2}} \right.$$

$$\left. \left(1 - \frac{2 - 2x - x^2}{x^2 + zy(x - y)\frac{\Delta^2}{m^2}} \right) \right] \right\} - \frac{\alpha}{2\pi}\, mi\bar{v}(p')\sigma_{j\mu}v(p'')\Delta_\mu \qquad (4.84)$$

$$\left[\int_0^1 dx \int_0^x dy \, \frac{x(1 - x)}{x^2 + y(x - y)\frac{\Delta^2}{m^2}} \right]$$

where B is the infinite constant

$$B = -2ie^2 \int \frac{dk}{(2\pi)^4} \int_0^1 dx \int_0^x dy \, \frac{k^2 + 4m^2(1 - x - x^2/2)}{[k^2 - m^2 x^3]^3}. \qquad (4.85)$$

Turning to the general expression for the current Eq. (4.76) we see that the second term is to order α strictly proportional to $\bar{v}\gamma v$ and is in fact

$$\left(1 - \frac{1}{N^2} \right) e\bar{v}\gamma v.$$

The dedicated (as opposed to the interested) reader can show that in second order $1/N^2 = 1 + B$, where the B in this expression is the same as the B in Eq. (4.85). Thus, the term in Eq. (4.84) which involves B is exactly cancelled by the second term in Eq. (4.76). This was to be anticipated, since

$$e \int dx'\bar{v}(x')\gamma v(x')\Box^2 D_f{}'(x - x')$$

contains the net charge e, so that all of the remaining terms cannot contribute to the total charge.

The exact expression, Eq. (4.84), is very clumsy, so that we shall consider only the limit $\Delta^2/m^2 \ll 1$. For the other limit, $\Delta^2/m^2 \gg 1$, the reader is referred to a paper by Schwinger.[3] In our limit the integrals over x, y, and z are easily performed. However, the x integral diverges logarithmically at the lower end. This is again an infra-red divergence. If the photon is given a mass μ then the x^3 in the denominator is replaced by $x^2 + (1 - x)\mu^2/m^2$. In this case the integral remains finite. Keeping only terms which do not vanish in the limit $\mu \to 0$ we find

$$\bar{v}(p')\Lambda_j v(p'') = \bar{v}\gamma_j v \left\{ B + \frac{\alpha}{3\pi} \Delta^2 \left[\ln\left(\frac{m}{\mu}\right) - \frac{3}{8} \right] \right\}$$

$$- \frac{\alpha}{4\pi} mi\bar{v}\sigma_{j\mu}v\Delta_\mu \tag{4.86}$$

or, within the approximations listed above, we have for the whole expression

$$(1 \mid j_j(x) \mid 1) = e \int \bar{v}(x')\gamma_j v(x')\Box^2 D_f'(x - x')\, dx'$$

$$- \frac{\alpha}{2\pi}\left[\ln\left(\frac{m}{\mu}\right) - \frac{3}{8} \right]\frac{\Box^2}{m^2} \bar{v}(x)\gamma_j v(x) - \frac{\alpha}{2\pi}\frac{\partial}{\partial x_k}\frac{\bar{v}(x)\sigma_{jk}v(x)}{2m}. \tag{4.87}$$

For a wave packet which is spread out sufficiently smoothly so that we may neglect $\Box^2/m^2$ we have for the current

$$(1 \mid j_j \mid 1) = \frac{ei}{2m} \bar{\psi}(\partial_j - \partial_j)\psi$$

$$- \frac{e}{2m}\left(1 + \frac{\alpha}{2\pi}\right)\frac{\partial}{\partial x_k}\frac{\bar{v}(x)\sigma_{jk}v(x)}{2m}. \tag{4.88}$$

The significance of $(1 \mid j \mid 1)$ can be seen by introducing an external current $\delta L = \mathcal{J}(x)\mathbf{A}(x)$. Because of the field equations, Eq. (4.71), we conclude that

$$(1 \mid \delta L \mid 1) = \int dx dx' j(x) D^{ret}(x - x')(1 \mid \mathbf{j}(x) \mid 1)$$

where the particular choice of the Green's function is irrelevant so long as $\mathcal{J}$ does not produce photons. Thus, to first order in $\mathcal{J}(x)$ all the corrections are included in $(1 \mid j(x) \mid 1)$.

In an external magnetic field only the last term in Eq. (4.88) contributes to the energy if the electron is taken to be at rest. Therefore,

[3] J. Schwinger, *Phys. Rev.* **76**, 790 (1949).

the electron has a magnetic moment associated with the spin which is $(1 + \alpha/2\pi)$ Bohr magnetons. There are, of course, no corrections to the total angular momentum of the electron, so that the g factor is $(1 + \alpha/2\pi)2$. This has been measured with great precision[4] and the α correction has been established to within 1 % accuracy.

The other terms in Eq. (4.88) represent the spreading of the electron due to the recoil of the virtual photons. This we have discussed in the introduction. For a bound electron in an atom there is no infra-red divergence, since the electron is not affected by photons with wave lengths which are large compared with atomic radius. A calculation for this case[5] shows that $\ln m/\mu \sim 8$. Therefore, in a Coulomb field we get a correction to the energy of the order

$$\alpha \int \frac{e^2}{4\pi r} \Delta\rho(x) \ln \left(\frac{m}{\mu}\right)$$

As discussed in the introduction, this is the main contribution to the Lamb shift.

If we are interested in the scattering of free electrons by an external field then to lowest order in this field the relevant quantity is the matrix element of $\mathbf{j}$ between the initial and final states. One sees immediately that the expression derived above for $\mathbf{j}$ also holds here. The infra-red divergence is cancelled out in this case. This comes about because one must add to the elastic cross section the cross section for slightly inelastic processes, i.e., the emission of one photon with an energy less than ΔE, say, which also diverges for $\mu \to 0$. The two cross sections are indistinguishable experimentally and hence are added together. In this addition the infra-red divergence drops out. Thus, one finds a scattering cross section of the form

$$d\sigma = d\sigma^{(2)} \left(1 - \frac{\alpha}{3\pi} \frac{(p - p')^2}{m^2} \ln \frac{m}{\Delta E}\right)$$

where $d\sigma^{(2)}$ is the second-order cross section expressed in renormalized quantities. The p and p' are the initial and final momenta of the electron. This expression is only valid, of course, so long as $d\sigma$ is greater than zero. Our results in Section 9 lead one to expect that

[4] See J. M. Jauch and F. Rohrlich, "Theory of Photons and Electrons," p. 15, Addison-Wesley, Reading, Massachusetts, 1955, for a list of references on the experimental papers.

[5] R. Karplus, A. Klein, and J. Schwinger, *Phys. Rev.* **86**, 288 (1952).

the exact expression will go like

$$d\sigma = d\sigma^{(2)}e^{-\frac{\alpha}{3\pi}\left(\frac{p-p'}{m}\right)^2 \ln\frac{m}{\Delta E}} = d\sigma^{(2)}\left(\frac{\Delta E}{m}\right)^{\frac{\alpha}{3\pi}\left(\frac{p-p'}{m}\right)^2}. \qquad (4.89)$$

Hence, there is no scattering without photon emission.

It is important to note that for $(p - p')^2/m^2 \to 0$ the corrections to $d\sigma^{(2)}$ go to zero and the effect of the higher-order terms is only to express everything in terms of renormalized quantities. Thus, Eq. (4.89) illustrates that the total charge is correctly normalized and that for long wave lengths the electron cannot detect the detailed form of the charge distribution. We shall see below that this is the general behavior of observable quantities and is the reason that the lowest-order expressions give good agreement with experiments of normal precision.

Finally, we turn to the study of states with several physical particles present. In our general discussion of the mass spectrum we concluded that such states correspond to physical particles which are widely separated for $t \to -\infty$. Hence in this limit the states become states of non-interacting physical particles. Correspondingly, we shall assume that they are created by applying the operator

$$\lim_{\sigma \to -\infty} \int d\sigma_\mu \bar{\Psi}\gamma_\mu v$$

several times to the vacuum. The basic idea is that in the limit $t \to -\infty$ the wave packets v are sufficiently thinned out so that on the average they are infinitely remote from each other. One may ask whether a complete set of states can be generated this way. The answer depends on the presence or absence of bound states. In the electron-photon system there is no bound state, positronium being only a sharp resonance in the scattering of two or three photons. Therefore, in electrodynamics all states must, in the limit $t \to -\infty$, go over to free particle states, and they can be constructed as indicated above.[6]

Using the standard boson normalization we can write, for instance, a state with one physical electron and one physical photon in the following fashion

$$\left|\begin{matrix} e + \gamma \\ \text{in} \end{matrix}\right) = \lim_{\substack{\sigma \to -\infty \\ \sigma' \to -\infty}} \int d\sigma_\mu d\sigma_\mu' \bar{\Psi}(x)\mathbf{A}_i(x) \mid 0 \,)\gamma^\mu v(x)\partial'^\mu f_i(x')$$

[6] H. Lehmann K. Symanzik, and W. Zimmermann, *Nuovo Cimento* **2**, 425 (1955), have derived far-reaching consequences of this fact.

with $\Box^2 f = 0$ and f having positive frequencies. The subscript "in" means that the electron and the photon come in with the wave functions v and f, respectively. This state will be different from the state in which they go out with such wave functions, since scattering processes can occur. The latter state is obtained by taking $\lim_{\sigma \to \infty, \ \sigma' \to \infty}$ in the above equation. For a single particle this does not make any difference but here the difference just defines the S-matrix which we write

$$(e' + \ ' \mid S \mid e + \gamma) = \left(\begin{matrix} e' + \gamma' \\ \text{out} \end{matrix} \middle| \begin{matrix} e + \gamma \\ \text{in} \end{matrix} \right)$$

$$= \lim_{\substack{\sigma \to \infty \\ \sigma' \to -\infty}} \int d\sigma_\mu d\sigma_\mu' f_i'^*(x') [\overset{\leftrightarrow}{\partial_\mu}{}'(e' \mid A_i(x')A_k(x) \mid e) \overset{\leftrightarrow}{\partial_\mu} f_k(x)].$$

(4.90)

Using the techniques employed previously in this section we find

$$(e' + \gamma' \mid S \mid e + \gamma)$$

$$= \int dx \, dx' f_i'^*(x') f_k(x) \Box^2 \Box'^2 P(e' \mid \mathbf{A}_i(x) \mathbf{A}_k(x') \mid e)$$

(4.91)

$$= \int dx \, dx' f_i'^*(x') P(e' \mid \mathbf{j}_i(x') \mathbf{j}_k(x) \mid e) f_k(x)$$

since the commutators are either zero or do not contribute because $\Box^2 f = \Box'^2 f' = 0$.

Upon approximating the wave packets f and f' by plane waves, we can rewrite the above expression in a form similar to the propagation functions in the last section

$$(e' + \gamma' \mid S \mid e + \gamma) = \int dx \, dx' e^{ik'x'} e^{-ikx}$$

$$\sum_n \{ \theta(x - x')(e' \mid \mathbf{j}_i(x') \mid n)(n \mid \mathbf{j}_k(x) \mid e) + \theta(x' - x)(e' \mid \mathbf{j}_k(x) \mid n)$$

$$(n \mid \mathbf{j}_i(x')e) \} = i(2\pi)7\delta(p + k - p' - k')$$

$$\sum_{\underline{p_n} = \underline{p} + \underline{k}} \left[\frac{(e' \mid \mathbf{j}_i(0) \mid n)(n \mid \mathbf{j}_k(0) \mid e)}{k_0 + p_0 - p_0{}^n + i\epsilon} + \frac{(e' \mid \mathbf{j}_k(0) \mid n)(n \mid \mathbf{j}_i(0) \mid e)}{p_0 - p_0{}^n - k_0} \right]$$

where the $\mid n)$ comprise a complete set of eigenstates of the energy-momentum vector with eigenvalue p^n, and p is the energy-momentum vector of the initial electron. Since $\mid e)$ is a state with one physical electron we have, of course, $p^2 = m^2$, where m is the renormalized mass of the electron. If in the above equation we replace all quantities by ones referring to the free fields we obtain our previous second-order expression.

We shall now show that in the limit $k \to 0$, Eq. (4.91) reduces to the second-order S-matrix expressed in terms of renormalized quantities. For this purpose we shall assume, for the moment, that the photons have a rest mass μ (but we still regard k_0 as a free variable). In the laboratory system $p_0 = m$, and the next lowest state has $p_0 = m + \mu$ for $k \to 0$. Thus, in this limit, the sum over n will look like

$$(e' + \gamma' \mid S \mid e + \gamma) = i(2\pi)^7 \frac{1}{k_0} [(e \mid \mathbf{j}_i \mid e)(e \mid \mathbf{j}_k \mid e)$$

$$- (e \mid \mathbf{j}_k \mid e)(e \mid \mathbf{j}_i \mid e)] + \frac{1}{k_0 + \mu} [(e \mid \mathbf{j}_i \mid e + \gamma)(e + \gamma \mid \mathbf{j}_k \mid e)$$

$$- (e \mid \mathbf{j}_k \mid e + \gamma)(e + \gamma \mid \mathbf{j}_i \mid e)] + \cdots$$

Therefore, the first term dominates as $k \to 0$. However, we have observed before that the integral over all space of a matrix element of $\mathbf{j}$ between one-electron states is the lowest order expression with the renormalized charge. The higher order corrections come in only with higher Fourier components of $\mathbf{j}$ and make themselves felt for $k_0 \sim m$. So again the conservation of total charge guarantees that there are no radiative corrections at low energies. For $\mu \to 0$ there is an infrared divergence which, as is to be expected, cancels if one adds the cross sections for the emission of low energy photons in the scattering process.[7] These, however, go to zero for $k \to 0$ and the Thompson formula is the exact low-energy limit for Compton scattering.

Summarizing, we can say that at low energies the higher order corrections only replace the unrenormalized quantities, in the expressions of lowest order, by the renormalized ones. The corrections are usually small, since for small momentum transfers they go in second order like $1 + \alpha(\Delta p/m)^2$. For $\Delta p \gg m$ one usually finds $1 + \alpha \ln (p/m)$. The important fact is that we have found, by explicit calculation to second order, that the divergent integrals are contained in the renormalization constants Z, N, and δm, and that all observables are finite after renormalization. In the next chapter we shall discuss whether this holds in all orders and whether the theory after renormalization provides a consistent scheme.

[7] See J. M. Jauch and F. Rohrlich, "Theory of Photons and Electrons," for Addison-Wesley, Reading, Massachusetts, 1955, for a calculation of these processes.

16. Outlook

In the previous section we have seen that to second order the theory gives finite relations between observable quantities. Since the renormalization constants are infinite, assigning finite properties to the physical particles implies that the bare particles are characterized by infinite quantities. We shall now determine whether this is so in all orders in the expansion. Obviously the propagation functions D' and S' will form parts of the terms of higher order, so that these will have at least the infinities that appear in such functions. We shall, in fact, show that there are no new types of infinities as one proceeds to higher order. The infinities encountered in the second-order calculation form a complete catalog.

To give a definite meaning to "higher order" let us consider a general term of the S-matrix, Eq. (4.10). We will now explore whether or not the infinities which it contains are compensated by the renormalization constants. In a general graph of nth order there may be F_e external (incoming or outgoing) photon lines and, say, E_e external electron lines. The number of internal lines E_i and F_i is given by

$$E_e/2 + E_i = n \qquad F_e + 2F_i = n.$$

Each vertex supplies a relation between the energy-momentum vectors of the joining lines. If we consider only connected graphs then there is just one relation between the momenta of the external lines, so that there are $E_i + F_i - n + 1$ independent energy-momentum vectors over which one must integrate. For discussing the convergence of these integrals it is convenient to define the concept of a primitively divergent graph as follows: For such a graph the integrals taken over all of the virtual energy-momentum vectors diverge. However, if one integrates over all but one of the energy-momenta, then the integral converges. From this definition it follows immediately that a divergent graph is either primitively divergent or contains primitively divergent subgraphs. We may therefore discuss only primitively divergent graphs.

Looking at the momentum integrals for a general graph we see that the divergences can come from various limits in the integration. (We have seen in the last chapter some examples of the low-momen-

191

TABLE I

F_e / E_e	0	1	2	3	4
0	4	3	2	1	0
2	1	0	−1		
4	−2				

tum infra-red divergence.) In what follows we shall just be concerned with the high-momentum divergences, since the others are more or less easily fixed up. To see whether a primitive graph diverges[1] at the high-momentum limits one has only to compare the powers of k_i in the numerator and denominator. The condition for convergence is evidently that the powers of k in the denominator exceed those in the numerator, including the volume element. Since each electron line gives $(\mathbf{k} - m)^{-1}$, i.e., one power in the denominator, and a photon line gives two powers, the condition for convergence is

$$K = -E_i - 2F_i + 4(E_i + F_i - n + 1) < 0.$$

Expressing E_i and F_i by the number of external lines this becomes

$$K = -\tfrac{3}{2}E_e + F_e + 4 < 0.$$

It is important to recognize that the last form does not depend on n. Therefore, whether or not a graph is primitively divergent depends on the number of its external lines, but not on its order. New types of primitive divergent graphs do not appear as one proceeds to higher order.

In Table I we list the value of K for the various choices of (E_e, F_e). The primitively divergent graphs are contained within the heavy lines. We shall discuss them one at a time.

The $(0, 0)$ graphs without external lines give a factor common to all elements of S. This factor when squared, equals the probability that the vacuum remains a vacuum, and must therefore have an absolute value of one. Actually, the exponential will take the form $e^{i\infty}$, but this infinity is without dynamical consequences.

---

[1] The following statements hold only for primitive graphs. For integrals like

$$\int \frac{dk\ dk'}{(k^2)^5}$$

this estimate would give convergence, whereas it obviously diverges.

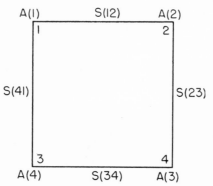

FIG. 22. This diagram illustrates the lowest order contribution.

The $(0, 1)$ is not possible because of energy-momentum conservation.

The $(0, 2)$ corresponds to graphs of the type we considered when we were discussing vacuum polarization. They give the photon propagation function and define, therefore, the charge renormalization.

The $(0, 3)$ gives zero because of charge conjugation. Such graphs lead to contributions propartional to e^{2n+1}, which must vanish since without external fields one sign of the charge cannot be distinguished from the other one.

The $(0, 4)$ converges because of gauge invariance. It yields an effective

$$\delta L \sim A^4$$

(Fig. 22 shows the lowest order contribution) and gauge invariance requires that such an addition to the Lagrangian must be expressible in terms of the field strengths. The field strengths correspond to derivatives of the graph with respect to external momenta, which render the integral convergent. One easily checks that the divergent terms actually compensate (problem 26). For slowly varying A's one finds to lowest order in e

$$\delta L = \frac{\alpha^2}{180 m^4} [5(F^{ik}F_{ik})^2 - 14(F_k{}^i F_l{}^k F_m{}^l F_i{}^m)]$$

which gives effects like the scattering of light by light or the scattering of light by a Coulomb field. This arises, for instance, from a scattering of a photon by a virtual pair produced by the Coulomb field. Formally such effects correspond to nonlinearities in the dielectric constant of the vacuum. As one can see by a simple probability argument the cross section is very small indeed, $\leq 10^{-30}$ cm^2. Since our experimental knowledge of these phenomena is meager we have just touched on them briefly.

The (2, 0) corresponds to the propagation function of the electron and defines the mass renormalization and the renormalization of the electric field.

The (2, 1) is in essence equivalent to calculating $(1 \mid \mathbf{j} \mid 1)$. The infinite charge renormalization coming from this graph is spurious and we have seen that to second order it is cancelled by the renormalization constant N of ψ. The consistency of our renormalization program requires this to happen to all orders, since the only contribution to the charge renormalization comes from (0, 2).

To show that by renormalization all infinities mentioned above are compensated by the renormalization constants in any order in e needs detailed considerations. Furthermore, since in all our formal proofs about limiting behavior and so on, we handled the infinities as if they were ordinary numbers, it is instructive to see how these techniques work out explicitly in nth order. However, we shall not attempt to detail such technical points[2] here, since first of all they do not lead to an additional understanding of the underlying physics, and secondly it is doubtful whether the scheme which is produced through these maneuvers is consistent.

Of course, one can attempt to apply renormalization to theories which contain particles other than electrons and photons. A particularly important prediction of the renormalization program is that the charge renormalization is the same for all particles and is, in fact, independent of the mass. If this were not true then one would have had to make the very implausible assumption that the bare charges of the various particles differ in just such a way that the observable charges are equal. But in a theory which contains several Fermi, fields, for example, one sees immediately[3] that the charge renormalization for the various fields is again determined by $(0 \mid \mathbf{AA} \mid 0)$, to which all the fields contribute. All charges are multiplied by the same factor $\sqrt{Z}$, so that equal observable charges mean equal bare charges.

Application of renormalization to other types of couplings does not

[2] See J. M. Jauch and F. Rohrlich, "Theory of Photons and Electrons," Addison-Wesley, Reading, Massachusetts, 1955, and the original literature quoted there.

[3] One might worry about possible exchange contributions via the exclusion principle, but since the virtual pairs occupy infinitely many states, the exclusion principle of one state is negligible.

always lead to the elimination of all infinities. For instance, if the coupling were to involve the electric field strength each vertex would give additional powers of k in the denominator. As a consequence, the condition for convergence would not be independent of the order of the term in the S-matrix n. This means that for any value of E_e and F_e one gets primitively divergent contributions as soon as one goes to sufficiently high orders. These cannot, of course, be absorbed by a finite number of constants. Electromagnetic couplings for particles with spin greater than $\frac{1}{2}$ are also of this type. One may consider the fact that there are no charged particles which are in the usual sense elementary and have spin greater than $\frac{1}{2}$, an indication that electric interactions have to be renormalizable.

It may have occurred to the reader by this point to wonder whether the renormalization program solves the classical problems of electromagnetic theory like the self stress of the electron. We have seen (problem 5) that from $T^{ik}_{,i} = 0$ and the assumption that in the rest system $T_{ik}(x)$ is time-independent it follows that in this system the self stress of the electron vanishes. In classical electrodynamics the condition $T^{ik}_{,i} = 0$ is not met, since the Lorentz-Maxwell equations are not satisfied inside the electron. Nonelectromagnetic forces are required to keep the electron from exploding, and they will contribute to the self stress. It seems that the renormalization program has resolved this question, since it was not necessary to introduce other fields which keep the electron together to get finite observable answers (at least in perturbation theory). The premise leading to a vanishing self stress is satisfied. An explicit calculation shows that a divergent and hence indeterminate expression is obtained for the self stress, although invariance arguments suggest that this term must be set equal to zero. Hence, inasmuch as renormalization defines a consistent scheme, it has resolved the problem of self stress. However, as we shall show now, the consistency of the renormalization program is a rather dubious affair, and in order to make the scheme consistent, one is led to the introduction of other (unrealistic) fields which cancel the infinities. Such fields contribute to the self stress and one is left in the same boat with the classical problem.

Our formulation of renormalization theory involves infinite constants (at least in second order) in the Lagrangian and therefore in all of the basic equations. The finite results appear only at the end as the differences of infinite terms. Furthermore, all of the formal proofs which are necessary for the consistency of the theory, like the unitarity of the S-matrix, also involve manipulations with infinite quantities. We may well ask whether these maneuvers are fallacious or whether they can be specified in a better way.

Toward these questions two basic attitudes have been taken. Either the attempt has been made to make the infinities finite by using a cutoff procedure and then defining the theory as the limit at which the cutoff goes to infinity[4] or one has tried to ignore the fact that the basic equations contain infinite quantities and hoped that the finite observable results which come out of the renormalization prescription define a consistent scheme. We shall now review the difficulties which each of these possibilities encounters.

A cutoff procedure can be formulated in a relativistic or nonrelativistic way. In the latter case one replaces $L'(x)$ by

$$\int dy^3 \, dy'^3 \, dy''^3 \bar{\psi}(t, \underline{y}) \gamma^k \psi(t, \underline{y}') \mathbf{A}_k(t, \underline{y}'') f(\underline{y}, \underline{y}', \underline{y}'', x). \qquad (4.92)$$

The coupled field problem generated by this Lagrangian can be treated with the same methods that we have used throughout, except that the resulting theory is not Lorentz invariant. By a suitable choice of f one can get rid of all infinities which occur in the power series expansion. However, since Lorentz invariance is such a powerful tool for determining the general form of expressions this approach has not attracted many investigators. Therefore, the convergence behavior of the power series is not known, although there are reasons for believing that the radius of convergence is larger than zero here. One is tempted to generalize Eq. (4.92) in such a way that the form factor f is an invariant function of all four coordinates. In this case the theory does, in fact, appear to be Lorentz invariant.

The quantization of such a theory, however, leads to grave difficulties. The formal reason is that $\mathbf{L}'(x)$ for this theory does not depend upon the field variables on one spacelike surface alone. Physically, the difficulties are quite analogous to those involved in the consideration of a rigid body of finite extent in the special theory of relativity. In a relativistic field theory with a point interaction the physical particle is, to be sure, an object of finite extent, but it does not act like a rigid body. A signal cannot be transmitted through it with a velocity greater than the velocity of light. In a theory with a form factor the bare particle acts like a rigid body of finite size rather than like a point particle. That is to say, $\mathbf{A}(x)$ can emit photons

---

[4] In momentum space.

at points which are not on the future light cone of x. Such behavior leads to the transmission of signals with a velocity greater than 1. It therefore violates the proper order of cause and effect, for in some Lorentz frames, photons will be created at times earlier than the electron creation time; that is, the Coulomb field will be formed before the electron is created. Although one such event may take place over microscopic regions only, by suitably iterating it, noncausalty can spread over macroscopic regions.

These difficulties lead to the consideration of another cutoff procedure, which keeps the relativistic invariance but which is not, unfortunately, meaningful physically. It consists of introducing an indefinite metric in Hilbert space and associating negative probabilities with some auxiliary fields which are coupled to the system of interest. In this case the spectral function $\Pi(a)$ which we introduced in Section 14 need not be taken as positive definite and one can cancel out the δ-functions which occur in the propagation functions and the infinities on the light cones. The masses of these pathological particles are to be taken as very large, so that they cannot be produced in a real process at low energies. As long as they do not show up in the probability balance of a real process the S-matrix will be unitary in the usual sense. Of course, there will be other meaningless predictions of the theory, like negative square fluctuations, but these will only appear at high energies or small distances. Hence, one can say that this method provides a mathematically well-defined scheme which is, within a limited domain, physically acceptable.

Finally, one can add a cutoff prescription without incorporating it into the basic equations. Such recipes can only be regarded as definitions of otherwise ambiguous expressions, like the definition of an improper integral.

In spite of all shortcomings, the cutoff methods may serve to give the theory some mathematical precision before the limit is taken. Thus one may consider a sequence of theories characterized by a cutoff L and regard the original parameters, like e_0, of the theory as being functions of L also, in such a way that in the limit the renormalized quantities can be matched with the experimental values

$$\frac{1}{137} = \frac{e^2}{4\pi} = \lim_{L \to \infty} \frac{e_0^2(L)}{4\pi} Z(L, e_0(L)). \tag{4.93}$$

Since Z presumably goes to zero for $L \to \infty$ this means that one has to let e_0 go to infinity in such a way that $e_0^2 Z$ stays finite. However, it is not at all certain that an increase in e_0 results in an increase of e.

Increasing e_0 will also enhance the vacuum polarization, which counteracts the increase in the bare charge. In fact, take, as an example, an ordinary dielectric in which our $1/Z$ corresponds to the static dielectric constant ϵ. Neglecting dipole interactions we have

$$\epsilon = 1 + e_0^2 \frac{v}{V} N$$

where v is the volume of the atom, V the volume of the dielectric, and N the number of atoms. In the terminology of field theory one has

$$e^2 = \frac{e_0^2}{1 + e_0^2 \frac{v}{V} N}$$

which is always less than the saturation value $V/(vN)$, regardless of the value of e_0. This form is similar to our second order formula, in which $(v/V)N$ is replaced by a logarithmically divergent quantity, which corresponds to an infinity of charged particles for arbitrarily high energies. However, for $N \to \infty$, with v/V fixed, the above upper limit of e^2 always goes to zero. Assigning a finite value to e implies complex values for e_0, which will ruin the consistency of the theory. There is a nonrelativistic model[5] of a field theory which shows exactly this behavior. By using a cutoff prescription it appears that in quantum electrodynamics too the observable charge goes to zero in this limit.[6] Thus, the definition of the renormalized theory in terms of a cutoff procedure does not seem very promising.

The alternative approach hinges on the question of whether all quantities, or just the coefficients in the expansion in powers of e, are finite after renormalization. In other words, does the renormalized power series expansion converge? To study this problem one might try to obtain an upper limit for the spectral function $\Pi(a)$ by inserting into the sum

$$\sum_n | (0 | \mathbf{j} | n) |^2$$

only a certain number of the states $| n)$, those for which $(0 | \mathbf{j} | n)$ is calculable. For instance, if we take just the states with n photons (n being an odd number), then to lowest order in α in the high energy

[5] T. D. Lee, *Phys. Rev.* **95**, 1329 (1954).

[6] See L. Landau, in "Niels Bohr and The Development of Physics" (W. Pauli, ed.), Pergamon Press, New York, 1955.

limit one has[7]

$$| (0 \mid \mathbf{j} \mid n) |^2 \simeq \alpha^n \frac{\ln (a)^{2n}}{n!}$$

similar to the result of the classical current in Section 9. Here, a is the total mass of the state $\mid n)$.

How the exact expression behaves is unknown, but intuitively one might expect that for high energies it will be larger than the one of lowest order, since at high energies the stronger bare charge comes into play. If this is so, then observable quantities like

$$D_f'(k) = \int_{9\mu^2}^{\infty} \frac{da \Pi(a)}{-k^2 + a^2} = \int_{9\mu^2}^{\infty} \frac{da}{a^2} \left(\frac{a}{m}\right)^{\alpha \ln (a/m)}$$

do not exist, since

$$\sum_n \alpha^n \int_{9\mu^2}^{\infty} \frac{da}{a^2} \frac{\ln (a/m)^{2n}}{n!}$$

diverges at the upper end. The exact expression for the integrand will be even bigger if the above conjecture is correct. Nonetheless, the expansion in powers of the integral over a converges for each term, but yields a sum which diverges like $\Sigma \, \alpha^n n!$. Such a divergence of the expansion has indeed been found in a simplified model[8] where the convergence behavior of the renormalized power series could be determined. In this model the essential simplification over electrodynamics is that the Fermi fields are replaced by Bose fields.

Although all of these speculations do not prove that renormalized quantum electrodynamics does not provide a consistent scheme they do suggest it very strongly. Nevertheless, owing to the logarithmic divergence of the theory, the breakdown is to be expected at very high frequencies or very small distances. For instance, if a formula like

$$e^2 = \frac{e_0^2}{1 + \frac{e_0^2}{4\pi} \ln \left(\frac{L}{m}\right)}$$

holds, then L can be as large as em^{137} before inconsistencies will appear. However, at much lower energies, namely, $\sim 2m.137$, mesons can be

---

[7] See M. Källen, Rept. CERN Conference, Geneva, 1956.

[8] See C. Hurst, *Proc. Cambridge Phil. Soc.* **48**, 625 (1952); W. Thirring, *Helv. Phys. Acta* **26**, 33 (1953); and A. Petermann, *Arch. sci. (Geneva)* **6**, 5 (1953).

created, so that a theory of electrons and photons alone does not tell the whole story. Thus, the validity of quantum electrodynamics is probably not curtailed primarily by the mathematical shortcomings of renormalization theory, because it very likely loses its physical meaning before such limitations make themselves manifest. We have a similar situation in classical electrodynamics, where the mathematical breakdown occurs at the classical electron radius, while in reality the theory loses its validity at the electron Compton wave length. Nevertheless, the inconsistency of a field theory which summarizes the basic laws of relativity and quantum mechanics shows that these laws must eventually break down and at small distances our present concepts will have to be modified. How this can be done is anyone's guess, and the solution will probably entail a theory which embodies all of the elementary particles and their interactions together.

APPENDIXES

Appendix I

The formal transformation properties of fields can be studied without reference to the quantization process. They are less familiar for the Dirac field than for the electromagnetic field. We shall therefore summarize and collect the relevant properties of the Dirac equation when viewed as a classical field rather than as the quantum mechanical description of a single particle. Whereas the field equations for Bose fields are more conveniently written as second-order equations, the first-order form is the more useful one for Fermi fields. Hence we begin with the Dirac equation

$$(\gamma^k(i\partial_k - eA_k(x)) - m)\psi(x) = 0 \qquad (A1.1)$$

where the numerical matrices γ, which act on the components of ψ to produce linear combinations, obey the commutation relations

$$\gamma^i\gamma^k + \gamma^k\gamma^i = 2g^{ik}. \qquad (A1.2)$$

Since we are not considering a Majorana field, which is constrained to be real, we do not impose a reality condition on the γ's. Thus, we are free to perform linear transformations with complex coefficients in spin space. In particular the Hermitian conjugate γ's themselves satisfy these commutation rules and are also a representation of the Dirac algebra. Therefore, a Hermitian[1] matrix β must exist with the property

$$\beta^{-1}\gamma^\dagger\beta = \gamma. \qquad (A1.3)$$

We define

$$\bar{\psi} = \psi^\dagger\beta \qquad (A1.4)$$

and write the equation conjugate to Eq. (A1.1) as

$$\bar{\psi}(x)(\gamma^k(i\partial_k + eA_k(x)) + m) = 0. \qquad (A1.5)$$

As one can see, $\bar{\psi}\psi$ and $\bar{\psi}\gamma\psi$ are Hermitian.[2] The Lorentz invariance

---

[1] By considering the Hermitian conjugate of the equation $\beta^\dagger\gamma\beta^{-1\dagger} = \gamma^\dagger$ it follows that $\beta^\dagger = C\beta$ with $CC^\dagger = 1$. However, $C^{1/2}\beta$ is Hermitian and satisfies Eq. (A1.3).

[2] Hermitian, but not real, since the ψ operators are in Hilbert space.

of this formalism can be achieved by postulating that a Lorentz transformation

$$x_i \rightarrow a_{ik}x^k$$

with

$$a_{ik}a^{il} = \delta_k{}^l \tag{A1.6}$$

induces a linear transformation S in the spin space, $\psi \rightarrow S\psi$, where S has the property

$$S^{-1}\gamma_i S = a_{ik}\gamma^k. \tag{A1.7}$$

The matrix S certainly exists, since Eq. (A1.6) implies that $\gamma_i' = a_{ik}\gamma^k$ also satisfies the commutation relations, Eq. (A1.2).

From the Hermitian conjugate equation to Eq. (A1.7) we learn,[3] using $a^\dagger_{ik} = a_{ik}$, that

$$S^\dagger = \beta S^{-1}\beta^{-1} \tag{A1.8}$$

from which it follows that $\bar{\psi} \rightarrow \bar{\psi}S^{-1}$. Thus $\bar{\psi}\psi$ is a scalar, $\bar{\psi}\gamma\psi$ a vector, and Eqs. (A1.1) and (A1.5) have the same form in the new system as in the old. Note that S is not unitary but that Eq. (A1.8) is the generalized unitarity relation with respect to the indefinite metric β. For the infinitesimal Lorentz transformations S is given as

$$S = 1 + \frac{i}{4}e^{ik}\sigma_{ik} \quad \text{with} \quad \sigma^{ik} = \frac{\gamma^i\gamma^k - \gamma^k\gamma^i}{2i}. \tag{A1.9}$$

One may readily show that this S, because of the commutation relations, Eq. (A1.2), has the property of Eq. (A1.7) if one drops the quadratic terms in a. This relation for infinitesimal a can be integrated into an exponential form for finite a, but we will not use this explicitly. Since the transposed γ's also form a representation of the Dirac algebra a matrix C exists such that

$$C\gamma^\dagger C^{-1} = -\gamma \tag{A1.10}$$

where one can prove[4] that $C^\dagger = -C$.

$$\psi' = C\bar{\psi}$$

---

[3] Here also one can only have $S^\dagger = C\beta S^{-1}\beta^{-1}$ with $C^\dagger = C$, since $SC^{-1/2}$ satisfies Eqs. (A1.7) and (A1.8).

[4] It is clear that $C^T = \pm C$. Thus, one has $\sigma_{ik}C = \mp(\sigma_{ik}C)^T$ and $\gamma_i C = \mp(\gamma_i C)^T$. There are, however, only six antisymmetric matrices in the algebra.

satisfies

$$(\gamma^k(i\partial_k + eA_k) - m)\psi' = 0 \tag{A1.11}$$

which is the same as Eq. (A1.1) except for a change in the sign of the charge. This suggests that ψ' and $\bar{\psi}' = -\psi C^{-1}$ describe particles of opposite charge to those described by ψ and $\bar{\psi}$. If one does not wish to single out any special sign of the charge, then the observable quantities must be invariant under "charge conjugation."

$$\psi \to \psi', \qquad \bar{\psi} \to \bar{\psi}', \qquad e \to -e. \tag{A1.12}$$

This program can only be performed within the framework of field quantization, since we have the relations

$$\bar{\psi}'\psi' = -\psi\bar{\psi} \quad \text{and} \quad \bar{\psi}'\gamma\psi' = \psi\gamma^T\bar{\psi}.$$

In a theory in which ψ and $\bar{\psi}$ commute, $T_i{}^i = m\bar{\psi}\psi$ and the current $e\bar{\psi}\gamma\psi$ are not charge symmetric.

According to the Dirac equation

$$\psi = \frac{1}{m}\gamma^k(i\partial_k - eA_k)\psi$$

one can split the current into a part which is the anaglog of the current due to charged scalar particles and a part arising from the magnetic moment[5]

$$e\bar{\psi}\gamma_k\psi = \frac{e}{2m}\bar{\psi}(i\partial_k - eA_k - i\overleftarrow{\partial}_k - eA_k)\psi - \frac{e}{2m}\partial^i\bar{\psi}\sigma_{kj}\psi \tag{A1.13}$$

($\overleftarrow{\partial}$ operates to the left on $\bar{\psi}$). Each part of Eq. (A1.13) separately satisfies the continuity equation. The influence of the magnetic moment on the field equations can best be seen by multiplying Eq. (A1.1) from the left with $(\gamma^k(i\partial_k - eA_k) + m)$. One then obtains

$$((i\partial_k - eA_k)(i\partial^k - eA^k) - m^2)\psi = \frac{e}{2}f^{kj}\sigma_{kj}\psi$$

where $f_{ik} = A_{i,k} - A_{k,i}$. A scalar particle satisfies the same equation with $\sigma_{kj} = 0$.

The trace of an odd number of γ matrices vanishes. This is most easily proved with the help of the matrix

[5] See W. Pauli, *in* "Handbuch der Physik" (S. Fluegge, ed.), Vol. 5, Part I. Springer, Berlin, 1958.

$$\gamma_5 = \gamma_0\gamma_1\gamma_2\gamma_3 \qquad \gamma_5^2 = -1 \qquad\qquad (A1.14)$$

which obviously anticommutes with all four γ's. From the fundamental property of the trace

$$\text{Tr}\,(AB) = \text{Tr}\,(BA) \qquad\qquad (A1.15)$$

we learn

$$\text{Tr}\,(\gamma_{\alpha_1} \cdots \gamma_{\alpha_{2n+1}}) = \text{Tr}\,(\gamma_5\gamma_{\alpha_1} \cdots \gamma_{\alpha_{2n+1}}\gamma_5)$$
$$= -\text{Tr}\,(\gamma_{\alpha_1} \cdots \gamma_{\alpha_{2n+1}}).$$

Equation (A1.2) implies that

$$\text{Tr}\,(\gamma_i\gamma_k) = 4\delta_{ik}$$

since the irreducible representation of the γ's is in terms of 4×4 matrices, implying that the trace of the unit matrix is 4. The trace of products of an arbitrary even number, $2n$, of γ's or γ invariants $\mathbf{A}_1 \cdots \mathbf{A}_{2n}$, can be found by commuting A_1 to the right and using the commutation relation $\mathbf{AB} = 2(AB) - \mathbf{BA}$ and Eq. (A1.15) to reduce to the case of $2n - 2$

$$\text{Tr}\,(\mathbf{A}_1 \cdots \mathbf{A}_{2n}) = (A_1A_2)\,\text{Tr}\,(\mathbf{A}_3 \cdots \mathbf{A}_n) - (A_1A_3)\,\text{Tr}\,(\mathbf{A}_2\mathbf{A}_4 \cdots \mathbf{A}_{2n})$$
$$+ \cdots + (A_1A_{2n})\,\text{Tr}\,(\mathbf{A}_2 \cdots \mathbf{A}_{2n-1}).$$

It follows by induction from Eq. (A1.16) that

$$\text{Tr}\,(\mathbf{A}_1 \cdots \mathbf{A}_n) = 4 \sum_P (-)^P (A_{\alpha_1}A_{\alpha_2}) \cdots (A_{\alpha_{2n-1}}A_{\alpha_{2n}}). \quad (A1.17)$$

Here $\alpha_1 \cdots \alpha_{2n}$ constitute a permutation of the numbers $1 \cdots 2n$ and the sum runs over all permutations P which contribute distinct terms to Eq. (A1.17). Each term in the sum is multiplied by $(-)^P$, the sign of the permutation. The sum in Eq. (A1.17) involves $1 \cdot 3 \cdot 5 \cdots (2n - 1) = (2n)!/2^n n!$ terms.[6] Two further relations which can be proved by induction using the commutation rules are

$$\gamma_k\mathbf{A}_1 \cdots \mathbf{A}_{2n+1}\gamma^k = -2\mathbf{A}_{2n+1} \cdots \mathbf{A}_1$$
$$\gamma_k\mathbf{A}_1 \cdots \mathbf{A}_{2n}\gamma^k = 2(\mathbf{A}_{2n}\mathbf{A}_1 \cdots \mathbf{A}_{2n-1} + \mathbf{A}_{2n-1} \cdots \mathbf{A}_1\mathbf{A}_{2n}). \qquad (A1.18)$$

Expressions of the form $\gamma_k M\gamma^k$ arise frequently in quantum electrodynamics when polarization directions of the photons are summed over. The relations above allow us to simplify terms of this form.

[6] Of the $(2n)!$ permutations $n!$ differ only by the sequence of pairs and 2^n only by the order of the factors in the bracket.

Appendix II

The most powerful tools for solving the partial differential equations arising in field theory are the Green's functions. We shall list here the properties of these and some related functions which occur in connection with the relativistic equations.

Because of the linearity of the wave equation, solutions of the inhomogeneous equation

$$(\Box^2 + m^2)f(x) = g(x) \tag{A2.1}$$

can be built up by superposing solutions of Eq. (A2.1) for a point source; i.e.,

$$(\Box^2 + m^2)\bar{\Delta}(x) = \delta(x) \tag{A2.2}$$

as follows

$$f(x) = \int dx' g(x')\bar{\Delta}(x - x'). \tag{A2.3}$$

The Fourier representation of the Green's function $\bar{\Delta}$ can be found by noting the Fourier representation of the δ function, Eq. (N.5), and recognizing that $\Box^2 + m^2$ becomes $-k^2 + m^2$ in momentum space

$$\bar{\Delta}(x) = (2\pi)^{-4} \int dk \, \frac{e^{-ikx}}{- k^2 + m^2}. \tag{A2.4}$$

Since the integrand of Eq. (A2.4) contains a pole for $k_0 = \pm \sqrt{k^2 + m^2}$, Eq. (A2.4) is not completely defined unless one specifies how the integration is to be taken around the poles. We now define the function $\bar{\Delta}$ by postulating that the principle part of the k_0 integration over the singularities is to be taken. If one chooses another integration path in the complex plane then one generates a different Green's function. This freedom corresponds to the fact that the Green's functions are only defined to within a solution of the homogeneous equation. Contributions from the poles satisfy $k^2 = m^2$ and are therefore solutions of the homogeneous equation. We shall now define three other Green's functions which are characterized by the integration paths shown in Fig. A2.1.

The relations below are clearly satisfied among the various Green's

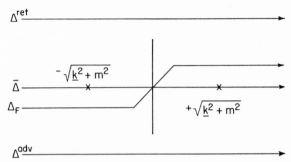

FIG. A2.1. This diagram shows the integration paths which define the various Green's functions.

functions

$$\bar{\Delta} = \tfrac{1}{2}(\Delta^{\text{ret}} + \Delta^{\text{adv}}) \qquad \bar{\Delta}(x) = \bar{\Delta}(-x)$$

$$\Delta^{\text{ret}}(x) = \Delta^{\text{adv}}(-x) \qquad\qquad \bar{\Delta}^\dagger = \bar{\Delta} \qquad\qquad \text{(A2.5)}$$

$$\Delta^{\text{ret}\dagger} = \Delta^{\text{ret}} \qquad\qquad \Delta^{\text{adv}\dagger} = \Delta^{\text{adv}}.$$

The differences between two solutions of the inhomogeneous equation is a solution of the homogeneous equation. We define special solutions of the homogeneous equation with particular invariance properties by the paths in the complex plane shown in Fig. A2.2.

We have the relations[1]

$$\Delta = \Delta^+ + \Delta^- \qquad \Delta^1 = \Delta^+ - \Delta^-$$

$$\Delta^{\text{ret}} = \bar{\Delta} + \frac{\Delta}{2} \qquad \Delta^{\text{adv}} = \bar{\Delta} - \frac{\Delta}{2} \qquad \Delta_f = \bar{\Delta} + \frac{\Delta^1}{2} \qquad \text{(A2.6)}$$

$$\Delta^+(-x) = -\Delta^-(x) \qquad \Delta^1(x) = \Delta^1(-x) \qquad \Delta(x) = -\Delta(-x)$$

$$(\Delta)^\dagger = \Delta \qquad\qquad (\Delta^1)^\dagger = -\Delta^1 \qquad (\Delta^-)^\dagger = \Delta^+.$$

For $x^0 < 0 (>0)$ one can, because of the factor $e^{-ik^0x^0}$, close the integration paths in Fig. A2.1 with an infinite semicircle above (or below) the real axis. In this way one obtains the following relations

$$\Delta^{\text{ret}} = 2\theta(x^0)\bar{\Delta}(x) \qquad \Delta^{\text{adv}} = 2\theta(-x^0)\bar{\Delta}(x)$$

$$\Delta(x) = 2\epsilon(x^0)\bar{\Delta}(x) \qquad \Delta_f(x) = \theta(x^0)\Delta^+(x) - \theta(-x^0)\Delta^-(x). \qquad \text{(A2.7)}$$

The analogy between the way one handles expressions of the form

[1] All the Δ's have an integral representation, Eq. (A2.4), with the path taken clockwise.

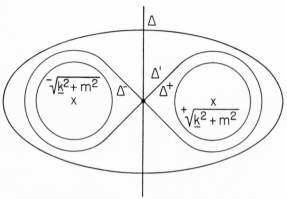

FɪG. A2.2. In this diagram the integration paths defining the various solutions of the homogeneous equation are shown.

$\delta(f(x))$ and evaluates the residue of $f^{-1}(x)$, Eq. (N.1), enables us to express solutions of the homogeneous equation in the form

$$(\Delta^1, \Delta, \Delta^+, \Delta^-) = i(2\pi)^{-3} \int dk e^{-ikx} \delta(k^2 - m^2)$$

$$(1, \epsilon(k^0), \theta(k^0), -\theta(-k^0)).$$

(A2.8)

If one remains within the continuous proper Lorentz group so that one does not consider time reversal, then the Δ functions are invariant,[2] as is clear from the forms (A2.4) and (A2.8). The functions depend, therefore, only on the four-dimensional distance x^2 and on the sign of the time $\epsilon(x^0)$. On symmetry grounds, in Eq. (A2.8) one must have $\Delta = 0$ for $x^0 = 0$. Thus, the invariant function disappears in the whole region in which $x^2 < 0$. Further, one may see from Eq. (A2.8) and

$$\int_{-\infty}^{\infty} |k_0| \, dk_0 \delta(k_0^2 - \underline{k}^2 - m^2) = 1$$

that

$$\left(\frac{\partial}{\partial x^0} \Delta^1, \Delta, \Delta^+, \Delta^-\right)_{x^0=0} = \left(0, \delta(x), \frac{\delta(x)}{2}, \frac{\delta(x)}{2}\right)$$ (A2.9)

[2] One often encounters the erroneous view that Lorentz invariance means the equality between space and time. It is almost impossible to imagine a greater difference than the one which the sign of the metric produces between space and timelike directions. Lorentz invariance just means that one timelike direction is as good as any other timelike direction.

or, in invariant integral form

$$\int_{x'_{\subset \sigma}} d\sigma_k f(x) \partial^k \Delta(x - x') = f(x') \qquad (A2.10)$$

for any f.

Since Δ is an invariant function which vanishes outside the light cone and is, furthermore, an odd function, so that we may define $\Delta(0) = 0$, we have, for a spacelike σ

$$\int_{x'_{\subset \sigma}} d\sigma_k f(x) \Delta(x - x') = \int d\sigma_k f(x) \partial^m \partial^n \Delta(x - x') = 0. \qquad (A2.11)$$

We shall now see that, as a consequence of Eqs. (A2.10) and (A2.11), Δ has the meaning of the solution to the Cauchy initial value problem; i.e., we are given a solution of the homogeneous equation $(\square^2 + m^2)f(x) = 0$ everywhere on a spacelike surface along with its derivative in the direction of the surface normal. We then seek the value of the function at an arbitrary space-time point x. The solution to this problem is

$$f(x) = \int d\sigma_k'(\Delta(x - x')\partial'^k f(x') - f(x')\partial'^k \Delta(x - x')). \qquad (A2.12)$$

Obviously, Eq. (A2.12) is a solution of the homogeneous equation and because of Eqs. (A2.10) and (A2.11) $f(x)$ and its normal derivative take on the prescribed values. The uniqueness follows from the fact that if f and $\partial/\partial t f$ are zero for all x at a certain time then the equation $(\square^2 + m^2)f = 0$ implies that f must be zero everywhere.

On evaluating the integrals over dk for the Green's functions to get explicit expressions one soon learns that the integrals do not converge. However, if we examine the expression for Δ^+ we can see that the integral converges if we subtract from x an imaginary vector $i\eta$ which is in the upper light cone. Thus Δ^+ will be defined as the limit of

$$(2\pi)^{-3} \int_{k_0 > 0} dk e^{-ik(x - i\eta)} \delta(k^2 - m^2)$$

for $\eta \to 0$. From invariance arguments this integral must depend only on $\lambda^2 = (x - i\eta)^2 = x^2 - \eta^2 - 2i\eta x$; $t > 0$ or $t < 0$ corresponds to the lower or upper half plane of this variable, respectively. Since the integral converges uniformly for η in the upper half light cone and it is $\neq 0$ we conclude that it is analytic in this variable save for the positive real axis. Therefore, Δ^+, being the limit for $\eta \to 0$, will be the boundary value of an analytic function. To determine Δ^+ we compute for x and η in the direction of k_0

$$\int \frac{dk}{(2\pi)^3} e^{-ik_0(t-i\eta)} \delta(k^2 - m^2) = (2\pi)^2 \int_m^\infty dk_0 \sqrt{k_0^2 - m^2} \, e^{-ik_0(t-i\eta)}$$

$$= \frac{m^2}{8\pi} \frac{H_1^{(1)}(m(t-i\eta))}{m(t-i\eta)} .$$

Because of the above-mentioned invariance properties we generally must have

$$\Delta^+(x) = \frac{m^2}{8\pi} \lim_{\eta \to 0} \frac{H_1^{(1)}(m\lambda)}{m\lambda} .$$

For working out the limit we must remember that

$$\lim_{\alpha \to 0} \text{Re} \, \frac{-i}{x - i\alpha} = \pm\pi\delta(x)$$

depending on whether α approaches zero from the positive or negative real axis. Splitting off the singular part we have[3]

$$\Delta(x) = 2 \, \text{Re} \, \Delta^+(x) = \epsilon(x) \left(\frac{\delta(x^2)}{2\pi} - \theta(x^2) \frac{m^2}{4\pi} \frac{J_1(m\sqrt{x^2})}{m\sqrt{x^2}} \right)$$

$$\Delta^1(x) = 2 \, \text{Im} \, \Delta^+(x) = \frac{im^2}{4\pi} \, \text{Im} \, \frac{H_{(1)}^1(m\sqrt{x^2})}{m\sqrt{x^2}} .$$

$$(A2.13)$$

Because of the relations (A2.5), (A2.6), and (A2.7), all of the other functions can be expressed in terms of these. For world intervals λ smaller than the Compton wave length we may develop the power series

$$\Delta(x) = \left[\frac{\delta(x^2)}{2\pi} + \frac{\theta(x^2)}{2\pi} \left(\frac{m^2}{4} + x^2 \frac{m^4}{32} + \cdots \right) \right] \epsilon(x)$$

$$\Delta^1(x) = \frac{i}{4\pi^2} \left[-\frac{2}{x^2} + m^2 \ln\left(\frac{\gamma}{2}\right) m\lambda - \frac{m^2}{2} + \cdots \right]$$

$$(A2.14)$$

with γ representing Euler's constant.

For large distances Δ^1 and $\bar{\Delta}$ oscillate in the timelike directions. For spacelike directions Δ^1 falls off like an exponential e^{-mr} and Δ van-

---

[3] It is interesting to check that these functions obey the Klein-Gordon equation without using the Fourier representation. See W. Thirring, *Acta Phys. Austriaca* **4**, 125 (1950).

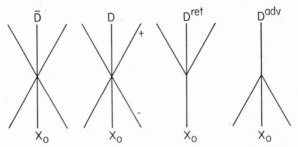

FIG. A2.3. These diagrams give the D-functions schematically.

ishes. In the special case in which $m = 0$ we denote the Δ–function by D and then we have

$$(\bar{D}, D, D^{\text{ret}}, D^{\text{adv}}) = \frac{\delta(x^2)}{2\pi}\left[\frac{1}{2}, \epsilon(x^0), \theta(x^0), \theta(-x^0)\right] \quad (\text{A2.15})$$

shown schematically in Fig. A2.3.

For the Dirac equation in the absence of an external field $(\partial - m)\psi = 0$ where $\partial = i\gamma_k\partial^k$ it is easy to specify the corresponding functions. Since $(\partial - m)(\partial + m) = -\Box^2 - m^2$ the functions[4] (A2, 16)

$$(\bar{S}, S, S^{\text{ret}}, S^{\text{adv}}, S_f, S^1, S^+, S^-)$$

$$= -(\partial + m)(\bar{\Delta}, \Delta, \Delta^{\text{ret}}, \Delta^{\text{adv}}, \Delta_f, \Delta^1, \Delta^+, \Delta^-)$$

have the same role for the Dirac equation[5] as the Δ's have for the Klein-Gordon equation, Eq. (A2.2).

In momentum space the S-functions can be written

$$S = (2\pi)^{-4}\int dp e^{-ipx}\frac{\mathbf{p} + m}{p^2 - m^2}$$

or

$$S = (2\pi)^{-4}\int dp e^{-ipx}(\mathbf{p} - m)^{-1} \quad (\text{A.217})$$

$(\mathbf{p} = \gamma^k p_k)$. The integration paths are the same as in the corresponding case of the Δ's. Since the Dirac equation with an external field $(\partial - m)\psi = e\gamma A\psi$ is a homogeneous equation we cannot solve it with

---

[4] The reader may discover which of the relations, Eq. (A2.5), (A2.6), or (A2.7), hold as well for the S-functions.

[5] Observe that $(\partial - m)_{x\beta}\bar{S}_{\beta\gamma} = \delta(x)\delta_{\alpha\gamma}$. Hence, in the spin $\frac{1}{2}$ case, the δ functions mean a δ in spin space as well.

a Green's function, but we may transform it into an integral equation

$$\psi(x) = \int dx' S^{\text{ret}}(x - x') e\gamma A(x')\psi(x')$$

which can then be solved using a Neumann series

$$\psi = \sum_i \psi^i \qquad \psi^{i+1} = \int S^{\text{ret}} e\gamma A \psi^i \qquad (A2.18)$$

with ψ^0 a solution to the vacuum equation $(A = 0)$.

S generates the solution to the Cauchy problem. It has the property that

$$\int_{x \subset \sigma'} d\sigma_k S(x - x')\gamma^k f(x')$$

$$= \int d\sigma_k'(-i\gamma^j\gamma^k\partial_j - m\gamma^k)[\Delta(x - x')f(x')]$$

$$= -i \int d\sigma_k'\partial^k[\Delta(x - x')f(x')] \qquad (A2.19)$$

$$- \frac{i}{2} \int d\sigma_k'(\gamma^j\gamma^k\partial_j - \gamma^k\gamma^j\partial_j)[\Delta(x - x')f(x')]$$

$$= -if(x).$$

Here we have used Eq. (A2.11) and the theorem (N.6), as a consequence of which the terms skew symmetric in j and k disappear. Since the Dirac equation is of the first order a knowledge of all components at a certain time suffices to determine them for all times. Correspondingly, we have for $\psi(x)$, if it satisfies the vacuum equation and is prescribed on a spacelike surface

$$\psi(x) = i \int d\sigma_k' S(x - x')\gamma^k\psi(x')$$

$$\bar{\psi}(x) = i \int d\sigma_k' \bar{\psi}(x')\gamma^k S(x' - x). \qquad (A2.20)$$

We shall now derive composition formulae for the invariant functions which turn out to be the basis of the calculation of self energy effects. To this end we note that the product of two Δ^+ functions $\Delta^+(x, a)\Delta^+(x, b)$ with the mass parameters a and b, for example, is also an invariant function with its Fourier vector in the upper light cone. Therefore, we should be able to express it as a superposition of Δ^+ functions with different masses. This is worked out most conveniently in Fourier space, where we have

$$\Delta^+(x, a)\Delta^+(x, b) = -(2\pi)^{-6} \int dk \, dq e^{-ix(k+q)}$$

$$\cdot \theta(k_0)\theta(q_0)\delta(k^2 - a^2)\delta(k^2 - b^2).$$

Introducing the variable $p = k + q$ we are led to the integral

$$\int d^4q \theta(q_0)\theta(p_0 - q_0)\delta(q^2 - p^2)\delta((p - q)^2 - a^2)$$

$$= \frac{4\pi}{8p^2} \sqrt{(p^2 - a^2 - b^2)^2 - 4a^2b^2} \, [\theta(p^2 - (a + b^2))\theta(p_0)]$$

which we readily evaluate in the rest frame of p. This gives us

$$\Delta^+(x, a)\Delta^+(x, b)$$

$$= -\frac{1}{16\pi^3} \int_{p_0>0} \frac{dp}{(2\pi)^3} \frac{e^{-ipx}}{p^2} \sqrt{(p^2 - a^2 - b^2)^2 - 4a^2b^2} \quad \text{(A2.21)}$$

$$= \int_0^\infty dc f_{\Delta\Delta}(abc)\Delta^+(x, c)$$

where

$$f_{\Delta\Delta}(abc) = \frac{i}{8\pi^2c} \sqrt{(c^2 - a^2 - b^2)^2 - 4a^2b^2} \, \theta(c^2 - (a + b)^2).$$

Similarly, we have

$$\Delta^-(x, a)\Delta^-(x, b) = -\int_0^\infty dc f_{\Delta\Delta}(abc)\Delta^-(c).$$

Since

$$\Delta_f = \theta(x_0)\Delta^+(x) - \theta(-x_0)\Delta^+(-x) \quad \text{and} \quad \theta^2(x_0) = \theta(x_0),$$

$$\theta(x_0)\theta(-x_0) = 0, \qquad \text{we would expect}$$

$$\Delta_f(x, a)\Delta_f(x, b) = \int_0^c dc f_{\Delta\Delta}(abc)\Delta_f(x_0c).$$

However, looking at the integral over c when Δ_f is expressed in Fourier space we recognize that it does not exist, since it does not converge at the upper limit. Nevertheless, it is possible to use this formula when integrated over a and b with suitable (not positive definite) weight factors $\rho(a)$ and $\bar{\rho}(b)$

$$\int_0^\infty da\, db \rho(a)\bar{\rho}(b)\Delta_f(x, a)\Delta_f(x, b)$$

$$= \int_0^\infty da\, db\, dc\rho(a)\bar{\rho}(b)f_{\Delta\Delta}(abc)\Delta_f(x, c)$$

provided all integrals exist.

In a similar fashion we can combine a product

$$\Delta^+(x, a)\, S^+\, (x, a) = \Delta^+(x, a)\left(-i\gamma\,\frac{\partial}{\partial x} - b\right)\Delta^+(x, b).$$

Here we are led in Fourier space to a new integral

$$\int dq\theta(q_0)\theta(p_0 - q_0)\delta(q^2 - b^2)\delta((p - q)^2 - a^2)q_\mu\,.$$

Invariance arguments tell us that it must be of the form $p_\mu G(a, b, c)$ with $c^2 = p^2$. The evaluation of G can be reduced to the previous case by multiplying with p_μ

$$c^2 G(a, b, c) = \tfrac{1}{2}(c^2 + b^2 - a^2)f(abc).$$

In this way we arrive at

$$\Delta^+(x, a)S^+(x, b) = \int_{-\infty}^\infty dc f_{\Delta s}(abc)S^+(x, c)$$

with

$$f_{\Delta s}(abc) = \frac{-i}{16\pi^2 c}\sqrt{(c^2 - a^2 - b^2) - 4a^2 b^2}$$

$$\cdot\frac{(c + b)^2 - a^2}{2c^2}\,\theta(c^2 - (|a| + |b|)^2). \tag{A2.22}$$

Finally, we shall need, for the vacuum polarization

$$\tfrac{1}{4}\mathrm{Tr}\,(S^+(x, a)\gamma_i S^+(x, -a)\gamma^i).$$

In Fourier space this expression is similar to what occurs for $\Delta^+\Delta^+$ except for the factor

$$\tfrac{1}{4}\text{Tr}\left((\mathbf{q}+a)\gamma_i(\mathbf{k}-a)\gamma^{i}\right) = -\tfrac{1}{2}\text{Tr}\left((\mathbf{q}+a)(\mathbf{k}+2a)\right)$$

$$= -2qk - 4a^2 = -(p^2 + 2a^2).$$

This gives us

$$\frac{1}{4}\,\text{Tr}\left(S^+(x,a)\gamma_i S^+(x,-a)\gamma^{i}\right) = \int_0^{\infty} dc f_{ss}(a,-a,c)\Delta^+(x,c)$$

$$f_{ss}(a,-a,c) = -i\,\frac{(c^2+2a^2)c}{8\pi^2}\,\sqrt{1-\frac{4a^2}{c^2}}\,\theta(c^2-4a^2).$$

(A2.23)

Problems

Part I

1. Deduce Eq. (1.8).

2. Show that $j^i_{,i} = T^{ik}_{,i} + \mathfrak{I}^{ik}_{,i} = 0$ if j and $\mathfrak{I}$ represent the current density vector and the energy-momentum tensor associated with a charge.

3. Show that for a particle at rest, $z = (s, 0, 0, 0)$, Eqs. (1.16) and (1.18) become the usual expressions for the Coulomb field.

4. Compute Eq. (1.20).

5. Prove that if $T_{ik}(x)$ is time-independent in a certain Lorentz frame, then the self stress, $\int d\underline{V} \, T_{ik}(x)$, $i, k = 1, 2, 3$, must vanish in this frame.

6. Compute the radiation lost by an electron in a linear accelerator and a synchrotron.

7. Calculate $(q't_1 \mid q''t_2)$ for a linear oscillator $L = \tfrac{1}{2}(\dot{q}^2 - \omega^2 q^2)$ with the aid of Eq. (1.54) for variations of t. Check that Eq. (1.54) also holds for variations of q' and ω.

8. Prove Eq. (1.70) by calculating directly with Eq. (1.65).

Part II

9. Using the vacuum definition $q^+(0) = 0$, determine the representation $(q \mid 0)$ for the ground state of an oscillator.

10. Compute the momentum representation of P_k by applying

$$A(x) = \frac{1}{(2\pi)^3} \int dk e^{-ikx} \delta(k^2) a(k)$$

and show, using Eq. (2.30), that P_0 is positive.

11. Find a state in the photon number representation which satisfies Eq. (2.30).

12. Prove that $[A_k, \Sigma] = i\lambda_{,k}$ and construct Σ from an infinitesimal gauge transformation of

$$L = f^{ik} f_{ik}/4 - (A^i_{,i})^2/2.$$

13. Discuss Eq. (2.36) in the momentum representation of problem 10.

14. Compute Eq. (2.34), using Eq. (1.61) and $L = f^{ik}f_{ik}/4$, and show that the difference between Eq. (2.34) and Eq. (2.28) does not contribute to P.

15. Find a representation for $\psi(x)$ and $\delta\psi(x)$ with the matrices

$$a = \begin{pmatrix} 0 & 1 \\ 0 & 0 \end{pmatrix}, \qquad \{a, a^\dagger\} = 1,$$

and $\quad c = \begin{pmatrix} 1 & 0 \\ 0 & -1 \end{pmatrix}, \qquad$ with $\qquad \{c, a\} = 0, \qquad c^2 = 1.$

16. Use a momentum representation similar to the one in problem 10 to represent, for a scalar field, P_μ, Q and N as integrals in momentum space. Prove, in particular, that

$$[N, \Phi^\pm] = \mp\Phi^\pm.$$

17. Quantize the field of particles, obeying the nonrelativistic Schrödinger equation. Show that the position and momentum operators obey the usual commutation relations. Find the eigenstates of the position operator (localized states) and check that the expectation values of the energy and charge densities have a δ character.

18. Prove that the commutation relations of Eq. (2.40) are invariant under charge conjugation.

Part III

19. Deduce Eq. (3.4) by integrating the equation for the time dependence of the state vector in the Schrödinger representation.

20. Show that Eq. (3.38) equals the classical radiation loss, Eq. (1.27).

21. Discuss under what conditions the trace Tr $QQ\dagger$ of Eq. (3.60) is finite.

Part IV

22. Prove Eq. (4.6) of the text.

23. Reduce Eq. (4.14) under the assumption that the wave length is much larger than the spatial extension of $j_{n,m}$ to the familiar form for dipole radiation.

24. Calculate the cross section for annihilation of an electron and positron into two photons.

25. Calculate the cross section for the elastic scattering of two electrons.

26. Show, in fourth order, that the divergent terms for the scattering of light by light cancel.

Solutions

1. $\quad T^k{}_{i,k} = f^m{}_{i,k}f^k{}_m + f^m{}_i f^k{}_{m,k} - \dfrac{f^m_k f^k_m{}_{,i}}{2}$

$\qquad = f_i{}^m j_m + f^{mk}\dfrac{(f_{im,k} + f_{ki,m} + f_{mk,i})}{2}$

$\qquad = -j^m f_{mi}.$

2. $\quad j^i{}_{,i}(x) = \displaystyle\int ds\,\frac{d}{ds}\,\delta(x - z(s)) = 0$

$\mathcal{J}^{ik}{}_{,i}(x) = \dfrac{\partial}{\partial x_i}\displaystyle\int ds\,m\dot{z}^i(s)\dot{z}^k(s)\delta(x - z) = m\int ds\,\ddot{z}^k\delta(x - z) = j^m f_{mk}.$

3. $\quad \dot{z} = (1, 0, 0, 0),\ \ddot{z} = 0,\ (\dot{z}, x - z) = x_0 - z_0$

$\qquad = |x - z| = r,\qquad A(x) = \dfrac{e}{4\pi r}(1, 0, 0, 0)$

$$f(x) = \frac{e}{4\pi r^3}\begin{vmatrix} 0 & -x & -y & -z \\ x & 0 & 0 & 0 \\ y & 0 & 0 & 0 \\ z & 0 & 0 & 0 \end{vmatrix}.$$

4. $\quad L \simeq f^{ik}f_{ik}$ disappears in the wave zone and the other part gives

$$f_i{}^{m(\dot{z})}f_{mk}{}^{(\ddot{z})} = \left(\frac{e}{4\pi(\dot{z}, x - z)^3}\right)^2[(\dot{z}, x - z)$$

$(\ddot{z}_i(x - z)^m - \ddot{z}^m(x - z)_i) - (\ddot{z}, x - z)(\dot{z}_i(x - z)^m$

$\qquad - \dot{z}^m(x - z)_i]\,[(\dot{z}, x - z)(\ddot{z}_m(x - z)_k$

$\qquad - \ddot{z}_k(x - z)_m) - (\ddot{z}, x - z)(\dot{z}_m(x - z)_k - \dot{z}_k(x - z)_m)].$

This expression, with the use of Eqs. (1.13) and (1.17), reduces to Eq. (1.20).

5. $\quad$ From $\dfrac{\partial}{\partial x_0}T_{0i} + \dfrac{\partial}{\partial x_\alpha}T_{\alpha i} = 0,\qquad \alpha = 1, 2, 3$

we conclude

$$\int d\underline{V} x_\beta \frac{\partial}{\partial x_\alpha} T_{\alpha i} = -\int dV T_{\beta i} = 0.$$

6.   For a linear accelerator the radiation loss is essentially zero and only becomes significant when the electron gains an energy equal to its rest mass in a distance corresponding to the classical electron radius! In circular motion there is an energy loss

$$\Delta E_{\text{per turn}} \cong \left(\frac{E}{10^4}\right)\frac{1}{R}$$

if the energy is measured in Bev (= 10^9 ev) and the radius of the circle, R, in meters.

7.   The equations of motion are integrated to give

$$q_t = q_0 \cos \omega t + p_0/\omega \sin \omega t$$

$$p_t = p_0 \cos \omega t - \omega x_0 \sin \omega t.$$

From $[q_t, p_t] = i$ we conclude that

$$[q_0, q_t] = i \frac{\sin \omega t}{\omega}.$$

Commuting q_t to the left we find

$$-i \frac{\partial}{\partial t} (q't \mid q''0) = (q't \mid H \mid q''0)$$

$$= \left(q't \left| \frac{\omega^2}{2} \left(\frac{((q_t - q_0) \cos \omega t)^2 + \sin^2 \omega t q_0^2}{\sin^2 \omega t} \right) \right| q''0 \right)$$

$$= \frac{\omega^2}{2 \sin^2 \omega t} \left(q'^2 + q''^2 - 2q'q'' \cos \omega t - i \frac{\cos \omega t \sin \omega t}{\omega} \right) (q't \mid q''0)$$

which is integrated to give

$$(q't \mid q''0) = \sqrt{\frac{\omega}{2\pi \sin \omega t}} \exp - i \frac{\omega}{2 \sin \omega t} \{(q' + q'')^2 \cos \omega t - 2q'q''\}.$$

This becomes more suggestive for an initial Gaussian wave packet

$$\left| \int dq'' e^{-(q''-a)^2 \omega/2} (q't \mid q''0) \right|^2 \simeq e^{-(q'-a \cos \omega t)^2 \omega}$$

which shows the classical motion. One also verifies

$$-i\frac{\partial}{\partial q''}\,(q't\mid q''0) = (q't\mid P\mid q''0)$$

$$-i\frac{\partial}{\partial\omega}\,(q't\mid q''0) = \omega\left(q't\left|\int_0^t dt'q^2\right|q''0\right).$$

8. $[\psi^\alpha(x), P_k] = i\dfrac{\delta P_k}{\delta\pi^\alpha(x)}$

$$\delta P_k = \delta\left(\int d\sigma\pi^\alpha\psi^\alpha{}_{,k} - \int d\sigma_k L\right)$$

$$d\sigma = d\sigma_i n^i$$

$$\int d\sigma_k\delta L = \int d\sigma_k\partial_i(\pi^{i\alpha}\delta\psi^\alpha) = \int d\sigma(\pi^\alpha{}_{,k}\delta\psi^\alpha + \pi^\alpha\delta\psi^\alpha{}_{,k}).$$

using Eq. (1.55)

$$\delta P_k = \int d\sigma(\delta\pi^\alpha\psi^\alpha{}_{,k} - \delta\psi^\alpha\pi^\alpha{}_{,k})$$

$$\frac{\delta P_k}{\delta\pi^\alpha} = \psi^\alpha{}_{,k}\,.$$

Part II

9. $\dot{p} = -q,\ \dot{q} = p$

$$q(t) = (q(0) + ip(0))e^{-it}/2 + (q(0) - ip(0))e^{it}/2$$

$$q\dagger\mid 0) = \left(q + \frac{\partial}{\partial q}\right)\mid 0) = 0$$

$$\mid 0) = \pi^{-1/4}e^{-q^2/2}$$

with

$$q(0) = q$$

$$p(0) = -i\frac{\partial}{\partial q}\,.$$

10. $P_k = \dfrac{1}{2}\int d\sigma^j\!:\!A^n{}_{,j}A_{n,k} - A_n A^n{}_{,jk}\!:$

when we make use of Eq. (N.6). Introducing the Fourier transform and using

$$\int d\sigma^j(k - k')_j \delta(k^2)\delta(k'^2)e^{-ix(k+k')} = \delta(k + k')\delta(k^2)(2\pi)^3\epsilon(k_0)$$

we obtain

$$P_i = -\frac{1}{2}\frac{1}{(2\pi)^3}\int dk\delta(k^2):a(k)a(-k):k_i\epsilon(k_0)$$

$$= -\frac{1}{(2\pi)^3}\int_{k_0>0} dk(a^-(k)a^+(k))k_i$$

with

$$a(k) = a^+(k) + a^-(-k), \qquad a^+(k) = a^-(k) = 0$$

for $k_0 < 0$ and therefore

$$:a(k)a(-k): = a^+(k)a^+(-k) + a^-(k)a^+(k)$$
$$+ a^-(-k)a^+(-k) + a^-(k)a^-(-k)$$

so that only the two middle terms are different from zero. The Fourier representation of Eq. (2.30) is, if $k = (k_0, k_0, 0, 0)$

$$k_0(a_0 - a_1)\,|\,) = 0$$

so that

$$-(\,|:a(k)a(-k):|\,) = (\,|\,a^-{}_2 a^+{}_2 + a^-{}_3 a^+{}_3\,|\,).$$

11.   From $a_0{}^\pm\,|\,) = a_1{}^\pm\,|\,)$ it follows, if we expand the state in eigen-states of the number $n_0 \cdots n_3$ of photons with polarization directions $0 \cdots 3$

$$|\,) = \sum_{n_i} c_{n_0\cdots n_3}\,|\,n_0 \cdots n_3)$$

that the c_{n_i} obey the relation $c_{n_0\pm 1,n_1,n_2,n_3} = c_{n_0,n_1\pm 1,n_2,n_3}$, which gives the solution

$$|\,) = \sum_{n_2,n_3} c'_{n_2 n_3}\{\,|\,0, 0, n_2, n_3) + |\,1, 1, n_2, n_4)$$

$$+ |\,2, 2, n_2, n_3) + \cdots\}$$

The form of a state which obeys Eq. (2.30) with respect to the numbers of timelike and longitudinal photons is therefore determined and, in fact, these states are not eigenstates of the number operator. This is often expressed by saying that this part of the field remains unquantized.

12.   The Lagrange function we have employed has an advantage over $f^{ik}f_{ik}$ since it produces Eq. (2.26) without using the subsidiary condition and, further, π^0 does not vanish identically. We have

$$\pi_k{}^i = f_k{}^i - \delta_k{}^i A^m{}_{,m}$$

$$\int d\sigma_k \pi_k{}^i \delta A_i = \int d\sigma_k \lambda_{,i}(f_k{}^i - \delta_k{}^i A^m{}_{,m}) = \int d\sigma_k(\lambda A_i{}^{i,k} - \lambda^{,k} A^i{}_{,i})$$

where we have made use of Eq. (N.6).

The equation we are seeking follows directly from the commutation relation, Eq. (2.29), since we observe that in the expression

$$[A^m(x), \pi_k{}^j(x')] = i(g^{mj}\partial_k - g_k{}^m \partial^j + g_k{}^j \partial^m)D(x - x')$$

the last two terms compensate each other. As must be the case, Σ is independent of σ

$$\delta\Sigma/\delta\sigma(x) = \partial_k(\lambda^{,k} A^i{}_{,i} - \lambda A_i{}^{i,k}) = 0$$

so that one can suppose that the integration point x' is contained in the spacelike surface which passes through x. Then one can use Eq. (A2.9) to give an explicit proof of the commutation relation between A and Σ.

13.   In momentum space

$$f(k) = \begin{pmatrix} 0, & a_1 - a_0, & a_2, & a_3 \\ & 0, & a_2, & a_3 \\ & & 0 & 0 \\ & & & 0 \end{pmatrix} k_0, \qquad f^+(k) \mid 0) = 0$$

gives, in addition to Eq. (2.30), the equations $a_2{}^+ \mid 0) = a_3{}^+ \mid 0) = 0$. Therefore, $\mid 0)$ is the vacuum state we have set out to construct for the transverse field.

14.

$$\pi^{ik} = \frac{\partial L}{\partial A_{i,k}} = f^{ki} \qquad f_{jik} = f_{ji}A_k$$

$$\pi^{mi}A_{m,k} - \partial_m f_{imk} = f_{im}f^{mk}.$$

The difference between the energy-momentum tensors is

$$-\partial^m(A_i f_{mk}) - A^m{}_{,i} A_{k,m} + \tfrac{1}{2}\, g_{ik} A_{m,s} A^{s,m}.$$

From Eq. (N.6) and $f_{mk} = -f_{km}$, $\displaystyle\int d\sigma_k \partial^m(A_i f_m^k) = 0$

so

$$\int d\sigma^k A_{k,m} A^m{}_{,i} = \frac{1}{2} \int d\sigma^k (A_{k,m} A^m{}_{,i} + A^m A_{k,mi}) = \frac{1}{2} \int d\sigma_i A_{k,m} A^{m,k}$$

if one applies this expression to a state which is supposed to satisfy Eq. (2.30).

15.   We develop ψ in the complete orthonormal system of eigenfunctions of the Dirac equation, $u_s(x)$ with $(\partial - m)u = 0$, where the coefficients are operators in Hilbert space

$$\psi^\alpha(x) = \frac{1}{\sqrt{V}} \sum_s u_s{}^\alpha(x) b_s$$

where α is the spin index and s is the running index which labels the eigenfunctions. If we demand that the b satisfy the commutation relations

$$\{b_s, b_t{}^\dagger\} = \delta_t{}^s \qquad \{b_s, b_t\} = 0$$

then we find

$$\{\psi_\alpha(x), \psi_\beta{}^\dagger(x')\} = \frac{1}{V} \sum_s u_s{}^\alpha(x) u_s{}^{\dagger\beta}(x') = \delta(x - x')\delta_{\alpha\beta}$$

$$\{\psi(x), \bar\psi(x')\} = 0.$$

We obtain a representation of the b as an infinite direct product of commuting matrices of type a and we set $b_s = a_s \prod_{t>s} c_t$. These matrices fulfill the desired commutation relations. For the quantity $\delta\psi$, which anticommutes with all other operators, we obtain the corresponding representation $\delta\psi = \prod_t c_t \delta u$ with arbitrary δu.

16. As in problem 10, we find

$$P_i = (2\pi)^{-3} \int d^4 k\, k_i a^-(k) a^+(k) \delta(k^2)$$

$$N = (2\pi)^{-3} \int dk\, a^-(k) a^+(k) \delta(k^2) \ .$$

From

$$\delta(k^2)[a(k),\, a(k')] = (2\pi)^3\delta(k - k')\,\epsilon\,(k - k').$$

it follows that

$$\left[N, \int dk\delta(k^2)a^+(k)e^{ikx}\right] = \int dk\delta(k^2)a^+(k)e^{ikx}.$$

17. The field equations and commutation relations are

$$\frac{1}{i}\dot{\psi} - \frac{\nabla}{2m}\psi = 0 \qquad \{\psi(x, t), \psi(x', t)\} = \delta(x - x').$$

The observable are defined as usual

$$N = \int dx\psi^{\dagger}\psi \qquad X_i = \int dx\psi^{\dagger}(x, t)x_i\psi(x, t)$$

$$P_j = \int dx\psi^{\dagger}(x, t)\frac{\nabla_j}{i}\psi(x, t)$$

and obey the commutation relations

$$[X_i,\, P_j] = i\delta_{ij}N.$$

A localized one-particle state

$$|\,x) = \psi^{\dagger}(x)\,|\,0) \quad\text{with}\quad \psi(x')\,|\,0) = 0$$

is not normalizable but is a limit of normalizable states. In this limit we find

$$\frac{(x\,|\,\psi^{\dagger}(x')\psi(x')\,|\,x)}{(x\,|\,x)} \to \delta(x - x') \qquad \frac{(x\,|\,X\,|\,x)}{(x\,|\,x)} = x.$$

18. The hypothesis

$$\{\psi_{\alpha}'(x),\, \bar{\psi}_{\beta}'(x')\} = i\int dp e^{ip(x-x')}\delta(p^2 - m^2)\epsilon(p)(\mathbf{p} + m)$$

$$= -c_{\alpha\alpha'}^{-1}\{\bar{\psi}_{\alpha'}(x)\psi_{\beta'}(x')\}c_{\beta'\beta}$$

actually leads to

$$\{\psi_{\beta}(x'),\, \bar{\psi}_{\alpha}(x)\} = -i\int dp e^{ip(x-x')}\delta(p^2 - m^2)(cpc^{-1} + m)_{\beta\alpha}\,\epsilon(p)$$

or

$$\{\psi_{\alpha}(x)\bar{\psi}_{\beta}(x')\} = iS(x - x').$$

Part III

19. In the equation of motion for the state vector $\mid s)$ in the Schrödinger representation

$$(H_0 + H') \mid s) = i \frac{\partial}{\partial t} \mid s)$$

one can transform away the energy of the free fields H_0 by the transformation $\mid s) = e^{-iH_0 t} \mid \omega)$. An equation of motion in the "interaction
representation" for the transformed state $\mid \omega)$ is then obtained in
which only the interaction energy $H'(t)$ appears

$$H'(t) \mid \omega) = i \frac{\partial}{\partial t} \mid \omega) \quad \text{with} \quad H'(t) = e^{iH_0 t} H' e^{-iH_0 t}.$$

This equation is readily integrated. However, one must bear in mind
that the $H'(t)$ at different times do not commute. Hence, the solution is expressed in terms of the time-ordered exponential function

$$\mid \omega, t) = P e^{-i \int_{t_0}^{t} dt H'(t)} \mid \omega, t_0).$$

Since the operators in the interaction representation satisfy the free
field equations, one easily sees that $H'(t)$ is identical with $\int d\underline{V} L'(x)$
when L' does not depend on the time derivatives of the field quantities.

20. The classical radiation loss in the total space-time region is

$$\Delta P_r = \frac{1}{2} \int dx \, dx' j_s(x) (j^s(x') \partial_r - j_r(x') \partial^s) D(x - x').$$

The second part disappears by partial integration and the observation
that $j^s_{,s} = 0$. The momentum representation of the first part is

$$\frac{1}{(2\pi)^3} \int dk k_r \epsilon(k_0) \delta(k^2) (j(k) j(-k)).$$

One can easily show that $(0_{\text{in}} \mid \mathbf{P}^{\text{out}} \mid 0_{\text{in}})$ is equal to the energy-
momentum vector of the radiation field $A^{\text{rad}} = A^{\text{ret}} - A^{\text{av}} = A^{\text{out}} -
A^{\text{in}}$. A^{in} plays the role of the vacuum field of A. Then we have

$$(0 \mid S^{-1} P^{\text{in}} S \mid 0) = (0 \mid P^{\text{out}} \mid 0) = (0 \mid P^{\text{rad}} \mid 0)$$

where the superscript to P indicates from which field quantities one
has constructed P in Eq. (2.28). In taking the vacuum expectation

value of P^{rad} only P^{out} survives, since the terms linear and bilinear in A^{in} have vanishing vacuum expectation values.

21. Writing $Tr(QQ\dagger)$ more explicitly we note that

$$| TrQQ\dagger | < \int dk_1 \, dk_2 \, dq_1 \, dq_2 Tr \mid A(q_1 - k_1)S_f(k_1)$$

$$A(k_1 - q_2)S_f(q_2)A(q_2 - k_2)S_f(k_2)A(k_2 - q_2)S_f(q_2) \mid.$$

Since for large momenta $| S_f(k) | \to 1/k$ we must have $A(k) \to 1/k^3$ which has, as a consequence

$$E = \int dk k^2 \mid A(k) \mid^2 < \infty.$$

Part IV

22. From the Dirac equation we have $L^{\text{el}} + eL' = 0$, and the π_α are unchanged.

23. By applying Eq. (A.28) we find for the emission probability for a photon with spatial polarization direction n

$$e^2 \int d\underline{V} \, d\underline{V}'((nj^\dagger(\underline{x})(nj(\underline{x}')) \int dx_0 \, dx_0' e^{i\omega(x_0 - x_0')}$$

$$\int_{k_0 > 0} \frac{dk}{(2\pi)^3} \, \delta(k^2) e^{-ik(x - x')}.$$

The integration over the time yields a δ function, which restricts the frequency in the k integration to k_0 and brings out the total time as a factor. For the emission probability per unit time we find

$$2\alpha\omega \int \frac{d\Omega_k}{4\pi} \int d\underline{V} \, d\underline{V}'(nj^\dagger(\underline{x}))(nj(\underline{x}'))e^{i\omega|x - x'| \cos \delta}.$$

If the spatial extension of j is much smaller than the wave length, the exponential function can be set equal to one. Then the spatial integration can be performed by using Eq. (N.6) and the continuity equation for the current

$$\int d\sigma_i \partial_s(x_k j^s) = \int d\sigma_i j_k = \int d\sigma_s j^s g_{ik} + \int d\sigma_s x_k \partial_i j_s$$

or

$$\int d\underline{V}j = \int d\underline{V}x \partial_0 j_0(x).$$

If one takes into account the time dependence of the transition current, one finds, for the total transition probability per unit time

$$w = 2\alpha\omega^3 \mid (Xn) \mid^2 \quad \text{with} \quad X = \int d\underline{V} x j_0(\underline{x}).$$

These formulae confirm the elementary arguments in the introduction.

24. If p and p' are the energy-momentum vectors of the electron and positron then, after summation over the photon polarization vectors, we find for the cross section

$$\sigma = \frac{\alpha^2}{((pp')^2 - 1)^{1/2}} \int dk \delta(k^2) \delta((p + p' - k)^2)$$

$$\left[\frac{(pk)}{(p'k)} + \frac{(p'k)}{(pk)} + 2 \left(\frac{1}{(pk)} + \frac{1}{(p'k)} \right) - \left(\frac{(p + p', k)^2}{(pk)(p'k)} \right) \right].$$

For simplicity we have set $m = 1$ here. The notation corresponds to that used in Eq. (4.13). With the abbreviation

$$\beta^2 = (pp' - 1)(pp' + 1)^{-1}$$

we may write the total cross section

$$\sigma = \pi\alpha^2 \frac{1 - \beta^2}{2\beta} \left[2(\beta^2 - 2) + \frac{3 - \beta^4}{\beta} \ln \left(\frac{1 + \beta}{1 - \beta} \right) \right].$$

For $\beta < 1$ we have the approximate expression $\sigma = \pi\alpha^2/\beta$. The β has the physical significance of the velocity of the electron in the center of mass system. The order of magnitude of the cross section is easily found, as we have pointed out in the introduction. The cross section is equal to the probability that the electron and positron come close enough together times the emission probability for two photons per unit time and volume of incident particles

$$\frac{1}{m^3 V} \cdot \alpha \cdot \frac{\alpha m}{v} V = \left(\frac{\alpha}{m} \right)^2 \bigg/ v.$$

25. $\sigma = \dfrac{e^4}{16} ((pq)^2 - 1)^{-1/2} \displaystyle\int \frac{dp'}{(2\pi)^2} \delta(p'^2 - 1)\delta(q'^2 - 1)$

$\{(p - p')^{-4}\text{Tr}((\mathbf{p} + 1)\gamma_n(\mathbf{p}' + 1)\gamma_m)\text{Tr}((\mathbf{q} + 1)\gamma^n(\mathbf{q}' + 1)\gamma^m)$

$+ (p - q')^{-4}\text{Tr}((\mathbf{p} + 1)\gamma_n(\mathbf{q}' + 1)\gamma_m)\text{Tr}((\mathbf{q} + 1)\gamma^n(\mathbf{p}' + 1)\gamma^m)$

$- 2(p - p')^{-2}(p - q')^{-2}\text{Tr}((\mathbf{p} + 1)\gamma_n(\mathbf{p}' + 1)\gamma^m(\mathbf{q} + 1)\gamma^n(\mathbf{q}' + 1)\gamma_m)\}.$

Here we have put $m = 1$ and introduced q' as the abbreviation for $p + q - p'$. Using the relations $pp' = qq'$, $pq = p'q'$, $pq' = qp'$, we are able to reduce the bracket above to

$$2(p - p')^{-4}[(pq)^2 - 2pq + (p'q)^2 + 2pq] + 2(p - q')^{-4}[(pq)^2$$

$$-2pq + (pp')^2 + 2pp'] - 4(p - p')^{-2}(q - q')^{-2}[(pq)^2 - 2pq].$$

Introducing twice the square of the momentum in the center of mass system $u = pq - 1$ and computing the cross section in this system by observing that the scattering angle is given by $(p - p')^2 = -2u \sin^2 (\theta/2)$ we find

$$\frac{d\sigma}{d\Omega} = \frac{\alpha^2 (u + 1)^2}{2u^2(u + 2)} \{ \sin^{-4} (\theta/2) + \cos^{-4} (\theta/2) - \sin^{-2} (\theta/2) \cos^{-2} (\theta/2)$$

$$+ u^2(1 + u)^{-2}(1 + \sin^{-2} (\theta/2) \cos^{-2} (\theta/2)) \}.$$

26. If the photon has no momentum then in fourth order the graphs will yield a term of the form

$$\int \frac{dp}{(p^2 - m^2)^4} \, \mathrm{Tr}(\mathbf{p}\gamma_a \mathbf{p}\gamma_b \mathbf{p}\gamma_c \mathbf{p}\gamma_d + \mathbf{p}\gamma_a \mathbf{p}\gamma_c \mathbf{p}\gamma_b \mathbf{p}\gamma_d + \mathbf{p}\gamma_a \mathbf{p}\gamma_b \mathbf{p}\gamma_d \mathbf{p}\gamma_c).$$

Since the denominator only depends on p^2 we can replace $p_i p_k p_m p_n$ by

$$\frac{p^4}{24} \left(\delta_{ik}\delta_{mn} + \delta_{in}\delta_{km} + \delta_{im}\delta_{kn} \right).$$

Thus, the trace can be done by applying Eq. (A1.18) and gives, for the first summand under the integral

$$\delta_{ab}\delta_{cd} + \delta_{ad}\delta_{bc} - 2\delta_{ac}\delta_{bd} .$$

If we add the corresponding contribution from both other terms the cancellation is immediately exhibited.

SUBJECT INDEX

A

Action integral, 26, 30
Action principle, 32
Adjoint spinor, 203
Angular momentum, 37, 48
Annihilation, electron pair (see Pair annihilation)
  operator (see also Operator), 46, 48
  positronium (see Positronium)
Anticommutation rules, 36, 60, 132
Auxiliary condition, 56

B

B-field, 169
Born approximation, 109
Bose-Einstein statistics, 63, 71, 84
Bremsstrahlung, 12, 102

C

Canonical momentum tensor (see Momentum tensor)
Canonical transformation, 36, 62
Charge conjugation (see also Invariance), 39, 53, 61, 193, 205
Charge-current density (see Current density)
Charge renormalization (see Renormalization)
Classical theory of point charge, 18 ff.
Closed loop, 192
Commutation relations, 36, 39 ff., 129, 137
Compton scattering, 10, 147
Compton wave length, 4, 69
Conservation laws, 37
  charge, 38
  parity, 73
Convergence of iteration solution for external field, 117
  of renormalized S-matrix, 198 ff.
Coulomb interaction, 156

Coulomb scattering, 4, 156
  radiative corrections, 187
Creation operator (see Operator)
Cross section, 150
  differential, 150
Current, orbital, 82, 205
  particle, 18
  spin, 81, 205
Current density, 53, 60
  measurement, 132
  operator, 38

D

Decomposition into plane waves (see Plane waves)
Delta functions
  Dirac, xi
  explicit expressions, 210
  homogeneous, 52, 208
  inhomogeneous, 207
  integral representations, 207
  relations between, 208
Destruction operator (see Operator)
Diagrams
  momentum space, 148
  primitive, 191
  scattering, 148
Differential cross section, 150
Differential symbols, xiii
Dirac equation, 59, 203
  boundary value problem, 212
  relativistic invariance, 204
Divergences
  classification, 192
  degree of, 192
  infra-red, 14, 104, 186, 192
  primitive, 191

E

Electron
  classical point, 18 ff.
  classical radius, 11

magnetic moment, 82, 187
  scattering, 157
Electron line, 151
Electron mass, 25
Electron path, 6
Electron-positron scattering, 157
Electron self energy, 175
Electron self stress, 195
Energy loss, 22
Energy-momentum tensor (see also
    Momentum tensor)
  classical field, 17
  coupled field, 138
  particle, 18
  quantum field, 35
Euler equations, 33
  Dirac field, 59
  photon field, 56
  scalar field, 51
External field
  Dirac particle in an, 109 ff.
  S-matrix, 114 ff.

F

Fermi-Dirac statistics, 63, 71, 84
Field
  equations (see Euler equations)
  measurability (see Measurability)
  variables, 31 ff.
  variations, 32 ff.
Fine structure, 5
Fine structure constant, 3
Fluctuations
  charge, 120
  current, 79
  effect on energy levels, 15
Functional derivative, 118

G

Gamma matrices, xii
Gauge invariance (see Invariance)
Gauge transformations, 57, 142
  infinitesimal, 58
Generating function
  gauge transformations, 58, 142
  infinitesimal canonical transforma-
    tions, 30, 35 ff.

infinitesimal Lorentz transforma-
    tions, 34, 204
Green's function, 207 ff.

H

Hamiltonian mechanics, 25, 30
Heisenberg picture, 27
Hermitian conjugate, xii
Hermitian operator (see Operator)
Hilbert space, 27

I

Incoming fields, 19, 93
Indefinite metric, 174, 197
Infinitesimal transformation, 29 ff.
Infra-red divergence (see Divergence)
Interaction operator, 137
Invariance properties of fields
  charge conjugation, 39, 53, 61, 139,
    193
  gauge transformations, 57, 138
  Lorentz transformations, 34
  phase transformations, 39, 153, 138
  space inversion, 73
  time inversion, 33
Invariant functions (see Appendix II,
    207 ff.)

K

Klein-Gordon equation, 51
Klein-Nishina formula, 154
Klein's paradox, 124

L

Lagrangian, 30
  coupled fields, 89, 137
  electron field, 59
  meson field, 51
  radiation field, 56
Lamb shift, 15, 26, 124, 187
Larmour formula, 7
Lifetime, 8
  positronium, 9
Light by light scattering (see Photon-
    photon scattering)
Localizability, 127 ff.
Lorentz condition, 56, 72
Lorentz group, 41

Lorentz transformation, 34
  infinitesimal, 34 ff.

M

Magnetic moment of electron, 82, 187
Mass
  electromagnetic, 25
  mechanical, 25
  observable, 25
Mass renormalization (see Renormalization)
Maxwell's equations, 17, 56
Measurability of fields, 127 ff.
Measurement of charge-current density, 132 ff.
Metric tensor, xii
Møller scattering, 157
Momentum operators, 36
  for interacting fields, 141
  for radiation field, 107
Momentum space, xiii
Momentum tensor, canonical, 35

N

Nonlocal field theories, 49, 196
Number operator (see Operator)

O

Observable, 27
One particle theory, 203
Operator, xii
  annihilation, 46, 48 ff.
  creation, 46, 48 ff.
  current density, 38
  electron number, 62, 92, 141
  Hermitian, 27
  meson number, 54
  unitary, 28
Ordered product, 51
  for anticommuting fields, 60
Outgoing fields, 19, 93

P

Pair annihilation, 155
  one quantum, 8
  two quantum, 9
Pair production
  by an external field, 109

  in photon-photon collisions, 155
  spontaneous, 6
Parity operator (see Invariance)
Phase transformations, 39, 53, 142
Photon-electron scattering (see Compton scattering)
Photon-photon scattering, 124, 193
Photon mass, 121, 168
Photon scattering by Coulomb field, 193
Pi meson, 55, 73
Plane wave decomposition of field, 45 ff.
  electron, 48
  scalar, 48
  vector, 48
Poisson brackets, 30
Poisson distribution, 84
Polarization
  circular, 48
  sums, 99, 147
Positrons, 50
Positron-positron scattering (see Møller scattering)
Positronium, 8
  lifetime, 73
  selection rules, 73
  space parity, 75
  two-photon annihilation, 75
Propagation functions
  causal character, 144
  electron in external field, 114
  exact, 162, 173

Q

Quantization of field, 47

R

Radiation field, 19, 56
Radiation field operator, 56
  longitudinal component, 57
Radiation loss, 107
Radiative corrections, 177 ff.
  to scattering, 187
Rayleigh-Jeans formula, 13
Renormalization
  charge, 122, 167, 194
  field, 167, 174

mass, 164
S-matrix, 190
Rutherford scattering, 11, 157

S

Scattering, 10, 94, 113, 143
Scattering matrix (see S-matrix)
Schrödinger equation, 31
Selection rules in
   pi decay, 73
   positronium, 73
Self energy, 166
   of electron, 175
Self force of electron, 24
Self stress of electron, 175
S-function, 61, 212 ff.
Signum function, 001
S-matrix
   definition, 93
   evaluation, 97, 147
   external field approximation, 97
   invariance, 142
   physical meaning, 93
   sign and numerical factors, 114
   unitarity, 118
   vacuum matrix elements, 114
Source function, 89
Space inversion, 73
Spacelike surface, xiii, 32
Spin sums, 78, 147
State
   one electron, 67
   one meson, 65
   one photon, 67
   two electron, 70

two meson, 69
two photon, 70
Surface term, 33
Symbols, xiv

T

Thompson formula, 190
Time inversion, 33
Time-ordered product, 91
Traces of gamma matrices, 205
Transformation matrix, 28, 91
Transition probability, 91, 150

U

Uncertainty relation, 4, 127 ff.
Unitary operator, 28
Units, 3

V

Vacuum
   definition of, 45, 161
   for photon field, 58
Vacuum expectation values, 78 ff.
Vacuum fluctuations, 79 ff.
Vacuum polarization, 118, 181, 193
Variables
   dynamical, 37
   field, 31 ff.
Vector space, linear, 27
Virtual quanta, 13, 93 ff.

Z

Zero point energy, 14
   fluctuation, 13
Zitterbewegung, 81